# GATEWAY TO THE GREAT BOOKS

# GATEWAY
## TO THE
# GREAT BOOKS

# Gateway
## to the
# Great Books

ROBERT M. HUTCHINS, MORTIMER J. ADLER
*Editors in Chief*

CLIFTON FADIMAN
*Associate Editor*

---

# 9

## MATHEMATICS

## Encyclopædia Britannica, Inc.

WILLIAM BENTON
*Publisher*

*Chicago, London, Toronto, Geneva, Sydney, Tokyo, Manila*

Portrait illustrations are by Fred Steffen

# Contents
# of Volume 9

# Lancelot Hogben

1895–

Lancelot Hogben, British scientist and economist, was born in Portsmouth in 1895. He was the son of a clergyman. Educated at Cambridge, he has held university posts in England, Scotland, South Africa and Canada.

Hogben's interest in the problems of man in society dates from a very early age when he was introduced to the plays of George Bernard Shaw and to the socialist literature of the Fabian Society by a schoolmistress at the Tottenham County School. One of man's problems arises from his failure to understand the scientific language of his culture. To bridge the gap that has developed between the average man and his scientific environment, Hogben wrote *Science for the Citizen* and *Mathematics for the Million*. The following selection is taken from the latter work.

Hogben has written and lectured not only on mathematics but on zoology, social biology, natural history, sociology, economics, medical statistics, and probability. He has also written an illustrated history of 30,000 years of human visual communication, *From Cave Painting to Comic Strips*.

In *Mathematics, the Mirror of Civilization*, Hogben brings the zeal of a social reformer to the task of rescuing mathematics from the fate of becoming a priestcraft.

Since much of man's relation to man and nature has come to be treated in mathematical terms, it is dangerous to ignore the new language. We run the risk of leaving the power to control our political and material welfare in the hands of specialists. If these specialists have, as did the ancient Egyptian priests, a vested interest in mystifying the people, an unhealthy situation develops. "No society," says Hogben, "is safe in the hands of its clever people." In our atomic age, Hogben's apprehensions seem particularly valid.

In contradistinction to most of the other authors represented in this volume, Hogben does not have much use for mathematics as a purely speculative activity. He is solidly planted in opposition to the view of mathematics that is usually associated with Plato.[1] Plato held that mathematics reflects absolute and eternal truths, but Hogben sees it as merely a useful language, with rules based on convenience, like ordinary grammar. In this respect, he has much in common with Poincaré.

But Poincaré, like Russell, Whitehead, and Forsyth,[2] argues for the study of mathematics as an esthetic experience which is undertaken for its own sake. To this, Hogben is opposed. His broad outline of the history of mathematics shows mathematical invention and discovery only as the result of man's effort to control his environment.

Many of Hogben's ideas are thus controversial. You may find yourself with him or against him. But if you are baffled and discouraged by the whole world of mathematics, Hogben is heartening. He flays with caustic wit those who have brought you to your present condition. They have concealed from you, he says, the story of the human origin of mathematics. It is this story that he tells.

---

[1] See *The Republic*, Book VII, in *Great Books of the Western World*, Vol. 7, pp. 392–398.
[2] See the selections from the writings of these authors in this volume.

# Mathematics, the Mirror
# of Civilization

There is a story about Diderot, the Encyclopaedist and materialist, a foremost figure in the intellectual awakening which immediately preceded the French Revolution. Diderot was staying at the Russian court, where his elegant flippancy was entertaining the nobility. Fearing that the faith of her retainers was at stake, the Tsaritsa commissioned Euler, the most distinguished mathematician of the time, to debate with Diderot in public. Diderot was informed that a mathematician had established a proof of the existence of God. He was summoned to court without being told the name of his opponent. Before the assembled court, Euler accosted him with the following pronouncement, which was uttered with due gravity: $\frac{a + b^n}{n} = x$, *donc Dieu existe répondez!*" Algebra was Arabic to Diderot. Unfortunately he did not realize that was the trouble. Had he realized that algebra is just a language in which we describe the *sizes* of things in contrast to the ordinary languages which we use to describe the *sorts* of things in the world, he would have asked Euler to translate the first half of the sentence into French.[1] Translated freely into English, it may be rendered: "A number $x$ can be got by first adding a number $a$ to a number $b$ multiplied by itself a certain number of times, and then dividing the whole by the number of $b$'s multiplied together. So God exists after all. What have you got to say now?" If Diderot had asked Euler to illustrate the first part of his remark for the clearer understanding of the Russian court, Euler might have replied that $x$ is 3 when $a$ is 1 and $b$ is 2 and $n$ is 3, or that $x$ is 21 when $a$ is 3 and $b$ is 3 and $n$ is 4, and so forth. Euler's troubles would have begun when the court wanted to know how the second part of the sentence follows from the first part. Like many of us, Diderot had stagefright when confronted with a sentence in size language. He left the court abruptly amid the titters of the

---

1. For a critical evaluation of this version of the Euler-Diderot anecdote, which incorrectly portrays Diderot as a mathematical illiterate, see A. M. Wilson, *Diderot* (1957), p. 91 [Ed.].

assembly, confined himself to his chambers, demanded a safe conduct, and promptly returned to France.

Though he could not know it, Diderot had the last laugh before the court of history. The clericalism which Diderot fought was overthrown, and though it has never lacked the services of an eminent mathematician, the supernaturalism which Euler defended has been in retreat ever since. One eminent contemporary astronomer in his Gifford Lectures tells us that Dirac has discovered $p$ and $q$ numbers. *Donc Dieu existe.* Another distinguished astronomer pauses, while he entertains us with astonishing calculations about the distance of the stars, to award M. le grand Architecte an honorary degree in mathematics. There were excellent precedents long before the times of Euler and Diderot. For the first mathematicians were the priestly calendar makers who calculated the onset of the seasons. The Egyptian temples were equipped with Nilometers with which the priests made painstaking records of the rising and falling of the sacred river. With these they could predict the flooding of the Nile with great accuracy. Their papyri show that they possessed a language of measurement very different from the pretentious phraseology with which they fobbed off their prophecies on the laity. The masses could not see the connection between prophecy and reality, because the Nilometers communicated with the river by underground channels, skilfully concealed from the eye of the people. The priests of Egypt used one language when they wrote in the proceedings of a learned society and another language when they gave an interview to the "sob sisters" of the Sunday press.

In the ancient world writing and reading were still a mystery and a craft. The plain man could not decipher the Rhind papyrus in which the scribe Ahmes wrote down the laws of measuring things. Civilized societies in the twentieth century have democratized the reading and writing of *sort language.* Consequently the plain man can understand scientific discoveries if they do not involve complicated measurements. He knows something about evolution. The priestly accounts of the creation have fallen into discredit. So mysticism has to take refuge in the atom. The atom is a safe place not because it is small, but because you have to do complicated measurements and use underground channels to find your way there. These underground channels are concealed from the eye of the people because the plain man has not been taught to read and write *size language.* Three centuries ago, when priests conducted their services in Latin, Protestant reformers founded grammar schools so that people could read the open Bible. The time has now come for another

Reformation. People must learn to read and write the language of measurement so that they can understand the open bible of modern science.

In the time of Diderot the lives and happiness of individuals might still depend on holding the correct beliefs about religion. To-day the lives and happiness of people depend more than most of us realize upon the correct interpretation of public statistics which are kept by government offices. When a committee of experts announce that the average man can live on his unemployment allowance, or the average child is getting sufficient milk, the mere mention of an average or the citation of a list of figures is enough to paralyse intelligent criticism. In reality half or more than half the population may not be getting enough to live on when the *average* man or child has enough. The majority of people living to-day in civilized countries cannot read and write freely in size language, just as the majority of people living in the times of Wycliff and Luther were ignorant of Latin in which religious controversy was carried on. The modern Diderot has got to learn the language of size in self-defence, because no society is safe in the hands of its clever people.

Long before clever people started reading and writing the ordinary languages in which we describe different sorts of things, other people who were not so terribly clever had learnt to talk. The plain man of to-day, that is to say, the reader or the writer of this book, has a great advantage over the audiences who listened to the priestly oracles of the ancient world. Though we may not read or write it, we have all learned to talk in *size language*. If we were asked what distinguishes the men of to-day, the men of the machine age, from the men who lived before the American or French Revolution, we might give many answers. Very few would give the answer that Burke gave. About forty years after the incident we have been discussing, Burke wrote a vitriolic denunciation of the social revolution heralded by the Encyclopaedists. With this difference that Burke wrote elegant, sonorous, and commanding prose, many passages in it recall familiar descriptions of current events in Russia, as they are reflected in the dented mirror of the daily press. In one of the most resonant and also the silliest passages of his reflections, Burke pronounces an eloquent obituary on the *ancien régime*. What raises his anger to white heat is not that Europe will become a continent of shopkeepers. It is that Europe will become a continent of calculators. "The Age of Chivalry is gone. That of sophists, economists, and *calculators* has succeeded, and the glory of Europe is extinguished for ever. . . ."

The first men who dwelt in cities were *talking* animals. The man of the

Machine Age is a *calculating* animal. We live in a welter of figures:
cookery recipes, railway time-tables, unemployment aggregates, fines,
taxes, war debts, overtime schedules, speed limits, bowling averages,
betting odds, billiard scores, calories, babies' weights, clinical temperatures, rainfall, hours of sunshine, motoring records, power indices,
gas-meter readings, bank rates, freight rates, death rates, discount,
interest, lotteries, wave-lengths, and tire pressures. Every night, when he
winds up his watch, the modern man adjusts a scientific instrument of a
precision and delicacy unimaginable to the most cunning artificers of
Alexandria in its prime. So much is commonplace. What escapes our
notice is that in doing these things we have learnt to use devices which
presented tremendous difficulties to the most brilliant mathematicians of
antiquity. Ratios, limits, acceleration are not remote abstractions, dimly
apprehended by the solitary genius. They are photographed upon every
page of our existence. In the course of the adventure upon which we are
going to embark we shall constantly find that we have no difficulty in
answering questions which tortured the minds of very clever mathematicians in ancient times. This is not because you and I are very clever people. It is because we inherit a social culture which has suffered the impact of material forces foreign to the intellectual life of the ancient world.
The most brilliant intellect is a prisoner within its own social inheritance.

An illustration will help to make this quite definite at the outset. The
Eleatic philosopher Zeno set all his contemporaries guessing by pro-
pounding a series of conundrums, of which the one most often quoted is
the paradox of Achilles and the tortoise. Here is the problem about
which the inventors of school geometry argued till they had speaker's
throat and writer's cramp. Achilles runs a race with the tortoise. He runs
ten times as fast as the tortoise. The tortoise has 100 yards' start. Now, says
Zeno, Achilles runs 100 yards and reaches the place where the tortoise
started. Meanwhile the tortoise has gone a tenth as far as Achilles, and
is therefore 10 yards ahead of Achilles. Achilles runs this 10 yards.
Meanwhile the tortoise has run a tenth as far as Achilles, and is therefore 1
yard in front of him. Achilles runs this 1 yard. Meanwhile the tortoise has
run a tenth of a yard and is therefore a tenth of a yard in front of Achilles.
Achilles runs this tenth of a yard. Meanwhile the tortoise goes a tenth of
a tenth of a yard. He is now a hundredth of a yard in front of Achilles.
When Achilles has caught up this hundredth of a yard, the tortoise is a
thousandth of a yard in front. So, argued Zeno, Achilles is always getting
nearer the tortoise, but can never quite catch him up.

You must not imagine that Zeno and all the wise men who argued the point failed to recognize that Achilles really did get past the tortoise. What troubled them was, where is the catch? You may have been asking the same question. The important point is that you did not ask it for the same reason which prompted them. What is worrying you is why they thought up funny little riddles of that sort. Indeed, what you are really concerned with is a *historical* problem. I am going to show you in a minute that the problem is not one which presents any *mathematical* difficulty to you. You know how to translate it into size language, because you inherit a social culture which is separated from theirs by the collapse of two great civilizations and by two great social revolutions. The difficulty of the ancients was not a historical difficulty. It was a mathematical difficulty. They had not evolved a size language into which this problem could be freely translated.

The Greeks were not accustomed to speed limits and passenger-luggage allowances. They found any problem involving division very much more difficult than a problem involving multiplication. They had no way of doing division to any order of accuracy, because they relied for calculation on the mechanical aid of the counting frame or abacus. They could not do sums on paper. For all these and other reasons which we shall meet again and again, the Greek mathematician was unable to see something that we see without taking the trouble to worry about whether we see it or not. If we go on piling up bigger and bigger quantities, the pile goes on growing more rapidly without any end as long as we go on adding more. If we can go on adding larger and larger quantities indefinitely without coming to a stop, it seemed to Zeno's contemporaries that we ought to be able to go on adding smaller and still smaller quantities indefinitely without reaching a limit. They thought that in one case the pile goes on for ever, growing more rapidly, and in the other it goes on for ever, growing more slowly. There was nothing in their number language to suggest that when the engine slows beyond a certain point, it chokes off.

To see this clearly we will first put down in numbers the distance which the tortoise traverses at different stages of the race after Achilles starts. As we have described it above, the tortoise moves 10 yards in stage 1, 1 yard in stage 2, one-tenth of a yard in stage 3, one-hundredth of a yard in stage 4, etc. Suppose we had a number language like the Greeks and Romans, or the Hebrews, who used letters of the alphabet. Using the one that is familiar to us because it is still used for clocks, graveyards, and law-courts, we might write the total of all the distances the tortoise ran before Achilles caught him up like this:

$$X + I + \frac{I}{X} + \frac{I}{C} + \frac{I}{M} \text{ and so on.}$$

We have put "and so on" because the ancient peoples got into great difficulties when they had to handle numbers more than a few thousands. Apart from the fact that we have left the tail of the series to your imagination (and do not forget that the tail is most of the animal if it goes on for ever), notice another disadvantage about this script. There is absolutely nothing to suggest to you how the distances at each stage of the race are connected with one another. To-day we have a number vocabulary which makes this relation perfectly evident when we write it down as:

$$10 + 1 + \frac{1}{10} + \frac{1}{100} + \frac{1}{1,000} + \frac{1}{10,000} + \frac{1}{100,000} + \frac{1}{1,000,000} \text{ and so on.}$$

In this case we put "and so on" to save ourselves trouble, not because we have not the right number-words. These number-words were borrowed from the Hindus, who learnt to write number language after Zeno and Euclid had gone to their graves. A social revolution, the Protestant Reformation, gave us schools which made this number language the common property of mankind. A second social upheaval, the French Revolution, taught us to use a reformed spelling. Thanks to the Education Acts of the nineteenth century, this reformed spelling is part of the common fund of knowledge shared by almost every sane individual in the English-speaking world. Let us write the last total, using this reformed spelling, which we call decimal notation. That is to say:

$$10 + 1 + 0{\cdot}1 + 0{\cdot}01 + 0{\cdot}001 + 0{\cdot}0001 + 0{\cdot}00001 + 0{\cdot}000001$$
$$\text{and so on.}$$

We have only to use the reformed spelling to remind ourselves that this can be put in a more snappy form:

$$11{\cdot}111111 \text{ etc.,}$$

or still better:

$$11{\cdot}\dot{1}.$$

We recognize the fraction 0.i as a quantity that is less than $\frac{2}{10}$ and more than $\frac{1}{10}$. If we have not forgotten the arithmetic we learnt at school, we may even remember that 0.i corresponds with the fraction $\frac{1}{9}$. This means that the longer we make the sum, 0·1 + 0·01 + 0·001, etc., the nearer it gets to $\frac{1}{9}$, and it never grows bigger than $\frac{1}{9}$. The total of all the yards the tortoise moves till there is no distance between himself and Achilles makes up just 11$\frac{1}{9}$ yards, and no more.

You will now begin to see what was meant by saying that the riddle presents no mathematical difficulty to you. You have a number language constructed so that it can take into account a possibility which mathematicians describe by a very impressive name. They call it the convergence of an infinite series to a limiting value. Put in plain words, this only means that, if you go on piling up smaller and smaller quantities as long as you can, you *may* get a pile of which the size is not made measurably larger by adding any more. The immense difficulty which the mathematicians of the ancient world experienced when they dealt with a process of division carried on indefinitely, or with what modern mathematicians call infinite series, limits, transcendental numbers, irrational quantities, and so forth, provides an example of a great social truth borne out by the whole history of human knowledge. Fruitful intellectual activity of the cleverest people draws its strength from the common knowledge which all of us share. Beyond a certain point clever people can never transcend the limitations of the social culture they inherit. When clever people pride themselves on their own isolation, we may well wonder whether they are very clever after all. Our studies in mathematics are going to show us that whenever the culture of a people loses contact with the common life of mankind and becomes exclusively the plaything of a leisure class, it is becoming a priestcraft. It is destined to end, as does all priestcraft, in superstition. To be proud of intellectual isolation from the common life of mankind and to be disdainful of the great social task of education is as stupid as it is wicked. It is the end of progress in knowledge. History shows that superstitions are not manufactured by the plain man. They are invented by neurotic intellectuals with too little to do. The mathematician and the plain man each need one another. Maybe the Western world is about to be plunged irrevocably into barbarism. If it escapes this fate, the men and women of the leisure state which is now within our grasp will regard the democratization of mathematics as a decisive step in the advance of civilization.

In such a time as ours the danger of retreat into barbarism is very real. We may apply to mathematics the words in which Cobbett explained the uses of grammar to the working-men of his own day when there was no public system of free schools. In the first of his letters on English grammar for a working boy, Cobbett wrote these words: "But, to the acquiring of this branch of knowledge, my dear son, there is one motive, which, though it ought, at all times, to be strongly felt, ought, at the present time, to be so felt in an extraordinary degree. I mean that desire which every man, and especially every young man, should entertain to be able to assert with effect the rights and liberties of his country. When you come to read the history of those Laws of England by which the freedom of the people has been secured . . . you will find that tyranny has no enemy so formidable as the pen. And, while you will see with exultation the long-imprisoned, the heavily-fined, the banished William Prynne, returning to liberty, borne by the people from Southampton to London, over a road strewed with flowers: then accusing, bringing to trial and to the block, the tyrants from whose hands he and his country had unjustly and cruelly suffered; while your heart and the heart of every young man in the kingdom will bound with joy at the spectacle, you ought all to bear in mind, that, without a knowledge of grammar, Mr. Prynne could never have performed any of those acts by which his name has been thus preserved, and which have caused his name to be held in honour."

To-day economic tyranny has no more powerful friend than the calculating prodigy. Without a knowledge of mathematics, the grammar of size and order, we cannot plan the rational society in which there will be leisure for all and poverty for none. If we are inclined to be a little afraid of the prospect, our first step towards understanding this grammar is to realize that the reasons which repel many people from studying it are not at all discreditable. As mathematics has been taught and expounded in schools no effort is made to show its social history, its significance in our own social lives, the immense dependence of civilized mankind upon it. Neither as children nor as adults are we told how the knowledge of this grammar has been used again and again throughout history to assist in the liberation of mankind from superstition. We are not shown how it may be used by us to defend the liberties of the people. Let us see why this is so.

The educational system of north-western Europe was largely moulded by three independent factors in the period of the Reformation. One was linguistic in the ordinary sense. To weaken the power of the Church as an economic overlord it was necessary to destroy the influence of the Church on the imagination of the people. The Protestant Reformers appealed to the recognized authority of scripture to show that the priestly practices were innovations. They had to make the scriptures an open book. The invention of printing was the mechanical instrument which destroyed the intellectual power of the Pope. Instruction in Latin and Greek was a corollary of the doctrine of the open Bible. This prompted the great educational innovation of John Knox and abetted the more parsimonious founding of grammar schools in England. The ideological front against popery and the wealthy monasteries strengthened its strategic position by new translations and critical inspection of the scriptural texts. That is one reason why classical scholarship occupied a place of high honour in the educational system of the middle classes.

The language of size owes its position in Western education to two different social influences. While revolt against the authority of the Church was gathering force, and before the reformed doctrine had begun to have a wide appeal for the merchants and craftsmen of the medieval boroughs, the mercantile needs of the Hanse had already led to the founding of special schools in Germany for the teaching of the new arithmetic which Europe had borrowed from the Arabs. An astonishing proportion of the books printed in the three years after the first press was set up were commercial arithmetics. Luther vindicated the four merchant gospels of addition, subtraction, multiplication, and division with astute political sagacity when he announced the outlandish doctrine that every boy should be taught to calculate. The grammar of numbers was chained down to commercial uses before people could foresee the vast variety of ways in which it was about to invade man's social life.

Geometry, already divorced from the art of calculation, did not enter into Western education by the same route. Apart from the stimulus which the study of dead languages received from the manufacture of Bibles, classical pursuits were encouraged because the political theories of the Greek philosophers were congenial to the merchants who were aspiring to a limited urban democracy. The appeal of the city-state democracy to the imagination of the wealthier bourgeois lasted till after the French Revolution, when it was laid to rest in the familiar funeral urns of mural decoration. The leisure class of the Greek city-states played with geometry as people play with crossword puzzles and chess to-day. Plato taught that geometry was the highest exercise to which human leisure could be devoted. So geometry became included in European education as a part of classical scholarship, without any clear connection with the contemporary reality of measuring Drake's "world encompassed." Those who taught Euclid did not understand its social use, and generations of schoolboys have studied Euclid without being told how a later geometry, which grew out of Euclid's teaching in the busy life of Alexandria, made it possible to measure the size of the world. Those measurements blew up the pagan pantheon of star gods and blazed the trail for the great navigations. The revelation of how much of the surface of our world was still unexplored was the solid ground for what we call the faith of Columbus.

Plato's exaltation of mathematics as an august and mysterious ritual had its roots in dark superstitions which troubled, and fanciful puerilities which entranced, people who were living through the childhood of civilization, when even the cleverest people could not clearly distinguish the difference between saying that 13 is a "prime" number and saying that 13 is an unlucky number. His influence on education has spread a veil of mystery over mathematics and helped to preserve the queer free-masonry of the Pythagorean brotherhoods, whose members were put to death for revealing mathematical secrets now printed in school-books. It reflects no discredit on anybody if this veil of mystery makes the subject distasteful. Plato's great achievement was to invent a religion which satisfies the emotional needs of people who are out of harmony with their social environment, and just too intelligent or too individualistic to seek sanctuary in the cruder forms of animism. The curiosity of the men who first speculated about atoms, studied the properties of the lodestone, watched the result of rubbing amber, dissected animals, and catalogued plants in the three centuries before Aristotle wrote his epitaph on Greek science, had banished personalities from natural and familiar objects. Plato placed animism beyond the reach of experimental exposure by inventing a world of "universals." This world of universals was the world as God knows it, the "real" world of which our own is but the shadow. In this "real" world symbols of speech and number are invested with the magic which departed from the bodies of beasts and the trunks of trees as soon as they were dissected and described.

The *Timaeus* is a fascinating anthology of the queer perversities to which this magic of symbolism could be pushed. Real earth, as opposed to the solid earth on which we build houses, is an equilateral triangle. Real water, as opposed to what is sometimes regarded as a beverage, is a right-angled triangle. Real fire, as opposed to fire against which you insure, is an isosceles triangle. Real air, as opposed to the air which you pump into a tire, is a scalene triangle [see drawing]. Lest you should find this hard to credit, read how Plato turned the geometry of the sphere into a magical explanation of man's origin. God, he tells us, "imitating the spherical shape of the universe, enclosed the two divine courses in a spherical body, that, namely, which we now term the head." In order that the head "might not tumble about among the deep and high places of the earth, but might be able to get out of the one and over the other," it was provided with "the body to be a vehicle and means of locomotion, which consequently had length and was furnished with four limbs extended and jointed. . . ." This supremacy of the head is very flattering to intellectuals who have no practical problems to occupy them. So it is not surprising that Plato's peculiar metaphysics retained its influence on education after his daring project for a planned society ceased to be thought a suitable doctrine for young people to study. An educational system which was based on Plato's teaching is apt to entrust the teaching of mathematics to people who put the head before the stomach, and who would tumble about the deep and high places of the earth if they had to teach another subject. Naturally this repels healthy people for whom symbols are merely the tools of organized social experience, and attracts those who use symbols to escape from our shadow world in which men battle for the little truth they can secure into a "real" world in which truth seems to be self-evident.

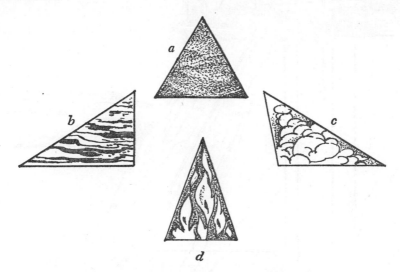

*Plato Took Measurement Out of Geometry*
*and Put Magic in Its Place*

*The real world of Plato was a world of form from which matter was banished.*
   (a)  *An equilateral triangle (i.e. one of which all three sides are equal) is the*
       *elemental earth form.*
   (b)  *A right-angled triangle is the spirit of water. (To find spirit in water is*
       *the most advanced kind of magic.)*
   (c)  *A scalene triangle with no equal sides is the spirit of the air.*
   (d)  *An isosceles triangle (i.e. one of which only two sides are equal) is the*
       *elemental fire.*
   *(If you do not know these names, note their meaning. You may meet them*
*again. You have been warned.)*

The fact that mathematicians are often like this may be why they are so inclined to keep the high mysteries of their Pythagorean brotherhood to themselves. To ordinary people, the perfection of their "real" world savours of unreality. The world in which ordinary people live is a world of struggle and failure, trial and error. In the mathematical world everything is obvious—once you have got used to it. What is rarely explained to us

*Mathematics in Everyday Life*

*This figure is taken from Agricola's famous sixteenth-century treatise on mining technology. At that time the miners were the aristocrats of labour, and the book called attention to a host of new scientific problems which had been neglected in the slave civilizations of antiquity, when there was little co-operation between theoretical speculation and practical experience. Having measured the distance HG which is the length of the stretched rope, you can get the distance you have to bore horizontally to reach the shaft, or the depth to which the shaft must be sunk, if you want to reach the horizontal boring. You will see easily with a scale diagram that the ratio of the horizontal cutting to the measured distance HG is the ratio of the two measurable distances N:M. Likewise the ratio of the shaft depth to HG is O:M. . . .*

is that it may have taken the human race a thousand years to see that one step in a mathematical argument is "obvious." How the Nilometer works is obvious to you if you are a priest in the temple. If you are outside the temple, it can only become obvious through tracing out the subterranean channel which connects the temple with the river of man's social experience. Educational methods which are mixed up with priestcraft and magic have contrived to keep the rising and falling, the perpetual movement of the river from our scrutiny. So they have hidden from us the romance of what might be the greatest saga of man's struggle with the elements. Plato, in whose school our teachers have grown up, did not approve of making observations and applying mathematics to arrange them and co-ordinate them. In one of the dialogues he makes Socrates, his master, use words which might equally well apply to many of the text-books of mechanics which are still used. "The starry heavens which we behold is wrought upon a visible ground and therefore, although the fairest and most perfect of visible things, must necessarily be deemed inferior far to the true motions of absolute swiftness and absolute intelligence. . . . These are to be apprehended by reason and intelligence but not by sight. . . . The spangled heavens should be used as a pattern and with a view to that higher knowledge. But the astronomer will never imagine that the proportions of night to day . . . or of the stars to these and to one another can also be eternal . . . and it is equally *absurd to take so much pains in investigating their exact truth. . . . In astronomy as in geometry we should employ problems, and let the heavens alone,* if we would approach the subject in the right way and so make the natural gift of reason to be of any use."

This book will narrate how the grammar of measurement and counting has evolved under the pressure of man's changing social achievements, how in successive stages it has been held in check by the barriers of custom, how it has been used in charting a universe which can be commanded when its laws are obeyed, but can never be propitiated by ceremonial and sacrifice. As the outline of the story develops, one difficulty which many people experience will become less formidable. The expert in mathematics is essentially a technician. So his chief concern in teaching is to make other technicians. Mathematical books are largely packed with exercises which are designed to give proficiency in workmanship. This makes us discouraged because of the immense territory which we have to traverse before we can get insight into the kind of mathematics which is used in modern science and social statistics. The fact is that modern mathematics does not borrow so very much from antiquity. To be sure, every useful development in mathematics rests on the historical foundation of some earlier branch. At the same time every new branch liquidates the usefulness of clumsier tools which preceded it. Although algebra, trigonometry, the use of graphs, the calculus all depend on the rules of Greek geometry, scarcely more than a dozen from the two hundred propositions of Euclid's elements are essential to help us in understanding how to use them. The remainder are complicated ways of doing things which can be done more simply when we know later branches of mathematics. For the mathematical technician these complications may provide a useful discipline. The person who wants to understand the place of mathematics in modern civilization is merely distracted and disheartened by them. What follows is for those who have been already disheartened and distracted, and have consequently forgotten what they may have learned already or fail to see the meaning or usefulness of what they remember. So we shall begin at the very beginning.

Two views are commonly held about mathematics. One comes from Plato. This is that mathematical statements represent eternal truths. Plato's doctrine was used by the German philosopher, Kant, as a stick with which to beat the materialists of his time, when revolutionary writings like those of Diderot were challenging priestcraft. Kant thought that the principles of geometry were eternal, and that they were totally independent of our sense organs. It happened that Kant wrote just before biologists discovered that we have a sense organ, part of what is called the internal ear, sensitive to the pull of gravitation. Since that discovery, the significance of which was first fully recognized by the German physicist, Ernst Mach, the geometry which Kant knew has been brought down to earth by Einstein. It no longer dwells in the sky where Plato put it. We know that geometrical statements when applied to the real world are only approximate truths. The theory of relativity has been very unsettling to mathematicians, and it has now become a fashion to say that mathematics is only a game. Of course, this does not tell us anything about mathematics. It only tells us something about the cultural limitations of some mathematicians. When a man says that mathematics is a game, he is making a private statement. He is telling us something about himself, his own attitude to mathematics. He is not telling us anything about the public meaning of a mathematical statement.

If mathematics is a game, there is no reason why people should play it if they do not want to. With football, it belongs to those amusements without which life would be endurable. The view which we shall explore is that mathematics is the language of size, and that it is an essential part of the equipment of an intelligent citizen to understand this language. If the rules of mathematics are rules of grammar, there is no stupidity involved when we fail to see that a mathematical truth is obvious. The rules of ordinary grammar are not obvious. They have to be learnt. They are not eternal truths. They are conveniences without whose aid truths about the sorts of things in the world cannot be communicated from one person to another. In Cobbett's memorable words, Mr. Prynne would not have been able to impeach Archbishop Laud if his command of grammar had been insufficient to make himself understood. So it is with mathematics, the grammar of size. The rules of mathematics are rules to be learnt. If they are formidable, they are formidable because they are unfamiliar when you first meet them—like gerunds or nominative absolutes. They are also formidable because in all languages there are so many rules and words to memorize before we can read newspapers or pick up radio news from foreign stations. Everybody knows that being able to chatter in several foreign languages is not a sign of great social intelligence. Neither is being able to chatter in the language of size. Real social intelligence lies in the use of a language, in applying the right words in the right context. It is important to know the language of size, because entrusting the laws of human society, social statistics, population, man's hereditary make-up, the balance of trade to the isolated mathematician without checking his conclusions is like letting a committee of philologists manufacture the truths of human, animal, or plant anatomy from the resources of their own imaginations.

You will often hear people say that nothing is more certain than that two and two make four. The statement that two and two make four is not a mathematical statement. The mathematical statement to which people refer, correctly stated, is as follows:

$$2 + 2 = 4.$$

This can be translated: "to 2 add 2 to get 4." This is not necessarily a statement of something which always happens in the real world. The illustration [on page 18] shows that in the real world you do not always find that you have 4 when you have added 2 to 2. To say $2 + 2 = 4$ merely illustrates the meaning of the verb "add" when it is used to translate the mathematical verb "+". To say that $2 + 2 = 4$ is a true statement is just a grammatical convention about the verb "+" and the nouns "2" and "4." In English grammar it is true in the same sense to say that the plural of "mouse" is "mice," or, if you prefer it, "add mouse to mouse to get mice." In English grammar it is untrue to say that the plural of "house" is "hice." Saying "$2 + 2 = 2$" is false in precisely the same sense. A slight change in the meaning of the word "add," as used to translate "+," makes it a perfectly correct statement about the apparatus [in the figure below]. Such changes of meaning are confusing. The object of grammar is to control the freedom of words so that there is no congestion of the intellectual traffic. As a statement about the real world, saying that

*In the real world you do not always find that you have got* four *when you add* two *and* two.

*Try filling this with water. Its laws of "addition" would be:*

$$1 +. 1 = 2$$
$$1 +. 2 = 3$$
$$1 +. 3 = 2$$
$$2 +. 2 = 2 \text{ etc.}$$

*The dot is put in to show that the kind of addition used here is not the kind of addition (+ without a dot) which applies to a vessel which cannot leak, and is so large that it cannot be filled.*

the British houses of Parliament are in Glasgow, is a plain lie. As a statement of grammar, it is a true example of how the plural of "house" is formed. If a British Radical member said that the Hice of Parliament were treating the unemployed of Glasgow with shameless frivolity, he might convey a profound and important truth about the real world to a few bright people. As a statement of grammar, it would be false. Many would miss the point and wonder whether he were certifiable. Unlike Mr. Prynne, who understood grammar, he would fail to advance the liberties of the people.

We must not be surprised if we find that the rules of mathematics are not always a perfect description of how we measure the distance of a star, or count heads in a population. The rules of English grammar are a very imperfect description of how English is used. The people who formulated them were preoccupied with translating the Bible and other classical texts. So they were over-anxious to find exact equivalents for the peculiarities of Greek and Latin. They were like the first zoologists who used words for the limbs and organs of the human body when describing the peculiar anatomy of the insect. The English grammar taught in English schools is rather primitive zoology. Also it is essentially a description of the habits of speech prevailing in the English professional class, from which writers of books on grammar are drawn. When the American from New England says "gotten," he is using what was the correct past participle of the strong verb "to get" in *Mayflower* times. When the English country labourer says "we be going," he is correctly using one of the three original verbs which have been used to make the roots of the modern mixed verb "to be." When he says "yourn," he is using one of two once equally admissible and equally fashionable forms introduced by analogy about the time when Chaucer wrote the *Canterbury Tales*. To say that "are" and "yours" are grammatically correct is merely to say that we have agreed to adopt the habits of the more prosperous townspeople. When Mr. Shaw is dead, and hence a topic for grammarians, we shall say that "dont" is the correct way to write "do not." Almost certainly we shall soon admit "it is me" as correct grammar. The rules of mathematical grammar also change. In modern vector analysis the rules for using "+" are not the rules we learned at school.

If we can unearth milestones of man's social pilgrimage in the language of everyday life, it is much more easy to do so when we study the grammar of mathematics. The language in which people describe the different *sorts* of things there are in the world is vastly more primitive and more conservative than the *size* languages which have been multiplied to cope with the increasing precision of man's control over nature. In the world which is open to public inspection, the world of inorganic and organic nature, man was not compelled to enlarge the scope of language to describe any new *sorts* of phenomena between 2000 B.C. and the researches of Faraday and Hertz, the father of radio. Even electric and magnetic attractions were recognized as a special sort of thing before there were any historians in the world. In the seventh century B.C. Thales recorded the attraction of small particles to a piece of amber (Greek "electron") when rubbed. The Chinese already knew about the lodestone or natural magnet. Since about 1000 B.C., when some men broke away from picture writing or script like the Chinese which associates sounds with picture symbols, and first began to use an alphabet based purely on how words sound, there has only been one conspicuous invention introduced for describing the qualities of things in the world. This was made by biologists in the eighteenth century, when the confusion existing in the old herbals of medicinal plants forced them to invent an international language in which no confusion is possible. The clear description of the immense variety of organic beings has been made possible by the deliberate introduction of unfamiliar words. These words, like *Bellis perennis,* the common daisy, or *Pulex irritans,* the common flea, are taken from dead languages. Any meaning for which the biologist has no use lies buried in a social context forgotten long ago. In much the same way the North Europeans had borrowed their alphabet of sound symbols from the picture scripts, and buried the associations of distracting metaphors in the symbols used by the more sophisticated people of the ancient world.

The language of mathematics differs from that of everyday life, because it is essentially a rationally planned language. The languages of size have no place for private sentiment, either of the individual or of the nation. They are international languages like the binomial nomenclature of natural history. In dealing with the immense complexity of his social life man has not yet begun to apply inventiveness to the rational planning of ordinary language when describing different kinds of institutions and human behaviour. The language of everyday life is clogged with sentiment, and the science of human nature has not advanced so far that we can describe individual sentiment in a clear way. So constructive thought about human society is hampered by the same conservatism as embarrassed the earlier naturalists. Nowadays people do not differ about what sort of animal is meant by cimex or pediculus, because these words are only used by people who use them in one way. They still can and often do mean a lot of different things when they say that a mattress is infested with bugs or lice. The study of man's social life has not yet brought forth a Linnaeus. So an argument about the "withering away of the state" may disclose a difference about the use of the dictionary when no real difference about the use of the policeman is involved. Curiously enough, people who are most sensible about the need for planning other social amenities in a reasonable way are often slow to see the need for creating a rational and international language.

The technique of measurement and counting has followed the caravans and galleys of the great trade routes. It has developed very slowly. At least four thousand years intervened between the time when men could calculate when the next eclipse would occur and the time when men could calculate how much iron is present in the sun. Between the first recorded observations of electricity produced by friction and the measurement of the attraction of an electrified body two thousand years intervened. Perhaps a longer period separates the knowledge of magnetic iron (or lodestone) and the measurement of magnetic force. Classifying things according to size has been a much harder task than recognizing the different sorts of things there are. It has been more closely related to man's social achievements than to his biological equipment. Our eyes and ears can recognize different sorts of things at a great distance. To measure things at a distance, man has had to make new sense organs for himself, like the astrolabe, the telescope, and the microphone. He has made scales which reveal differences of weight to which our hands are quite insensitive. At each stage in the evolution of the tools of measurement man has refined the tools of size language. As human inventiveness has turned from the counting of flocks and seasons to the building of temples, from the building of temples to the steering of ships into chartless seas, from seafaring plunder to machines driven by the forces of dead matter, new languages of size have sprung up in succession. Civilizations have risen and fallen. At each stage a more primitive, less sophisticated culture breaks through the barriers of custom thought, brings fresh rules to the grammar of measurement, bearing within itself the limitation of further growth and the inevitability that it will be superseded in its turn. The history of mathematics is the mirror of civilization.

The beginnings of a size language are to be found in the priestly civilizations of Egypt and Sumeria. From these ancient civilizations we see the first-fruits of secular knowledge radiated along the inland trade routes to China and pushing out into and beyond the Mediterranean, where the Semitic peoples are sending forth ships to trade in tin and dyes. The more primitive northern invaders of Greece and Asia Minor collect and absorb the secrets of the pyramid makers in cities where a priestly caste is not yet established. As the Greeks become prosperous, geometry becomes a plaything. Greek thought itself becomes corrupted with the star worship of the ancient world. At the very point when it seems almost inevitable that geometry will make way for a new language, it ceases to develop further. The scene shifts to Alexandria, the greatest centre of shipping and the mechanical arts in the ancient world. Men are thinking about how much of the world remains to be explored. Geometry is applied to the measurement of the heavens. Trigonometry takes its place. The size of the earth, the distance of the sun and moon are measured. The star gods are degraded. In the intellectual life of Alexandria, the factory of world religions, the old syncretism has lost its credibility. It may still welcome a god beyond the sky. It is losing faith in the gods within the sky.

In Alexandria, where the new language of star measurement has its beginnings, men are thinking about numbers unimaginably large compared with the numbers which the Greek intellect could grasp. Anaxagoras had shocked the court of Pericles by declaring that the sun was as immense as the mainland of Greece. Now Greece itself had sunk into insignificance beside the world of which Eratosthenes and Poseidonius had measured the circumference. The world itself sank into insignificance beside the sun as Aristarchus had measured it. Ere the dark night of monkish superstition engulfed the great cosmopolis of antiquity, men were groping for new means of calculation. The bars of the counting frame had become the bars of a cage in which the intellectual life of Alexandria was imprisoned. Men like Diophantus and Theon were using geometrical diagrams to devise crude recipes for calculation. They had almost invented the third new language of algebra. That they did not succeed was the nemesis of the social culture they inherited. In the East the Hindus had started from a much lower level. Without the incubus of an old-established vocabulary of number, they had fashioned new symbols which lent themselves to simple calculation without mechanical aids. The Moslem civilization which swept across the southern domain of the Roman Empire brought together the technique of measurement, as it had evolved in the hands of the Greeks and the Alexandrians, adding the new instrument for handling numbers which was developed through the invention of the Hindu number symbols. In the hands of Arabic mathematicians like Omar Khayyām, the main features of a language of calculation took shape. We still call it by the Arabic name, algebra. We owe algebra and the pattern of modern European poetry to a non-Aryan people who would be excluded from the vote in the Union of South Africa.

Along the trade routes this new arithmetic is brought into Europe by Jewish scholars from the Moorish universities of Spain and by gentile merchants trading with the Levant, some of them patronized by nobles whose outlook had been unintentionally broadened by the Crusades. Europe stands on the threshold of the great navigations. Seafarers are carrying Jewish astronomers who can use the star almanacs which Arab scholarship had prepared. The merchants are becoming rich. More than ever the world is thinking in large numbers. The new arithmetic or "algorithm" sponsors an amazing device which was prompted by the need for more accurate tables of star measurement for use in seafaring. Logarithms were among the cultural first-fruits of the great navigations. Mathematicians are thinking in maps, in latitude and longitude. A new kind of geometry (what we call graphs in everyday speech) was an inevitable consequence. This new geometry of Descartes contains something which Greek geometry had left out. In the leisurely world of antiquity there were no clocks. In the bustling world of the great navigations mechanical clocks are displacing the ancient ceremonial function of the priesthood as timekeepers. A geometry which could represent time and a religion in which there were no saints' days are emerging from the same social context. From this geometry of time a group of men who were studying the mechanics of the pendulum-clock and making fresh discoveries about the motion of the planets devise a new size language to measure motion. To-day we call it "the" calculus.

For the present this crude outline of the history of mathematics as a mirror of civilization, interlocking with man's common culture, his inventions, his economic arrangements, his religious beliefs, may be left at the stage which had been reached when Newton died. What has happened since has been largely the filling of gaps, the sharpening of instruments already devised. Here and there are indications of a new sort of mathematics. We see a hint of it in social statistics and the study of the atom. We begin to see possibilities of new languages of size transcending those we now use, as the calculus of movement gathered into itself all that had gone before.

---

*The foregoing consists of Chapter I*
*from Hogben's* MATHEMATICS FOR THE MILLION.

# Andrew Russell Forsyth

## 1858–1942

Every now and then a mathematician is called upon to justify his craft to nonmathematicians. The occasion may be an address delivered before some learned body (learned in other fields), or it may be an informal after-dinner conversation. In either case the usual approach is to show how useful mathematics is. Too often, however, this consists essentially in pointing out that everyone needs to do sums at some time in his life. It remains for the gifted teacher to try to define what he considers to be the mathematical way of thinking, and to describe precisely the nature of the relationship between mathematics and the other sciences. Forsyth was such a teacher.

Andrew Russell Forsyth, Scottish mathematician, was born in Glasgow in 1858. After studying at University College in Liverpool and at Trinity College in Cambridge, he became a professor of mathematics, lecturing at Trinity College, Cambridge, and at the Imperial College of Science and Technology in London. He was a creative mathematician in the field of pure mathematics, and wrote widely on the subject of differential equations. In addition to his own contributions to mathematics, Forsyth stimulated interest in the work of other mathematicians. He died in 1942.

Mathematics, in Life and Thought, delivered as a lecture in 1928, is an example of Forsyth's ability to excite interest in a subject usually regarded with either awe or dislike. Much of it is devoted to a description of the mental processes which led Newton from the observation of the falling apple to the theory of universal gravitation. Though such a description in nonmathematical terms requires considerable simplification, it is an interesting account of the facts then available to Newton, and the puzzles that he had to solve in order to arrive at his theory. In placing Newton's work in its historical context as the culmination of investigations by Copernicus, Galileo, and Kepler, and followed by radical modifications by Einstein, Forsyth illustrates the nonstatic nature of scientific theory. The last word is never said.

After mentioning the many areas in which mathematics serves in the market place, Forsyth makes a special plea for mathematics as a pure science. In many cases scientific theories can come into being only because the forms in which they can be expressed have been created by mathematicians years or even centuries before anyone foresaw their possible usefulness.

# Mathematics, in Life
# and Thought

There is an ancient adage, certainly as old as the naturalist Pliny, who perished in the famous eruption of Vesuvius, that "a shoemaker should not look above his last." The wisdom of the adage is always being ignored. The newspapers give evidence of the neglect in their daily spate of ingenuous letters. Every publishing season adds to the evidence by the recurring deluge of new books which seem no nearer an end now than they were in the days of the troubled preacher who, like many another student, found much study a weariness of the flesh. The neglect is not unknown even in the range of occasional lecturers of the strictest academic credentials. Physicists, whose main concern has been with the inanimate matter of the universe, have been heard to pontificate on the origins of life and its continuity after death. Men of science will discourse on philosophy with no more success and no more clarity than are achieved by Beatrice in Dante's *Divina Commedia*. Philosophers, in all the precision of metaphysics, will enunciate canons for the progress of observational science. Nay, theologians have been known to formulate fundamental principles which, as being the eternal verities, are the unchanging limits of scientific attainment. Even the citizen in the bus will settle the policy of a nation, though his knowledge of an issue at stake could be written on a picture postcard, leaving plenty of space for the picture. So let me, very respectfully, for once be the obedient shoemaker of the adage, not look above my last, and offer you a sample of my own wares.

The subject of mathematics, to some aspects of which my lecture will invite your attention, is regarded variously: sometimes with respect, rising through awe to wonder; sometimes with dislike, degenerating through repulsion to hatred. Occasionally it is regarded as a key, even as the guide, to trustworthy knowledge; sometimes as the dismal process of calculations to be performed by hired computers. In any event, why take it as the matter of a lecture? For there are at least two diverging views as to the nature of such a performance. One view is that the lecture should give a tabloid summary of what is hidden in books that are not read: yet, in the case of my choice, who wants a summary of what seems the infinitely arid and the absolutely incomprehensible, as so obviously appears whenever a mathematical book is opened? Another view is that the lecture should give what is not to be found in any of the books, so that the exposition of novelties shall induce, in a sympathetic listener, the frame of mind that is willing to acquire fuller knowledge through patient labour. On this view the listener must indeed be sympathetic, very willing to provide the patient labour for the acquisition of mathematical knowledge: for he will find, as Euclid told a bored and discontented pupil in words that have lived for more than two thousand years, "There is no royal road to learning."

My purpose differs from both of these implied aims. It is to invite you to note one or two of the uses, some simple, some recondite, of mathematics, and, by noting them, to attempt an appreciation of the issues which are forced into daily discussion and daily action.

For the ordinary course of affairs a great English divine declared that "probability is the very guide of life." Usually certainty is lacking: and probability can be taken as the only reasonable guide amid an occasional maze of possibilities. Yet, when sifted and analysed, this probability often reduces itself to a more or less mathematical (chiefly, I fear, less mathematical) measure of moral and material advantages to follow. The spirit of mathematics, if not its method, dominates the sifting analysis: we can sometimes regret that the method is lacking. Let me offer a couple of illustrations.

Some of you may remember a legend of wide circulation in 1914 before the Great War was many weeks old: how a force of 80,000 Russians had been landed in the north of England, transported from the north-east coast to Portsmouth, and thence shipped to France. The moral support of those Russians was a comforting belief at the moment. There had been days, only a human generation earlier, when everything Russian had been anathema to patriotic Englishmen: but those days were past. Though we might be martially arrogant enough to feel that we did not need the help, it still was good to think that we had it: so comforting that the news was accepted without question. Retired military men in clubs, an unfailing source of trustworthy wisdom, were supposed to know it: the unverified gossip of the smoking-room gathered confidence in statement as it spread: the good news was believed. I was staying on the Dorsetshire coast at the time: and during a week-end a visitor brought information from a London club that the stationmaster at Dorchester had seen the Russians pass through his station in the train. My mathematical scepticism was roused: my informant, by successive queries mildly posed, was induced to estimate the number of men in a compartment, the number of compartments in a carriage, the number of carriages in a train even in a period of emergency, and the consequent number of trains needed to convey the said 80,000 Russians. When, on the basis of his own estimates, he informed me (correctly) that over one hundred trains would be required for the transport, I asked him whether the Dorchester stationmaster had seen over one hundred trains pass through his station. His answer was blank silence: for him, as for me, the Russians vanished into thin air—a little salutary arithmetic had dissipated a hopelessly false legend that was fostering false confidence. Probability had not been the guide of my informant's judgment.

I suppose that, in Swansea as in other communities, considerable industry is devoted by eager optimists to competitions anticipating the results of football matches. Newspapers (all of them prudent enough to insure against loss in the venture) vie with one another in offering large sums of money for merely filling up slips of paper: in those slips entries are to be made estimating the result for each one of a dozen matches, a win, or a draw, or a loss, for a specified side. To the person who antici-pates all the twelve results correctly, a large sum of money is paid. So the competitors, eager for wealth but niggardly in constructive labour, spend long periods in hatching their prophetic guesses. It is not a game: it is not a business; it is a gamble. I sometimes wonder whether the competitors have the faintest idea of the minuteness of the chance of individual success in the competition, if it can be dignified by such a title. There are more than four thousand different ways of getting every guess wrong; there are more ways of getting eight guesses wrong and the other four right than there are of getting any other distribution; there are more than half a million ways of having one or more errors in the selection: there is only one way of getting them all right. Need I say more? To this fatuous occupation, Bishop Butler might have hesitated before declaring probability to be the very guide of life.

Let us pass to consider matters somewhat more serious and more precise.

A copious definition of mathematics can be given by describing it as the craft of counting as in the arithmetic of daily life, as the craft of measuring as in the original needs of surveying and engineering, as the craft of observing and noting as in the early days of astronomy. When the simple processes of counting, of measuring, and of recording observations are pursued systematically, it is found that the repetition of some particular issue requires the particular repetition of some unchanging and appropriate process—a rule is evolved: the rules aggregate into a science. Moreover, there arises the necessity for some discrimination between the nebulous inspiration of a guess, which in our graver moods we call an "idea," and the comparative certainty of a systematic inference, which those graver moods dignify with the title of a "theory." As a mere fact, speculations and ideas may be almost as old as the hills: laborious methods can lead to a theory which, new to-day, may be discarded or be confirmed tomorrow in the light of fuller knowledge.

Again let me offer a couple of illustrations, more academic than imaginary Russians or a gambling quest for an unearned increment. One shall be from astronomy, the other from the structure of matter or (as the old Latin poet Lucretius styled it) the nature of things.

Systematic astronomy had its establishment in observations as accurate as time and patience and simple instruments would allow. A marvellous collection of facts, relating to such abstruse phenomena as the sequence of eclipses of the sun and of the moon, was made by the ancient Chaldeans. Later the Greeks, whose passion for geometry was almost a rule of life, began to describe the heavens geometrically as they saw and we see the heavens. The natural, the almost inevitable, consequence was that, because the Greek observers described accurately what they saw, they made the earth the centre of the universe. (Here let me say that these old Greek descriptions remain as accurate as man could make them: where we part company from the Greeks is in the assumption, obvious but untrue, that the phenomena require the earth to be the centre of all things.) Yet nearly three centuries before the Christian era the Greek philosopher, Aristarchus of Samos, was an early astronomical heretic—he groped towards a heliocentric theory of the universe: with him it was a speculation, an idea, based upon an inference that the sun is seven times as large as the earth, at a time when there was little knowledge of the size of the earth and less of the size of the sun. His speculation remained in the region of fancy: the traditional trust in Aristotle maintained the acceptance of the old geocentric theory; there were not enough facts to achieve the tragedy of killing a theory. In their turn the theologians of the West, conservative as are all orders of organized priesthood, made the geocentric theory an article of orthodox faith: and for centuries the universe, thus theocratic in matters outside religion and faith, could be described only in the vocabulary of the schoolmen in theology. A Catholic monk, Copernicus, opened the path to a change of estimate, though the innocent dedication of his book to the Pope saved his name from contumely: had he lived, it might not have saved him from the fate of Galilei. Gradually, almost painfully, methods systematized from facts killed the old theory: and the inspired guess of Aristarchus passed from the range of happy surmise into a knowledge of the solar system of which even the most exuberant imagination had not dared to dream.

My second illustration is taken from a more speculative range of thought—more speculative because less openly amenable to observation and to experiment. Many of you doubtless are familiar with the recent predominance of the word "atom" in scientific discussions. There was a time, even now easily recalled, when the use of the word was an implicit declaration that finality had been attained: human knowledge could not penetrate the indivisible. In the interval, a school of mathematical physicists has devoted itself to the study of the atom: its apostles have concluded that, mathematically, an atom is a universe in itself, a sort of solar system with recurrent revolutions of its members that can be subjected to calculation. Different atoms, in present speculation, are different universes which, under the compulsion of electric bombardment, may lose some of their constituents and, in doing so, become a changed universe. But mark the history. The atom was the irresoluble element by which Democritus, four centuries before the Christian era, explained the phenomena of matter to one of the most critical nations of thinkers the world has known: the atom became the explanation of animate, as well as of inanimate, nature. The culmination of that ancient theory came in the doctrine of Epicurus; and its fine exposition by Lucretius is nearly two thousand years old. In varying forms, with changing adaptations, it was tried, was found wanting, was driven from pillar to post, until it seemed to have reached a secure haven in chemistry. Where is the atomic theory now? Thirty years ago chemists were shocked by the resolution of the atom, the absolutely irresoluble element; now the more elusive electron has taken the field. The scientific world is in pursuit of the electron: Sir Ernest Rutherford is battering the atom by an electric attack under staggering voltage; and the negative electrons thus violently expelled from the domain of the positive nucleus are realizing the speculative guess made, centuries ago, by Hipparchus, that atoms could lose portions of themselves and thereby change their essence. Sir Joseph Thomson, the brilliant master of Rutherford, goes further than his pupil and suggests that the electron itself is a universe, perhaps another mathematical solar system; and only two short months ago the distinguished son of Sir Joseph Thomson was able, as the result of investigations, to compare the size of the electron and that of the atom, neither of which has been seen by man. Physical speculation is outrunning its mathematics: but, as so often before, the return to mathematics is ever made as soon as there are facts amenable to calculation. The facts remain, and the calculations based on the facts remain. Theories spring up and flourish while they conform to the facts and the calculations: they wilt, when new facts come that demand requirements which the theories cannot supply. It resembles the historic cult in the Arician grove: an old theory of yesterday is forsaken for a new one of to-day, itself to be forsaken to-morrow, like

> The priest who slew the slayer
> And shall himself be slain.

What part does the science of mathematics play in all this scientific tornado? And, indeed, what does the science include, and what may it claim to achieve? Broadly speaking, as soon as any progressive subject attains a stage where its phenomena admit of some kind of measurement, then and there the science of calculation can begin to deal with the measurements: thereafter the subject can be assisted by mathematics. Calculations can predict some results that must ensue from combinations of facts, and so can render some experiments superfluous. Calculations can even anticipate experiment and observation: such has been the case with Hamilton's conical refraction in optics and with the electric waves which first emerged from the mathematical labours of Maxwell and Hertz. Calculations can utilize facts in nonexperimental fashion and produce results that lay concealed. But no calculation can produce results that do not belong to the range of the subject-matter: thus astrology, and alchemy, and necromancy, bound to be scientific failures, were and are successful frauds owing to the undying gullibility of human nature in its wistful yearning for the unknown and the unattainable.

Briefly, the science of mathematics cannot be a substitute for essential experiment: but it can show how experiments and observations, duly systematized, can be elucidated so as to discriminate between what is principle and what is detailed consequence of principle. Sometimes it can lead, though its guidance is unrecognized, to simple devices which economize labour to an extent almost beyond credibility. Thus some of you know the slide-rule by practice; many of you will know it by name; but I am not sure that every student, or even every professor, would be prepared to furnish a reasoned statement justifying the various processes for which that admirable instrument is used. Yet it can be regarded as a compendium of logarithms, without tables and without any necessity for calculation: and logarithms are but a means of turning abstruse multiplication into simple addition and abstruse division into simple subtraction. Again, your Russian peasant usually is illiterate: but he will make out his invoice for wool, or furs, or timber, or corn and rye, as accurately as your western clerk by surprisingly simple means that mark a limit of his attainments. He can multiply by the number two, but no other number; he can divide by the number two, but by no other number; and he can perform simple addition. By these three operations he effects all that he needs for business transactions, and he effects it accurately. But he could not give you one word of explanation of a process which to him has become a habit; and if you explained the mathematical argument that justifies his action, he could not understand one word of the explanation. Does his process strike you as wonderful? It is no more wonderful, it is less wonderful, than the process employed by the smallest shopkeeper. Your Welsh shopkeeper calculates in what mathematicians call the scale of four for farthings, in the scale of twelve for pence, in the scale of twenty for shillings; he adds and he multiplies in the scale of ten. But he knows nothing of numerical scales; and probably he would not understand a word of reasoned explanation of such scales. The Russian peasant actually calculates, in essence though not in obvious form, in the scale of two: and some kind though unknown genius, in a dim and distant past, has turned the simple mathematics of the scale of two into the Russian peasant's process of arithmetic.

And if such is the fact in simple matters, you need not be surprised if the science of mathematics is used to high economic purpose where, at some stage, its calculations are obtrusively significant. Another couple of examples will justify such a statement.

At the present time, parts of the country are soon to be covered with a vast network of wires, stretching from pier to pier, for the transmission of electric power from central stations to relatively remote places where the power cannot be generated and cannot otherwise be obtained or concentrated. All sorts of complicated questions of an engineering kind arise, as fundamental in their way as questions connected with the construction of a liner to cross the Atlantic or a bridge to span the Ganges: questions of stress, of strain, of strength to face unknown but imaginable conditions which may become grimly real; and the answers are the results of mathematical calculations. These calculations are made in an office, but they do not remain in the office: they are utilized to indicate critical tests and to adapt given possibilities for the making of those tests in a variety of external conditions. Not until all the tests are satisfied would the engineers be justified in proceeding to their work: and engineers know, and can imagine, better than all others concerned, how much superfluous labour has been saved by the mathematical calculations.

There were days when the telegraph, overhead or submarine, was at once a new toy and a new mystery. Once the springs of action were known, their doings were regularized by instruments devised on a mathematical basis. Systematic processes were thus possible: their mathematical basis was worked out by Lord Kelvin (then Professor William Thomson) especially for submarine cables; and through his double genius for mathematics and for engineering applications of mathematics, the telegraph took its place in the routine of daily life. Now it is so ordinary, almost so stale and so old-fashioned, as to seem on the verge of supersession. For you are surrounded by wireless telegraphy at every turn; the beginnings of telephotography are being made whereby you may see in your evening paper a transmitted photograph of some event occurring only a few hours earlier perhaps some thousands of miles away. Does it ever occur to jaded satisfaction to inquire how so much has come into ordinary life which even in our grandfathers' age would have been declared impossible or fanciful? The story is not long, though the labour has been multitudinous.

Probably any historian of modern electrical science would be prepared to acknowledge Faraday's researches as the beginning of a new epoch. Great as was his genius, and valuable as were those researches, Faraday left them largely as a treasury of rich results, fundamental in bearing, capable of ordered development from their experimental stage and wisely formulated laws, but still undeveloped. Then another genius with another bent, Maxwell the mathematician, regarded the quantitative results obtained by Faraday as the material for systematic mathematical analysis; and the monument of his life is his ordered mathematical exposition of a new mathematical theory of electricity and magnetism founded on the Faraday results. But, as so often has been the fact in the movements of human knowledge, when once the accurate scientific observations received their systematic treatment by mathematics, interesting possibilities were revealed that hitherto had not even been surmised; and one immediate consequence of Maxwell's work was his creation of an electro-magnetic theory of light, through the identification of a relation between certain electrical constants and the speed of the transmission of light. The notion of waves and vibrations now entered boldly into the discussion. Another mathematical genius, Hertz, developed the consequences of the Maxwell theory and, by his calculations, obtained inferences in advance of observed results. The constructive genius of engineers—Marconi is a typical and outstanding example—was fired to new efforts in practical application. Soon there was the initial sending of messages through space (call it the ether, if you choose, but do not suppose that a name implies knowledge) from one land to another, from land to ocean and ocean to land: last Sunday's armistice service in Trafalgar Square in London was heard in New Zealand. Let me leave you in the middle of sounds, which may come from a studio near at hand or a continental orchestra perhaps in Rome or Madrid: and in all your surprise and happiness do not entirely forget that, throughout the development, the science of mathematics has played, is playing, and will continue to play, its significant part in every endeavour. Electrical engineering is not wholly electrical, in practice or in theory: its successes are achieved not solely through its machinery, however elaborate. Behind all its progress, as part of the reasoning mind of it all, there labours the science of mathematics as an angel of human thought.

Perhaps it is in astronomy that the most picturesque instances of the use of mathematics have occurred. You all have read of the fall of an apple in a Norfolk garden: how that fall made Newton ponder: and how the scribes (sparing us details perhaps not always known to them) tell us that Newton thence discovered the theory of gravitation. Will you be indulgent if, with only a fragment of calculation and confessedly for an ulterior purpose, I attempt to give you an outline of the process of thought which led to that theory?

Without going back to the beginnings of dynamical science, it will be sufficient to recall one of the experimental observations of Galilei, now almost commonplace enough to be ignored; then novel enough to startle old conceptions, ultimately to destroy some dogmas of theological (I do not say religious) belief, and to recast human ideas of the cosmic universe. He inferred that a dropped stone fell straight down, that is, towards the centre of the earth, because the descent, wherever tried, is always straight down. He also inferred that, in its movement, the stone fell

four times as far in the first two seconds as it did in the first, nine times
as far in the first three seconds as it did in the first: and so on for the
succession of seconds from the beginning: the distance fallen in any
number of seconds is measured by the result of taking that number and
multiplying it by itself, "squaring it," as we mathematicians call the
calculation. But this only gives a comparative measure among different
periods: something more is wanted in order to state what we popularly
call an exact measure. Such a statement demands a knowledge of the
exact distance that the stone would fall in a specified time; for example,
the exact distance the stone would fall in five seconds from the beginning
of its movement. He had noted observations also which answered the
demand: the result of calculations (always there is calculation) showed
that there is a number, very slightly larger than sixteen (but let me call
it sixteen for brevity of statement), which is of crucial importance. Return
now to the measure of the distance through which the stone falls. We saw
that the distance is, first of all, measured by a number which is the square
of the number of seconds (the number of seconds multiplied by itself).
We take that square number, which gives the first and the sort of relative
estimate of the fall, and we multiply that square number by the crucial
number sixteen, no matter what the square number may have been. The
product—what a schoolboy calls the "answer"—is the exact distance
through which the stone has fallen in the specified time, when the
distance is measured in English feet. Thus in three seconds the distance
would be 144 ft.: for the square of three (that is, three multiplied by
three) is 9, and the result of multiplying 9 by the crucial number 16 is
144. In five seconds the fall would be 400 ft.: for the square of five (that
is, five multiplied by five) is 25, and the result of multiplying 25 by the
crucial number 16 is 400. And so on. Let me ask you to remember that the
fall of the stone is measured by the square of the number of seconds in the
duration of the fall: above all, to remember that there is a crucial number
sixteen.

Now an explanation of the movements of the planets was being
attained, though very gradually. The Copernican opinion, that they
moved round the sun as a fixed body, was making its way, because the
more it was tested the more continually did it accord with facts. The
observations of Tycho Brahe had been reduced to systematic results by
the industry of Kepler, who found that planets move almost in circles,
actually in oval curves (mathematicians call them ellipses), with the sun
in the supreme position at the focus: and these ovals differ from circles
only very slightly. But that discovery of Kepler's was only descriptive,

corresponding to the description of a stone as falling straight down: it was no sort of measure of the movement of a planet. Such a measure came, once more, from Kepler's labours: he established two great inferences, laws as they are called. One law was concerned with the constant rate of speed round the sun, as measured by the area swept out by an imagined line drawn from the sun to the planet, thus giving one sort of measure. The other law was concerned with a relation between the size of the oval described by the planet round the sun, and the time which the planet required to effect one complete revolution round the sun: thus giving a second sort of measure. Knowledge had passed out of the describing stage into the measuring stage.

The genius of Newton comes upon the scene. According to the chronicles in summary, he saw an apple fall: it made him think of the moon; and thought led him to the theory of universal gravitation. Perhaps the sequence of ideas, a falling apple, a steady moon, and an abstract theory, does not seem very coherent; and it sounds like an extract from *Alice in Wonderland* to be told that the abstract theory can account for the fall of the apple and the steadiness of the moon. Yet it is true, and the explanation comes in this wise.

The Galilei stone and the Newton apple both fall straight down, that is, to the centre of the earth, supposed to be a globe: that qualitative result happens wherever the fall takes place; it is reasonable to suppose that the fall is due to the earth. There had been another discovery of Galilei's which, at first, had shocked even intellectual belief: stones of different weights and kinds and sizes fall through the same height in the same time; and so it is reasonable to suppose that, in the fall of a stone, the earth is the principal agent, perhaps the only agent, that leads to the fall of any stone anywhere through any height. It is true that the distances which can actually be observed for falling stones are ludicrously small compared with the size of the earth; and the crucial number seems to be a lonely fact, unrelated to anything except a falling stone, unexplained, so far inexplicable. But everything connected with the observation and with the calculations remains unaffected if a hypothesis be propounded under which the earth attracts the stone and is the sole cause of its fall: and there is no other observation, reserved in a background, to render that hypothesis open to objection.

Next, the moon goes round the earth steadily: so far as that movement is concerned, the moon can be declared (always descriptively, and with sufficient accuracy) to move round the earth in a circle with a steady speed. But the stone falls straight to the earth, always with an increasing speed; the moon moves round the earth, always with a steady speed; what earthly connection can there be between the two movements? It is here that the hypothetical attracting faculty of the earth enters, through another discovery which had been made by Galilei and formulated precisely by Newton. Under this law a movable body, if subjected to no influence of any kind, and if it moves at all, will only move in a straight line, and only at an unchanging speed in that line; and variation from the straightness of path, or variation of speed even in a straight path, can be effected only by outside influence. Our falling stone moves in a straight path downwards, but with an ever-gathering speed; this change of speed is due to some influence: all falling stones make in a direction towards the very centre of the earth; can the influence, affecting the speed, be due to the earth attracting the stone down to itself? Our moon does not move in a straight line; the deviation from straightness must be due to some influence; we must, for the moment, leave the uniform speed out of count, for the law makes no declaration concerning uniform speed not along a straight line. Can this influence upon the moon be due to the earth for ever attracting the moon out of the straight line which would be an uninfluenced path, drawing the moon to itself, with just enough influence to keep it at a steadily unchanging distance from itself? On the hypothesis of an attracting quality in the earth, the said quality must explain the deviation of the moon from a straight path, while it can explain the changing speed of the falling stone. The hypothesis must be tested; it is not to be declared true because it has not been disproved.

Critical tests are ready in the observed facts and in the inferences from the facts. But how are the facts to be used? Simply and solely by the application of mathematics, never constructed in this direction by any man before Newton, now the possession of any reasonably capable mathematical undergraduate.

Remember that we have the crucial number, sixteen, for Galilei's falling stone: let us now pay some attention to the moon. As the moon moves steadily in a circle round the earth, in a period of 29½ days roughly, and as the distance of the moon from the earth otherwise is known to be approximately sixty times the radius of the earth, the steady speed of the moon in her circle is easily calculated: the inferred estimate will, of course, be based upon the estimated size of the radius of the earth. An entirely different calculation gives our estimate of the pull to be exercised upon the moon, to drag her regularly and always into the circle away from the straight line which would be her path if there were no influence. Had there been no influence she would have gone along a straight line, for ever moving away from the earth farther and farther: as things are, she remains at a steady distance that on the average remains unchanged. Consequently the difference, say at the end of one second, between her actual distance from the earth and what would have been her distance had she moved along a straight line, is the distance through which, during that second, the supposed effective influence would have pulled her. That distance is a measure of the influence: but how is the influence to be estimated?

The estimate manifestly cannot come in the same way as for the falling stone. For the stone, only a few hundred feet at the utmost came to account. The moon is 240,000 miles away from the earth and remains at that distance. An assumption that the measure of the attracting influence of the earth is the same for all stones falling upon its surface causes no mental hesitation: the few hundred feet, which are the utmost traversed by a stone, are such a triviality in magnitude compared with the four-thousand-mile radius of the earth that there is no real opportunity for modification of the influence of the earth. But what is to be the assumption made for an attracted moon, if it is attracted? In thought we have to go far to reach the moon: we may as well be bold, go out boldly in thought into the vast space of the solar system, and use the knowledge provided by the Kepler laws which, be it noted, are not hypotheses but are the systematic expression of observed facts.

An easy mathematical calculation indicates the character of the supposed terrestrial influence which does no more than keep the moon going round in a circle at an unchanging distance, but does not bring the moon any nearer as it brings a stone nearer. This calculation uses the Kepler law establishing the relation between the size of a planetary path and the time of revolution along the whole path, and the result of the calculation is to show that the attracting influence of the earth, if it is to be the controlling cause of the movement, must decrease as the square of the number which represents the distance of the attracted body from the centre of the earth. The distance of the moon from the earth is, roughly, sixty times the radius of the earth; and the square of the number 60 is 3,600. Therefore, according to the result of the calculation, the attracting influence of the earth at the distant moon is only one 3,600th part of its attracting influence upon a stone falling at its surface.

Now we know that the earth's influence is the same for all falling stones and, ultimately, is measured by the crucial number sixteen. We want to know whether the earth's attracting influence, if any, upon the moon can be the same in kind as upon the falling stone, while, of course, its magnitude will be diminished in proper proportion owing to the difference in distance. Let us denote the crucial number, connected solely with the attracting power of the earth, by the symbol $x$, so dear to mathematicians. For a falling stone at the surface of the earth this number $x$ is known to be sixteen. If our hypothesis, that the earth's attracting influence is the sole cause dominating the movement of the moon, can be justified, the number at the distance of the moon would be $\frac{1}{3600} x$, just as $x$ is sixteen at the surface of the earth. We therefore have to calculate this number $\frac{1}{3600} x$ for the moon, in the same way as 16 is the calculated number for the stone. When it has been found for the moon, we at once have the value of $x$ by a simple operation; and this value of $x$ is as crucial for the moon's motion under our hypothesis as is the number 16 for the falling stone. If this crucial number $x$ for the moon is inferred from the calculation to be the same as the crucial number 16 for the falling stone, the hypothesis concerning the attracting influence of the earth is so far justified. If it is not, the moon sails on, serenely unexplained. The crucial number for the moon must be found.

Here, Newton was at the crisis of his investigation. He had his facts: there were the established laws, expressing accumulations of observations: there were the old measurements in the accepted units, the foot as the precise unit for distance in the case of the falling stone, the radius of the earth to be expressed in miles as a less precise unit in estimating the distance of the moon. Newton was now to test his theory in the furnace of fact. Everything depended upon the crucial number $x$: would it come out, for the moon, the same as it was for the stone, the critical sixteen?

When this crucial number $x$ first emerged from Newton's calculations about the moon, it turned out to amount to something very slightly less than fourteen—let us call it fourteen, as approximately as the critical sixteen. Certainly the $x$ had been found to be the number sixteen for the stone, which was as surely sixteen as human observation could make it. The theory was not established as a working hypothesis. Unless unknown and apparently undiscoverable errors had crept in, of such a kind as to vitiate the calculation, the theory could not be maintained. Something must be wrong somewhere: hardly imaginable in the facts or in the data; perhaps—a reluctant perhaps—in the assumption that the earth was the attracting influence upon the stone and the moon. At that stage there was nothing to be done by a mind and a temperament such as were Newton's: he kept silence, consigned his soul not to perdition but to patience, and proceeded to ponder over other riddles of the physical universe.

Now what is the secret of the situation? It is implied in what has already been said, as though it were a clue in a crossword puzzle. The calculations involved, through the moon's distance, an estimate of the radius of the earth in miles; and in Newton's day the mile, a geographical or nautical mile, was the sixtieth part of a degree. The calculations involved, through the distances traversed by the stone, the adoption of the foot as the unit. The two different units of length had to be brought into relation. We, of course, take 5,280 feet as equivalent to a mile; so did Newton. But that mile of 5,280 feet is not a geographical mile, the sixtieth part of a degree of latitude; the geographical mile survives solely in one usage, the maritime knot of 6,080 feet, and Newton did not know the fact. A correct estimate had, it is true, been published some thirty years earlier by a London schoolmaster based upon his own observations during a holiday tramp from London to York; but in the Stuart days of the first Charles, England was more concerned with political turmoil than with a pedagogue's estimate of a mile, and the schoolmaster's contribution to knowledge remained unnoticed and unknown.

Some thirteen years passed in silence for Newton. In 1679 a friend told him of a recent French research in geodesy which gave a corrected estimate of the length of a degree of latitude: still, of course, the sixty geographical miles, but a little over sixty-nine of the customary civic miles of 5,280 feet. Thus one datum in Newton's calculation had been wrong: he had used a wrong number, 60, instead of a right number, 69. In the light of this new knowledge Newton returned to his old calculations: the use of the more accurate measure of the radius of the earth brought out the crucial number $x$ for the moon to be in exact and complete agreement with the crucial number 16 for a falling stone. His hypothesis concerning the attracting influence of the earth was verified. It became a trustworthy working hypothesis which, in due course of its development, though then he knew it not, was to achieve a revolution in thought as regards the human knowledge of the physical cosmos.

But his mathematical triumph was only the beginning of new mathematical work. Suddenly there loomed before him a portentous difficulty. All his calculations had treated the moon, the earth, the sun, as points— points which, in Euclid's definition familiar to Newton, had no parts and no magnitude: an earth of no magnitude; a sun of no magnitude; truly portentous assumptions! To Newton's mind a fresh difficulty was only a fresh problem to be solved: and, here, he made another mathematical discovery which was of supreme importance for his theory. The moon, the earth, the sun, the planets, all of them round bodies, are very nearly spherical in shape; and Newton's fresh discovery was that the complete attraction of a sphere on an outside body was the same, in all respects, as if the whole of the matter were condensed at the centre. In fact, his mathematics showed that he could regard the moon, the earth, the sun, as attracting points. The difficulty disappeared: the theory could stand. Now he could go forward, to test the theory further by further extension: the result was his theory of universal gravitation according to which every particle of matter in the universe attracts every other particle according to a definite law: the attraction was measured by dividing one fixed number by a number which represented the square of the distance between the attracting particles. He worked out the theory in detail, under this law; the calculated results everywhere agreed with the observed phenomena; and the result was the publication, in 1687, of his *Mathematical Principles of Natural Philosophy*, one of the great books of the world. It was an achievement made through mathematics by a mathematician. It has been confirmed and amplified since Newton's day by generations of mathematicians of all the ages and all climes: by means of it, and still using their mathematics, they have made predictions that are daily verified in the movement of the planets; they have predicted the return of comets, they discovered a new planet, and, passing from fact as commonplace as the creation of the Nautical Almanac to the shadowy realms of high speculation, they measure the bounds of the universe, assign a limit in the past to its evolution from chaos, nay, they will even assign a limit to its future—a very remote limit, happily for our sense of ease—when it may subside into an exhausted extinction. Personally, I prefer fact to speculation.

Behind my account of the emergence of the theory of universal gravitation, there stands a purpose of warning rather than edification. Often in recent years you will have heard the name of Einstein: the journals and newspapers appeared to palpitate with excitement over his discovery, which was very real and of real importance: but there always was, and there remains, a grave dearth of comprehensible explanation as to the gist of his discovery. The writers found the word relativity: it used to bear a philosophical significance mainly connected with a doctrine that existence and observation are not independent of the living and observing mind. The association with the physical universe was rather nebulous in explanation: that mattered little; was not Einstein's important (but dimly understood) discovery connected with relativity? So, imitating the image-makers at Ephesus in the days of the apostle Paul, the expositors proclaimed that "Great is relativity." Here are the facts, so far as they are concerned with the theory of gravitation.

That theory of gravitation was found to embrace all astronomical observations. By the assumption of that theory as a working basis, Halley in 1706 had predicted the periodic return of a particular comet: it duly verified the prediction in 1758, in 1835, in 1910; and its next coming is due only fifty-eight years hence. By the assumption of that theory Adams and Leverrier, independently, through a vast mathematical calculation applied to some seeming irregularities of the planet Uranus, discovered the existence of a still more distant planet Neptune, never observed before the discovery made in their studies. The mathematical genius of Laplace had set the phenomena of the astronomical heavens in mathematical order. Everything was settled into its place, or almost everything. There remained one or two minute somethings. When the most elaborate calculations had been completed, there remained a little unexplained fluctuation in the movement of the moon, so often accused of fickleness by the poets; and one planet, fitly named after Mercury, the not over-righteous messenger of the gods in classical mythology, was found to be acting in a manner inconsistent with strict mathematical propriety. The vagaries of Mercury were very slight: its orbit is far more tilted than that of any other planet, and is more swiftly traversed than that of any other planet; but the vagaries could not be explained by tilt or speed, and their source (that is, the cause of the difference between what is actually seen and what calculation led astronomers to expect) could not be discovered. The irregularities made no difference to daily life: they made no other difference to astronomical life: but there they were. Nature would not change so as to conform to man's explanation, so man's explanation must be examined in order to be brought into conformity with nature. The accuracy of the calculations could not humanly be challenged, for they obeyed every test that human reason could devise. Perhaps there was something, an extremely tiny something somewhere (for, remember, the deviations are extremely slight), something wrong in the fundamental assumptions upon which the calculations were based. And here is an illustration of the difference between practice and thought: "to stop that nonsense" an engineer would have driven a rivet, would have inserted a guiding slot, would have added a tightening chain round the dome of St. Paul's. But rivets and slots and chains are devastations in thought, not remedies: so the fundamental assumptions must be revised. It had been assumed that the solar system is fixed, absolutely fixed, in the universe: is that dogma true? Even if it is not true, the alternative of a wandering solar system would hardly explain the minute domestic vagaries of one rather insignificant member. It had been assumed that the measurement of the same thing, in varying circumstances and at diverse times, made as accurate as human skill can achieve, and corrected for every incidental error that human skill can detect, is always the same, whatever be the time and the place of the thing measured and the measurement made. The dogma seems an obvious inference from what we are pleased to call common sense: like so many obvious things, it cannot be proved and it cannot be submitted to adequate test: in fact, common sense continues to call it obvious. But how if it be not true? Your standard of measurement, used to measure a magnitude in passing time and on a moving body, would change in the same way (if at all) as the measured magnitude, and you could not detect the change, if there be change: and, in that case, your measures would no longer be absolute: they would be relative, perhaps to time, perhaps to place or change of place, perhaps to the way of change. Nothing remains absolute: yet that was a fundamental assumption, stated explicitly, in the Newtonian philosophy.

Now this notion of relativity is not new: it did not come into scientific thought with Einstein: it was not unknown to Newton himself: and men have pondered over it often in the last fifty years. But there is the customary difficulty: an idea may come into the range of thought: how can it be garbed in expression, for discussion, for calculation? You will remember the wisdom of a character in George Eliot's *Theophrastus Such,* "There's some as thinks one thing: there's some as thinks another thing: but my opinion's different." Men, charging themselves with the formulation of relativity, have devised various modes of its mathematical expression; and, so far as concerns astronomy, there is not the unanimity of expression which, if there, would be a rudimentary recommendation. It was the work of Einstein which was the first to explain—or, at any rate, to account for—the behaviour of Mercury: and therefore it is to Einstein that the glory rightly accrues. The method of Einstein, however, is not the sole one that gives an explanation; for the mathematical methods of other men have also led to that result, after Einstein. But neither the method of Einstein nor the method of any other mathematician has yet succeeded in explaining the slight caprice of the moon.

How far the popular expositors had made themselves acquainted with the investigations in all accessible issues, before some of them tried to make our flesh creep with their pronouncement upon the passing of gravitation, might be the curious quest of some doubting scientific Thomas Didymus. But of one thing we may be reasonably sure: neither in that theory, nor in any other living theory, has the last word been said. For the last words of all are the epitaph on a tomb: and the Newtonian theory is still alive sufficiently to provide man with a working hypothesis of the natural universe in which he lives.

Before I close, there are two inferences which I would appeal to you not to draw from my lecture. It is not the fact that the services of mathematics are restricted to the subjects that have been selected for mention or illustration. It is not the fact that the science of mathematics exists or thrives, solely or mainly in order to find or to further applications in other sciences.

The range of human activities, within which mathematics and the ideas of mathematics are called upon or are utilized for service, is so vast and so varied that I can do no more, at this stage, than mention the names of some of the regions where the science of mathematics is active. Enough has been said on the score of astronomy. In engineering of every type, ranging from the ancient ship of the sea to the modern ship of the air, in your buildings, in your bridges, in your tunnels, its help is indispensable. Is it an occupation so sedate as book-keeping, say by double entry? That process is but an iterated application of the use of the plus and minus signs of algebra, though the book-keeper is not usually aware of the fact. Is it a science so relatively modern as physical chemistry? Much of that science is based upon the mathematical expression of some of the laws of change in physical nature. Is it a science which apparently is so far remote from the usual conception of mathematics as is physiology, the science of the processes of living organisms? That human science is examining the phenomena of the activities of such organisms, is expressing quantitatively those activities, is dealing mathematically with those quantitative expressions: there are the researches on the expenditure of muscular energy, the researches on industrial fatigue. Did not a sectional president startle the British Association the other day by hinting (though without adequate justification) that a distinguished physiologist, trained as a mathematician and using his knowledge, was on the verge of discovering the mystery of life itself? Is it the spotting of invisible guns on a far-flung battlefield? My friend and former colleague, your worthy professor of mathematics in this College, could tell you of the combined efforts of mathematicians and physicists who, by means of instruments and calculations connected with the properties of sound, were able to devise means of approximate location. And those same properties were used, in connection with mathematical instruments constructed for the purpose, to detect, from the surface of the sea, not merely the fact, but the direction of approach, of a hostile submarine. The citations of utility could be continued almost without limit: only one other subject will be indicated. If there is anything that appeals to the average inhabitant of these islands and is a frequent topic of unfruitful conversation, it is the weather: and a feature of our morning newspaper is the forecast issued by the Meteorological Office. But the occupants of that office are not like the ancient soothsayers, waiting for inspiration from gifts tendered and from sacrifices rendered. They collect scattered information, co-ordinate that information by settled mathematical processes, draw their mathematical diagrams to represent that co-ordinated information, and, inferring tendencies from movements indicated by their diagrams, issue their calculated forecast.

All these—there are more that crowd into the mind—may be an adequate recital showing how essential and how extensive is the service rendered by the rather silent science of mathematics to the practical life of mankind.

Most of all, I would not wish to have you possessed by the notion that the pursuit of mathematics by human thought must be justified by its utility for practical uses in life. Such a justification would, it is true, require the inclusion of mathematics in the scheme of any university where technical studies are deemed important; and in the growing prosperity of your University College, the more generously you open your technical courses to mathematics, even in their utilitarian aspect, the more will the professional students ultimately benefit. But having paid tribute to the demands of the market-place, let me speak for mathematics as a pure science of progressive knowledge, worthy to claim the devotion of the finest intellects to its pursuit, worthy to challenge the respect of man towards the world of learning. One of the high ideals of mankind through all the ages, and in all civilizations, has inspired the search for more knowledge wherever it can be found or be attained. Ever since man has attempted to acquire ordered knowledge, the science that deals with number and deals with form has been pursued for its own sake because, thereby, the human spirit can find unending satisfaction and unending occupation. And the creations of mathematical science have been the glory of the nations. We may recall the lost dominion of Babylon, we may think of her hanging gardens as, in their time, a wonder of the world; we may sigh over her pomp and her luxury, gone like a dream in the visions of the night; but the contributions of her Chaldean priests to astronomy survive to this day. Greece has an immortal name from her art, from her literature, from her philosophy: her rival schools of Plato and of Aristotle still dominate the Western world; but her fame is no less immortal by her bequest of geometry and of number, two of the purest theories ever devised by the human mind. We may hold Semitic science in low regard: but Arabic learning kept science alive when the rest of the intellectual world was torpid; it created algebra as the marvellous extension of the Greek arithmetic, and gave us the very digits we use and the scale of ten, so familiar to us as to seem part of our existence: we can pay our mental homage of remembrance to those ancient Arabs in southern Spain. What the modern peoples have thus inherited they have amplified beyond recognition; and the nations of the West—France, Germany, Italy, America across the ocean, our own people—have lived in an unending life-giving rivalry in the creation of mathematical knowledge, sought for its own sake, its domain as boundless as human thought itself.

For there is progress still in mathematical science; there will always be progress of increasing knowledge in a world that is not dead. Results have been achieved by the noble army of great spirits of the past, and their achievements are the possession of the living. But those very achievements are the stimulus to the living that they, in their turn, shall endeavour to advance knowledge. And this pursuit is to be made by the living spirits for the sake of new knowledge, not for the sake of new glory, not for the sake of new benefit. If utility should come, well and good: but we need trouble no more about immediate utility as an aim than the Greeks troubled about the utility of their conic sections or Newton troubled about the utility of the gravitation theory. So here, amid this community in a centre of commercial activity, in this home of high learning which has been established for the betterment of men and women as human citizens, let me plead, if pleading be needed, for the highest consideration to be given to the pursuit of pure knowledge as well as technical training, not neglecting mathematics, once called the Queen of the Sciences. The wind bloweth where it listeth, and the spirit of knowledge does not follow the quest for wealth and power; but the creation of new knowledge makes for the high repute of a nation, alike in the days when its influence is dominant and in the more distant days when its doings shall have been recorded on the scroll of time.

# Alfred North Whitehead

## 1861–1947

Alfred North Whitehead, one of the most outstanding philosophers of recent times, was born in Ramsgate, England, in 1861. He was the son of the Reverend Alfred W. Whitehead, who was then headmaster of a private school. The educational and religious atmosphere of his home, the participation of his family in community affairs, and the surrounding countryside, rich in historical relics, all exerted a permanent influence on the younger Whitehead. He had a deep sense of the past, and a secure feeling of being at home in the world.

In 1880 Whitehead entered Trinity College, Cambridge, where he remained as student and Fellow until 1910. Then, for thirteen years, he was at the Imperial College of Science and Technology in Kensington. In 1924, rather than accept retirement because of old age, he moved to America and became professor of philosophy at Harvard. It was there that he was able to give the fullest expression to his own philosophy. He once remarked: "From twenty on I was interested in philosophy, religion, logic and history. Harvard gave me a chance to express myself." During this time he wrote *Science and the Modern World, Process and Reality,* and *Adventures in Ideas.* He was senior member of Harvard's Society of Fellows until his death in 1947.

The first phase of Whitehead's intellectual development was devoted to logic and mathematics. During this period, he wrote *A Treatise on Universal Algebra* and, together with Bertrand Russell, *Principia Mathematica.* This second work, which undertakes to establish the logical foundations of mathematics, has been called one of the greatest contributions to logic since Aristotle. The *Principia,* like that of Isaac Newton, set the fashion for decades to come, so that research in symbolic language became a major branch of mathematics. This program of "logicalizing" all of mathematics took ten years and ran into three volumes. The patience of investigation required is illustrated by the fact that the proof of the proposition $1 + 1 = 2$, which appears as Theorem 110.643, is not given until page 83 of the second volume.

In his second phase of development, Whitehead turned to the philosophy of science. He wrote *Enquiry Concerning the Principles of Natural Knowledge, The Concept of Nature, The Principles of Relativity,* and *Introduction to Mathematics,* a classic popularization of the subject. The following selection, "On Mathematical Method," is taken from this last work. Here Whitehead examines the fundamental ideas that form the foundations of mathematics rather than the technical processes by which problems are actually solved.

Whitehead once said: "It is a profoundly erroneous truism, repeated by copybooks and by eminent people when they are making speeches, that we should cultivate the habit of thinking of what we are doing. The precise opposite is the case. Civilization advances by extending the number of important operations which we can perform without thinking about them." In mathematics, "not thinking of what we are doing" is, Whitehead points out, the essence of abstraction, the importance of which lies in the fact that it is only by abstracting that we can form ideas of the universe.

Whitehead illustrates how abstraction leads to new ways of thinking, so that facts and relationships hitherto unknown come to light. The invention of variables, possible only after the invention of algebra, led to the formulation of laws about things that change. With the concept of variability, and using the method of abstraction, Newton was able to establish the law of gravity.

Whitehead defends the unworldly quality of mathematical inquiry, saying that "the really profound changes in human life all have their ultimate origin in knowledge pursued for its own sake."

---

*Notes from the artist: "Strong contrasts were used in the portrait of Whitehead. . . . Bold blacks and open whites frame the picture, while within it calculations from his* Principia Mathematica— *twisted into semiabstract forms—dance above the head of Whitehead, who is seen in an attitude of quiet concentration."*

Alfed north Whitehead

Abstract theorizing led Faraday to important discoveries in electricity. It took practical ability to develop the modern uses of electricity, but, to Whitehead, a world dominated by practical men is symbolized in the fate of Archimedes as told by Plutarch.

*On the Nature of a Calculus* examines the way in which tools for abstracting are forged. Such a tool is called a calculus. It is the art of manipulating signs according to certain fixed rules. Arithmetic is a calculus; so are algebra and trigonometry. The branch of mathematics invented by Newton and Leibniz was considered so important that it was called *the* calculus.

The most significant thing about these tools is that after they have been invented they seem to lead a life of their own. A mathematician often feels that he is in the position of simply watching them to see what they will do. If we can imagine one set of tools making another set of tools, we have a picture of the growth of mathematics. "Device is piled upon device," says Whitehead. But he rejects the idea that mathematics can become completely divorced from the world of things. A calculus may consist of symbols that stand for other symbols, but, if it is not to be frivolous, it must ultimately refer to some reality.

The rarefied atmosphere of Abstract Thought is not an outer space reserved for professional mathematicians. If you have learned to add two and five without asking "Two and five what?" you already have both feet off the ground—higher than you think. You are now air-borne. The rest is just a matter of gaining altitude.

# On Mathematical Method

## from *An Introduction to Mathematics*

### THE ABSTRACT NATURE
### OF MATHEMATICS

The study of mathematics is apt to commence in disappointment. The important applications of the science, the theoretical interest of its ideas, and the logical rigour of its methods, all generate the expectation of a speedy introduction to processes of interest. We are told that by its aid the stars are weighed and the billions of molecules in a drop of water are counted. Yet, like the ghost of Hamlet's father, this great science eludes the efforts of our mental weapons to grasp it—" 'Tis here, 'tis there, 'tis gone"—and what we do see does not suggest the same excuse for illusiveness as sufficed for the ghost, that it is too noble for our gross methods. "A show of violence," if ever excusable, may surely be "offered" to the trivial results which occupy the pages of some elementary mathematical treatises.

The reason for this failure of the science to live up to its reputation is that its fundamental ideas are not explained to the student disentangled from the technical procedure which has been invented to facilitate their exact presentation in particular instances. Accordingly, the unfortunate learner finds himself struggling to acquire a knowledge of a mass of details which are not illuminated by any general conception. Without a doubt, technical facility is a first requisite for valuable mental activity: we shall fail to appreciate the rhythm of Milton, or the passion of Shelley, so long as we find it necessary to spell the words and are not quite certain of the forms of the individual letters. In this sense there is no royal road to learning. But it is equally an error to confine attention to technical processes, excluding consideration of general ideas. Here lies the road to pedantry.

The object of the following chapters is not to teach mathematics, but to enable students from the very beginning of their course to know what the science is about, and why it is necessarily the foundation of exact thought as applied to natural phenomena. All allusion in what follows to detailed deductions in any part of the science will be inserted merely for the purpose of example, and care will be taken to make the general argument comprehensible, even if here and there some technical process or symbol which the reader does not understand is cited for the purpose of illustration.

The first acquaintance which most people have with mathematics is through arithmetic. That two and two make four is usually taken as the type of a simple mathematical proposition which everyone will have heard of. Arithmetic, therefore, will be a good subject to consider in order to discover, if possible, the most obvious characteristic of the science. Now, the first noticeable fact about arithmetic is that it applies to everything, to tastes and to sounds, to apples and to angels, to the ideas of the mind and to the bones of the body. The nature of the things is perfectly indifferent, of all things it is true that two and two make four. Thus we write down as the leading characteristic of mathematics that it deals with properties and ideas which are applicable to things just because they are things, and apart from any particular feelings, or emotions, or sensations, in any way connected with them. This is what is meant by calling mathematics an abstract science.

The result which we have reached deserves attention. It is natural to think that an abstract science cannot be of much importance in the affairs of human life, because it has omitted from its consideration everything of real interest. It will be remembered that Swift, in his description of Gulliver's voyage to Laputa, is of two minds on this point. He describes the mathematicians of that country as silly and useless dreamers, whose attention has to be awakened by flappers. Also, the mathematical tailor measures his height by a quadrant, and deduces his other dimensions by a rule and compasses, producing a suit of very ill-fitting clothes. On the other hand, the mathematicians of Laputa, by their marvellous invention of the magnetic island floating in the air, ruled the country and maintained their ascendancy over their subjects. Swift, indeed, lived at a time peculiarly unsuited for gibes at contemporary mathematicians. Newton's *Principia* had just been written, one of the great forces which have transformed the modern world. Swift might just as well have laughed at an earthquake.

But a mere list of the achievements of mathematics is an unsatisfactory way of arriving at an idea of its importance. It is worth-while to spend a little thought in getting at the root reason why mathematics, because of its very abstractness, must always remain one of the most important topics for thought. Let us try to make clear to ourselves why explanations of the order of events necessarily tend to become mathematical.

Consider how all events are interconnected. When we see the lightning, we listen for the thunder; when we hear the wind, we look for the waves on the sea; in the chill autumn, the leaves fall. Everywhere order reigns, so that when some circumstances have been noted we can foresee that others will also be present. The progress of science consists in observing these interconnections and in showing with a patient ingenuity that the events of this ever-shifting world are but examples of a few general connections or relations called laws. To see what is general in what is particular and what is permanent in what is transitory is the aim of scientific thought. In the eye of science, the fall of an apple, the motion of a planet round a sun, and the clinging of the atmosphere to the earth are all seen as examples of the law of gravity. This possibility of disentangling the most complex evanescent circumstances into various examples of permanent laws is the controlling idea of modern thought.

Now let us think of the sort of laws which we want in order completely to realize this scientific ideal. Our knowledge of the particular facts of the world around us is gained from our sensations. We see, and hear, and taste, and smell, and feel hot and cold, and push, and rub, and ache, and tingle. These are just our own personal sensations: my toothache cannot be your toothache, and my sight cannot be your sight. But we ascribe the origin of these sensations to relations between the things which form the external world. Thus the dentist extracts not the toothache but the tooth. And not only so, we also endeavour to imagine the world as one connected set of things which underlies all the perceptions of all people. There is not one world of things for my sensations and another for yours, but one world in which we both exist. It is the same tooth both for dentist and patient. Also we hear and we touch the same world as we see.

It is easy, therefore, to understand that we want to describe the connections between these external things in some way which does not depend on any particular sensations, nor even on all the sensations of any particular person. The laws satisfied by the course of events in the world of external things are to be described, if possible, in a neutral universal fashion, the same for blind men as for deaf men, and the same for beings with faculties beyond our ken as for normal human beings.

But when we have put aside our immediate sensations, the most serviceable part—from its clearness, definiteness, and universality—of what is left is composed of our general ideas of the abstract formal properties of things; in fact, the abstract mathematical ideas mentioned above. Thus it comes about that, step by step, and not realizing the full meaning of the process, mankind has been led to search for a mathematical description of the properties of the universe, because in this way only can a general idea of the course of events be formed, freed from reference to particular persons or to particular types of sensation. For example, it might be asked at dinner: "What was it which underlay my sensation of sight, yours of touch, and his of taste and smell?" the answer being "an apple." But in its final analysis, science seeks to describe an apple in terms of the positions and motions of molecules, a description which ignores me and you and him, and also ignores sight and touch and taste and smell. Thus mathematical ideas, because they are abstract, supply just what is wanted for a scientific description of the course of events.

This point has usually been misunderstood, from being thought of in too narrow a way. Pythagoras had a glimpse of it when he proclaimed that number was the source of all things. In modern times the belief that the ultimate explanation of all things was to be found in Newtonian mechanics was an adumbration of the truth that all science as it grows towards perfection becomes mathematical in its ideas.

### VARIABLES

Mathematics as a science commenced when first someone, probably a Greek, proved propositions about *any* things or about *some* things, without specification of definite particular things. These propositions were first enunciated by the Greeks for geometry; and, accordingly, geometry was the great Greek mathematical science. After the rise of geometry centuries passed away before algebra made a really effective start, despite some faint anticipations by the later Greek mathematicians.

The ideas of *any* and of *some* are introduced into algebra by the use of letters, instead of the definite numbers of arithmetic. Thus, instead of saying that $2 + 3 = 3 + 2$, in algebra we generalize and say that, if $x$ and $y$ stand for *any* two numbers, then $x + y = y + x$. Again, in the place of saying that $3 > 2$, we generalize and say that if $x$ be *any* number there exists *some* number (or numbers) $y$ such that $y > x$. We may remark in passing that this latter assumption—for when put in its strict ultimate form it is an assumption—is of vital importance, both to philosophy and to mathematics; for by it the notion of infinity is introduced. Perhaps it required the introduction of the arabic numerals, by which the use of letters as standing for definite numbers has been completely discarded in mathematics, in order to suggest to mathematicians the technical convenience of the use of letters for the ideas of *any* number and *some* number. The Romans would have stated the number of the year in which this is written in the form MDCCCCX, whereas we write it 1910, thus leaving the letters for the other usage. But this is merely a speculation. After the rise of algebra the differential calculus was invented by Newton and Leibniz, and then a pause in the progress of the philosophy of mathematical thought occurred so far as these notions are concerned; and it was not till within the last few years that it has been realized how fundamental *any* and *some* are to the very nature of mathematics, with the result of opening out still further subjects for mathematical exploration.

Let us now make some simple algebraic statements, with the object of understanding exactly how these fundamental ideas occur.

(1) For *any* number $x$, $x + 2 = 2 + x$;

(2) For *some* number $x$, $x + 2 = 3$;

(3) For *some* number $x$, $x + 2 > 3$.

The first point to notice is the possibilities contained in the meaning of *some*, as here used. Since $x + 2 = 2 + x$ for any number $x$, it is true for *some* number $x$. Thus, as here used, *any* implies *some* and *some* does not exclude *any*. Again, in the second example, there is, in fact, only one number $x$, such as $x + 2 = 3$, namely only the number 1. Thus the *some* may be that one number only. But in the third example, any number $x$ which is greater than 1 gives $x + 2 > 3$. Hence there are an infinite number of numbers which answer to the *some* number in this case. Thus *some* may be anything between *any* and *one only*, including both these limiting cases.

It is natural to supersede the statements (2) and (3) by the questions:

(2′) For what number $x$ is $x + 2 = 3$;

(3′) For what numbers $x$ is $x + 2 > 3$.

Considering (2′), $x + 2 = 3$ is an equation, and it is easy to see that its solution is $x = 3 - 2 = 1$. When we have asked the question implied in the statement of the equation $x + 2 = 3$, $x$ is called the unknown. The object of the solution of the equation is the determination of the unknown. Equations are of great importance in mathematics, and it seems as though (2′) exemplified a much more thoroughgoing and fundamental idea than the original statement (2). This, however, is a complete mistake. The idea of the undetermined "variable" as occurring in the use of "some" or "any" is the really important one in mathematics; that of the "unknown" in an equation, which is to be solved as quickly as possible, is only of subordinate use, though of course it is very important. One of the causes of the apparent triviality of much of elementary algebra is the preoccupation of the text-books with the solution of equations. The same remark applies to the solution of the inequality (3′) as compared to the original statement (3).

But the majority of interesting formulae, especially when the idea of *some* is present, involve more than one variable. For example, the consideration of the pairs of numbers $x$ and $y$ (fractional or integral) which satisfy $x + y = 1$ involves the idea of two correlated variables, $x$ and $y$. When two variables are present the same two main types of statement occur. For example, (1) for *any* pair of numbers, $x$ and $y$, $x + y = y + x$, and (2) for *some* pairs of numbers, $x$ and $y$, $x + y = 1$.

The second type of statement invites consideration of the aggregate of pairs of numbers which are bound together by some fixed relation—in the case given, by the relation $x + y = 1$. One use of formulae of the first type, true for *any* pair of numbers, is that by them formulae of the second type can be thrown into an indefinite number of equivalent forms. For example, the relation $x + y = 1$ is equivalent to the relations

$$y + x = 1, \ (x - y) + 2y = 1, \ 6x + 6y = 6,$$

and so on. Thus a skilful mathematician uses that equivalent form of the relation under consideration which is most convenient for his immediate purpose.

It is not in general true that, when a pair of terms satisfy some fixed relation, if one of the terms is given the other is also definitely determined. For example, when $x$ and $y$ satisfy $y^2 = x$, if $x = 4$, $y$ can be $\pm 2$, thus, for any positive value of $x$ there are alternative values for $y$. Also in the relation $x + y > 1$, when either $x$ or $y$ is given, an indefinite number of values remain open for the other.

Again there is another important point to be noticed. If we restrict ourselves to positive numbers, integral or fractional, in considering the relation $x + y = 1$, then, if either $x$ or $y$ be greater than 1, there is no positive number which the other can assume so as to satisfy the relation. Thus the "field" of the relation for $x$ is restricted to numbers less than 1, and similarly for the "field" open to $y$. Again, consider integral numbers only, positive or negative, and take the relation $y^2 = x$, satisfied by pairs of such numbers. Then whatever integral value is given to $y$, $x$ can assume one corresponding integral value. So the "field" for $y$ is unrestricted among these positive or negative integers. But the "field" for $x$ is restricted in two ways. In the first place $x$ must be positive, and in the second place, since $y$ is to be integral, $x$ must be a perfect square. Accordingly, the "field" of $x$ is restricted to the set of integers $1^2$, $2^2$, $3^2$, $4^2$, and so on, i.e., to 1, 4, 9, 16, and so on.

The study of the general properties of a relation between pairs of numbers is much facilitated by the use of a diagram constructed as follows:

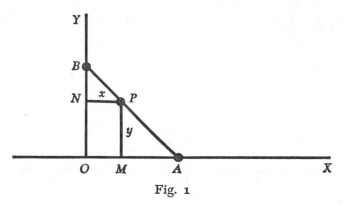

Fig. 1

Draw two lines $OX$ and $OY$ at right angles; let any number $x$ be represented by $x$ units (in any scale) of length along $OX$, any number $y$ by $y$ units (in any scale) of length along $OY$. Thus if $OM$, along $OX$, be $x$ units in length, and $ON$, along $OY$, be $y$ units in length, by completing the parallelogram $OMPN$ we find a point $P$ which corresponds to the pair of numbers $x$ and $y$. To each point there corresponds one pair of numbers, and to each pair of numbers there corresponds one point. The pair of numbers are called the co-ordinates of the point. Then the points whose co-ordinates satisfy some fixed relation can be indicated in a convenient way, by drawing a line, if they all lie on a line, or by shading an area if they are all points in the area. If the relation can be represented by an equation such as $x + y = 1$, or $y^2 = x$, then the points lie on a line, which is straight in the former case and curved in the latter. For example, considering only positive numbers, the points whose co-ordinates satisfy $x + y = 1$ lie on the straight line $AB$ in Fig. 1, where $OA = 1$ and $OB = 1$. Thus this segment of the straight line $AB$ gives a pictorial representation of the properties of the relation under the restriction to positive numbers.

Another example of a relation between two variables is afforded by considering the variations in the pressure and volume of a given mass of some gaseous substance—such as air or coal-gas or steam—at a constant temperature. Let $v$ be the number of cubic feet in its volume and $p$ its pressure in lb. weight per square inch. Then the law, known as Boyle's law, expressing the relation between $p$ and $v$ as both vary, is that the product $pv$ is constant, always supposing that the temperature does not alter. Let us suppose, for example, that the quantity of the gas and its other circumstances are such that we can put $pv = 1$ (the exact number on the right-hand side of the equation makes no essential difference).

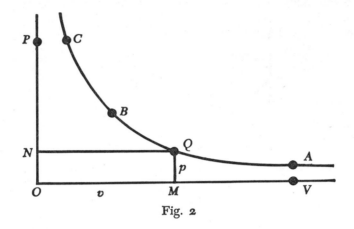

Fig. 2

Then in Fig. 2 we take two lines, $OV$ and $OP$, at right angles and draw $OM$ along $OV$ to represent $v$ units of volume, and $ON$ along $OP$ to represent $p$ units of pressure. Then the point $Q$, which is found by completing the parallelogram $OMQN$, represents the state of the gas when its volume is $v$ cubic feet and its pressure is $p$ lb. weight per square inch. If the circumstances of the portion of gas considered are such that $pv = 1$, then all these points $Q$ which correspond to any possible state of this portion of gas must lie on the curved line $ABC$, which includes all points for which $p$ and $v$ are positive, and $pv = 1$. Thus this curved line gives a pictorial representation of the relation holding between the volume and the pressure. When the pressure is very big the corresponding point $Q$ must be near $C$, or even beyond $C$ on the undrawn part of the curve; then the volume will be very small. When the volume is big $Q$ will be near to $A$, or beyond $A$; and then the pressure will be small. Notice that an engineer or a physicist may want to know the particular pressure corresponding to some definitely assigned volume. Then we have the case of determining the *unknown* $p$ when $v$ is a known number. But this is only in particular cases. In considering generally the properties of the gas and how it will behave, he has to have in his mind the general form of the whole curve $ABC$ and its general properties. In other words the really fundamental idea is that of the pair of *variables* satisfying the relation $pv = 1$. This example illustrates how the idea of *variables* is fundamental, both in the applications as well as in the theory of mathematics.

## METHODS OF APPLICATION

The way in which the idea of variables satisfying a relation occurs in the applications of mathematics is worth thought, and by devoting some time to it we shall clear up our thoughts on the whole subject.

Let us start with the simplest of examples: Suppose that building costs 1s. per cubic foot and that 20s. make £1. Then in all the complex circumstances which attend the building of a new house, amid all the various sensations and emotions of the owner, the architect, the builder, the workmen, and the onlookers as the house has grown to completion, this fixed correlation is by the law assumed to hold between the cubic content and the cost to the owner, namely that if $x$ be the number of cubic feet, and £$y$ the cost, then $20y = x$. This correlation of $x$ and $y$ is assumed to be true for the building of any house by any owner. Also, the volume of the house and the cost are not supposed to have been perceived or apprehended by any particular sensation or faculty, or by any particular man. They are stated in an abstract general way, with complete indifference to the owner's state of mind when he has to pay the bill.

Now think a bit further as to what all this means. The building of a house is a complicated set of circumstances. It is impossible to begin to apply the law, or to test it, unless amid the general course of events it is possible to recognize a definite set of occurrences as forming a particular instance of the building of a house. In short, we must know a house when we see it, and must recognize the events which belong to its building. Then amidst these events, thus isolated in idea from the rest of nature, the two elements of the cost and cubic content must be determinable; and when they are both determined, if the law be true, they satisfy the general formula

$$20y = x.$$

But is the law true? Anyone who has had much to do with building will know that we have here put the cost rather high. It is only for an expensive type of house that it will work out at this price. This brings out another point which must be made clear. While we are making mathematical calculations connected with the formula $20y = x$, it is indifferent to us whether the law be true or false. In fact, the very meanings assigned to $x$ and $y$, as being a number of cubic feet and a number of pounds sterling, are indifferent. During the mathematical investigation we are, in fact, merely considering the properties of this correlation between a pair of variable numbers $x$ and $y$. Our results will apply equally well, if we interpret $y$ to mean a number of fishermen and $x$ the number of fish caught, so that the assumed law is that on the average each fisherman catches twenty fish. The mathematical certainty of the investigation only attaches to the results considered as giving properties of the correlation $20y = x$ between the variable pair of numbers $x$ and $y$. There is no mathematical certainty whatever about the cost of the actual building of any house. The law is not quite true and the result it gives will not be quite accurate. In fact, it may well be hopelessly wrong.

Now all this no doubt seems very obvious. But in truth with more complicated instances there is no more common error than to assume that, because prolonged and accurate mathematical calculations have been made, the application of the result to some fact of nature is absolutely certain. The conclusion of no argument can be more certain than the assumptions from which it starts. All mathematical calculations about the course of nature must start from some assumed law of nature, such, for instance, as the assumed law of the cost of building stated above. Accordingly, however accurately we have calculated that some event must occur, the doubt always remains—Is the law true? If the law states a precise result, almost certainly it is not precisely accurate; and thus even at the best the result, precisely as calculated, is not likely to occur. But then we have no faculty capable of observation with ideal precision, so, after all, our inaccurate laws may be good enough.

We will now turn to an actual case, that of Newton and the law of gravity. This law states that any two bodies attract one another with a force proportional to the product of their masses, and inversely proportional to the square of the distance between them. Thus if $m$ and $M$ are the masses of the two bodies, reckoned in lbs. say, and $d$ miles is the distance between them, the force on either body, due to the attraction of the other and directed towards it, is proportional to $\dfrac{mM}{d^2}$; thus this force can be written as equal to $\dfrac{kmM}{d^2}$, where $k$ is a definite number depending on the absolute magnitude of this attraction and also on the scale by which we choose to measure forces. It is easy to see that, if we wish to reckon in terms of forces such as the weight of a mass of 1 lb., the number which $k$ represents must be extremely small; for when $m$ and $M$ and $d$ are each put equal to 1, $\dfrac{kmM}{d^2}$ becomes the gravitational attraction of two equal masses of 1 lb. at the distance of one mile, and this is quite inappreciable.

However, we have now got our formula for the force of attraction. If we call this force $F$, it is $F = k\dfrac{mM}{d^2}$, giving the correlation between the variables $F$, $m$, $M$, and $d$. We all know the story of how it was found out. Newton, it states, was sitting in an orchard and watched the fall of an apple, and then the law of universal gravitation burst upon his mind. It may be that the final formulation of the law occurred to him in an orchard, as well as elsewhere—and he must have been somewhere. But for our purposes it is more instructive to dwell upon the vast amount of preparatory thought, the product of many minds and many centuries, which was necessary before this exact law could be formulated. In the first place, the mathematical habit of mind and the mathematical procedure explained in the previous two chapters had to be generated; otherwise Newton could never have thought of a formula representing the force between *any* two masses at *any* distance. Again, what are the meanings of the terms employed, Force, Mass, Distance? Take the easiest of these terms, Distance. It seems very obvious to us to conceive all material things as forming a definite geometrical whole, such that the distances of the various parts are measurable in terms of some unit length, such as a mile or a yard. This is almost the first aspect of a material structure which occurs to us. It is the gradual outcome of the study of geometry and of the theory of measurement. Even now, in certain cases, other modes of thought are convenient. In a mountainous country distances are often reckoned in hours. But leaving distance, the other terms, Force and Mass, are much more obscure. The exact comprehension of the ideas which Newton meant to convey by these words was of slow growth, and, indeed, Newton himself was the first man who had thoroughly mastered the true general principles of Dynamics.

Throughout the middle ages, under the influence of Aristotle, the science was entirely misconceived. Newton had the advantage of coming after a series of great men, notably Galileo, in Italy, who in the previous two centuries had reconstructed the science and had invented the right way of thinking about it. He completed their work. Then, finally, having the ideas of force, mass, and distance, clear and distinct in his mind, and realizing their importance and their relevance to the fall of an apple and the motions of the planets, he hit upon the law of gravitation and proved it to be the formula always satisfied in these various motions.

The vital point in the application of mathematical formulae is to have clear ideas and a correct estimate of their relevance to the phenomena under observation. No less than ourselves, our remote ancestors were impressed with the importance of natural phenomena and with the desirability of taking energetic measures to regulate the sequence of events. Under the influence of irrelevant ideas they executed elaborate religious ceremonies to aid the birth of the new moon, and performed sacrifices to save the sun during the crisis of an eclipse. There is no reason to believe that they were more stupid than we are. But at that epoch there had not been opportunity for the slow accumulation of clear and relevant ideas.

The sort of way in which physical sciences grow into a form capable of treatment by mathematical methods is illustrated by the history of the gradual growth of the science of electro-magnetism. Thunderstorms are events on a grand scale, arousing terror in men and even animals. From the earliest times they must have been objects of wild and fantastic hypotheses, though it may be doubted whether our modern scientific discoveries in connection with electricity are not more astonishing than any of the magical explanations of savages. The Greeks knew that amber (Greek, electron) when rubbed would attract light and dry bodies. In A.D. 1600, Dr. Gilbert, of Colchester, published the first work on the subject in which any scientific method is followed. He made a list of substances possessing properties similar to those of amber; he must also have the credit of connecting, however vaguely, electric and magnetic phenomena. At the end of the seventeenth and throughout the eighteenth century knowledge advanced. Electrical machines were made, sparks were obtained from them; and the Leyden jar was invented, by which these effects could be intensified. Some organized knowledge was being obtained; but still no relevant mathematical ideas had been found out. Franklin, in the year 1752, sent a kite into the clouds and proved that thunderstorms were electrical.

Meanwhile from the earliest epoch (2634 B.C.) the Chinese had utilized the characteristic property of the compass needle, but do not seem to have connected it with any theoretical ideas. The really profound changes in human life all have their ultimate origin in knowledge pursued for its own sake. The use of the compass was not introduced into Europe till the end of the twelfth century A.D., more than 3,000 years after its first use in China. The importance which the science of electromagnetism has since assumed in every department of human life is not due to the superior practical bias of Europeans, but to the fact that in the West electrical and magnetic phenomena were studied by men who were dominated by abstract theoretic interests.

The discovery of the electric current is due to two Italians, Galvani in 1780, and Volta in 1792. This great invention opened a new series of phenomena for investigation. The scientific world had now three separate, though allied, groups of occurrences on hand—the effects of "statical" electricity arising from frictional electrical machines, the magnetic phenomena, and the effects due to electric currents. From the end of the eighteenth century onwards, these three lines of investigation were quickly interconnected and the modern science of electro-magnetism was constructed which now threatens to transform human life.

Mathematical ideas now appear. During the decade 1780 to 1789, Coulomb, a Frenchman, proved that magnetic poles attract or repel each other, in proportion to the inverse square of their distances, and also that the same law holds for electric charges—laws curiously analogous to that of gravitation. In 1820, Öersted, a Dane, discovered that electric currents exert a force on magnets, and almost immediately afterwards the mathematical law of the force was correctly formulated by Ampère, a Frenchman, who also proved that two electric currents exerted forces on each other.

> The experimental investigation by which Ampère established the law of the mechanical action between electric currents is one of the most brilliant achievements in science. The whole, theory and experiment, seems as if it had leaped full grown and full armed, from the brain of the 'Newton of Electricity.' It is perfect in form, and unassailable in accuracy, and it is summed up in a formula from which all the phenomena may be deduced, and which must always remain the cardinal formula of electrodynamics.

The momentous laws of induction between currents and between currents and magnets were discovered by Michael Faraday in 1831–32. Faraday was asked: "What is the use of this discovery?" He answered: "What is the use of a child—it grows to be a man." Faraday's child has grown to be a man and is now the basis of all the modern applications of electricity. Faraday also reorganized the whole theoretical conception of the science. His ideas, which had not been fully understood by the scientific world, were extended and put into a directly mathematical form by Clerk Maxwell in 1873. As a result of his mathematical investigations, Maxwell recognized that, under certain conditions, electrical vibrations ought to be propagated. He at once suggested that the vibrations which form light are electrical. This suggestion has since been verified, so that now the whole theory of light is nothing but a branch of the great science of electricity. Also Hertz, a German, in 1888, following on Maxwell's ideas, succeeded in producing electric vibrations by direct electrical methods. His experiments are the basis of our wireless telegraphy.

In more recent years even more fundamental discoveries have been made, and the science continues to grow in theoretic importance and in practical interest. This rapid sketch of its progress illustrates how, by the gradual introduction of the relevant theoretic ideas, suggested by experiment and themselves suggesting fresh experiments, a whole mass of isolated and even trivial phenomena are welded together into one coherent science, in which the results of abstract mathematical deductions, starting from a few simple assumed laws, supply the explanation to the complex tangle of the course of events.

Finally, passing beyond the particular sciences of electro-magnetism and light, we can generalize our point of view still further, and direct our attention to the growth of mathematical physics considered as one great chapter of scientific thought. In the first place, what in the barest outlines is the story of its growth?

It did not begin as one science, or as the product of one band of men. The Chaldean shepherds watched the skies, the agents of government in Mesopotamia and Egypt measured the land, priests and philosophers brooded on the general nature of all things. The vast mass of the operations of nature appeared due to mysterious unfathomable forces. "The wind bloweth where it listeth" expresses accurately the blank ignorance then existing of any stable rules followed in detail by the succession of phenomena. In broad outline, then as now, a regularity of events was patent. But no minute tracing of their interconnection was possible, and there was no knowledge how even to set about to construct such a science.

Detached speculations, a few happy or unhappy shots at the nature of things, formed the utmost which could be produced.

Meanwhile land surveys had produced geometry, and the observations of the heavens disclosed the exact regularity of the solar system. Some of the later Greeks, such as Archimedes, had just views on the elementary phenomena of hydrostatics and optics. Indeed, Archimedes, who combined a genius for mathematics with a physical insight, must rank with Newton, who lived nearly two thousand years later, as one of the founders of mathematical physics. He lived at Syracuse, the great Greek city of Sicily. When the Romans besieged the town (in 212 to 210 B.C.), he is said to have burned their ships by concentrating on them, by means of mirrors, the sun's rays. The story is highly improbable, but is good evidence of the reputation which he had gained among his contemporaries for his knowledge of optics. At the end of this siege he was killed. According to one account given by Plutarch, in his life of Marcellus, he was found by a Roman soldier absorbed in the study of a geometrical diagram which he had traced on the sandy floor of his room. He did not immediately obey the orders of his captor, and so was killed. For the credit of the Roman generals it must be said that the soldiers had orders to spare him. The internal evidence for the other famous story of him is very strong; for the discovery attributed to him is one eminently worthy of his genius for mathematical and physical research. Luckily, it is simple enough to be explained here in detail. It is one of the best easy examples of the method of application of mathematical ideas to physics.

Hiero, King of Syracuse, had sent a quantity of gold to some goldsmith to form the material of a crown. He suspected that the craftsman had abstracted some of the gold and had supplied its place by alloying the remainder with some baser metal. Hiero sent the crown to Archimedes and asked him to test it. In thcsc days an indefinite number of chemical tests would be available. But then Archimedes had to think out the matter afresh. The solution flashed upon him as he lay in his bath. He jumped

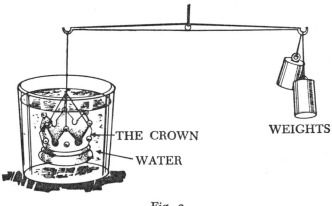

THE CROWN

WEIGHTS

WATER

Fig. 3

up and ran through the streets to the palace, shouting *Eureka! Eureka!* (I have found it, I have found it). This day, if we knew which it was, ought to be celebrated as the birthday of mathematical physics; the science came of age when Newton sat in his orchard. Archimedes had in truth made a great discovery. He saw that a body when immersed in water is pressed upwards by the surrounding water with a resultant force equal to the weight of the water it displaces. This law can be proved theoretically from the mathematical principles of hydrostatics and can also be verified experimentally. Hence, if $W$ lb. be the weight of the crown, as weighed in air, and $w$ lb. be the weight of the water which it displaces when completely immersed, $W - w$ would be the extra upward force necessary to sustain the crown as it hung in water.

Now, this upward force can easily be ascertained by weighing the body as it hangs in water, as shown in Fig. 3. If the weights in the right-hand scale come to $F$ lb., then the apparent weight of the crown in water is $F$ lb.; and we thus have

$$F = W - w$$

and thus

$$w = W - F,$$

and

$$\frac{W}{w} = \frac{W}{W - F} \qquad (A)$$

where $W$ and $F$ are determined by the easy, and fairly precise, operation of weighing. Hence, by equation $(A)$, $\dfrac{W}{w}$ is known. But $\dfrac{W}{w}$ is the ratio of the weight of the crown to the weight of an equal volume of water. This ratio is the same for any lump of metal of the same material: it is now called the specific gravity of the material, and depends only on the intrinsic nature of the substance and not on its shape or quantity. Thus to test if the crown were of gold, Archimedes had only to take a lump of indisputably pure gold and find its specific gravity by the same process. If the two specific gravities agreed, the crown was pure; if they disagreed, it was debased.

This argument has been given at length, because not only is it the first precise example of the application of mathematical ideas to physics, but also because it is a perfect and simple example of what must be the method and spirit of the science for all time.

The death of Archimedes by the hands of a Roman soldier is symbolical of a world change of the first magnitude: the theoretical Greeks, with their love of abstract science, were superseded in the leadership of the European world by the practical Romans. Lord Beaconsfield, in one of his novels, has defined a practical man as a man who practises the errors of his forefathers. The Romans were a great race, but they were cursed with the sterility which waits upon practicality. They did not improve upon the knowledge of their forefathers, and all their advances were confined to the minor technical details of engineering. They were not dreamers enough to arrive at new points of view, which could give a more fundamental control over the forces of nature. No Roman lost his life because he was absorbed in the contemplation of a mathematical diagram.

---

*The foregoing consists of Chapters I–III from Whitehead's* AN INTRODUCTION TO MATHEMATICS.

# On the Nature
# of a Calculus

1. *Signs*

ords, spoken or written, and the symbols of Mathematics are alike signs. Signs have been analysed into ($a$) suggestive signs, ($\beta$) expressive signs, ($\gamma$) substitutive signs.

A suggestive sign is the most rudimentary possible, and need not be dwelt upon here. An obvious example of one is a knot tied in a handkerchief to remind the owner of some duty to be performed.

In the use of expressive signs the attention is not fixed on the sign itself but on what it expresses; that is to say, it is fixed on the meaning conveyed by the sign. Ordinary language consists of groups of expressive signs, its primary object being to draw attention to the meaning of the words employed. Language, no doubt, in its secondary uses has some of the characteristics of a system of substitutive signs. It remedies the inability of the imagination to bring readily before the mind the whole extent of complex ideas by associating these ideas with familiar sounds or marks; and it is not always necessary for the attention to dwell on the complete meaning while using these symbols. But with all this allowance it remains true that language when challenged by criticism refers us to the meaning and not to the natural or conventional properties of its symbols for an explanation of its processes.

A substitutive sign is such that in thought it takes the place of that for which it is substituted. A counter in a game may be such a sign: at the end of the game the counters lost or won may be interpreted in the form of money, but till then it may be convenient for attention to be concentrated on the counters and not on their signification. The signs of a Mathematical Calculus are substitutive signs.

The difference between words and substitutive signs has been stated thus, "a word is an instrument for thinking about the meaning which it expresses; a substitute sign is a means of not thinking about the meaning which it symbolizes."[1] The use of substitutive signs in reasoning is to economize thought.

2. *Definition of a Calculus.* In order that reasoning may be conducted by means of substitutive signs, it is necessary that rules be given for the manipulation of the signs. The rules should be such that the final state of the signs after a series of operations according to rule denotes, when the signs are interpreted in terms of the things for which they are substituted, a proposition true for the things represented by the signs.

The art of the manipulation of substitutive signs according to fixed rules, and of the deduction therefrom of true propositions is a Calculus.

We may therefore define a sign used in a Calculus as "an arbitrary mark, having a fixed interpretation, and susceptible of combination with other signs in subjection to fixed laws dependent upon their mutual interpretation."[2]

The interpretation of any sign used in a series of operations must be fixed in the sense of being the same throughout, but in a certain sense it may be ambiguous. For instance in ordinary Algebra a letter $x$ may be used in a series of operations, and $x$ may be defined to be any algebraical quantity, without further specification of the special quantity chosen. Such a sign denotes any one of an assigned class with certain unambiguously defined characteristics. In the same series of operations the sign must always denote the same member of the class; but as far as any explicit definitions are concerned any member will do.

When once the rules for the manipulation of the signs of a calculus are known, the art of their practical manipulation can be studied apart from any attention to the meaning to be assigned to the signs. It is obvious that we can take any marks we like and manipulate them according to any rules we choose to assign. It is also equally obvious that in general such occupations must be frivolous. They possess a serious scientific value when there is a similarity of type of the signs and of the rules of manipulation to those of some calculus in which the marks used are substitutive signs for things and relations of things. The comparative study of the various forms produced by variation of rules throws light on the principles of the calculus. Furthermore the knowledge thus gained gives facility in the invention of some significant calculus designed to facilitate reasoning with respect to some given subject.

1. Cf. Stout, "Thought and Language," *Mind,* April, 1891.
2. Boole, *Laws of Thought,* Ch. ii.

It enters therefore into the definition of a calculus properly so called that the marks used in it are substitutive signs. But when a set of marks and the rules for their arrangements and rearrangements are analogous to those of a significant calculus so that the study of the allowable forms of their arrangements throws light on that of the calculus, or when the marks and their rules of arrangement are such as appear likely to receive an interpretation as substitutive signs or to facilitate the invention of a true calculus, then the art of arranging such marks may be called—by an extension of the term—an uninterpreted calculus. The study of such a calculus is of scientific value. The marks used in it will be called signs or symbols as are those of a true calculus, thus tacitly suggesting that there is some unknown interpretation which could be given to the calculus.

3. *Equivalence*. It is necessary to note the form in which propositions occur in a calculus. Such a form may well be highly artificial from some points of view, and may yet state the propositions in a convenient form for the eliciting of deductions. Furthermore it is not necessary to assert that the form is a general form into which all judgments can be put by the aid of some torture. It is sufficient to observe that it is a form of wide application.

In a calculus of the type here considered propositions take the form of assertions of equivalence. One thing or fact, which may be complex and involve an interrelated group of things or a succession of facts, is asserted to be equivalent in some sense or other to another thing or fact.

Accordingly the sign $=$ is taken to denote that the signs or groups of signs on either side of it are equivalent, and therefore symbolize things which are so far equivalent. When two groups of symbols are connected by this sign, it is to be understood that one group may be substituted for the other group whenever either occurs in the calculus under conditions for which the assertion of equivalence holds good.

The idea of equivalence requires some explanation. Two things are equivalent when for some purpose they can be used indifferently. Thus the equivalence of distinct things implies a certain defined purpose in view, a certain limitation of thought or of action. Then within this limited field no distinction of property exists between the two things.

As an instance of the limitation of the field of equivalence consider an ordinary algebraical equation, $f(x, y) = 0$. Then in finding $\dfrac{dy}{dx}$ by the formula, $\dfrac{dy}{dx} = - \dfrac{\partial f}{\partial x} \Big/ \dfrac{\partial f}{\partial y}$, we may not substitute 0 for $f$ on the right-hand side of the last equation, though the equivalence of the two symbols has been asserted in the first equation, the reason being that the limitations under which $f = 0$ has been asserted are violated when $f$ undergoes partial differentiation.

The idea of equivalence must be carefully distinguished from that of mere identity. No investigations which proceed by the aid of propositions merely asserting identities such as $A$ is $A$, can ever result in anything but barren identities. Equivalence on the other hand implies non-identity as its general case. Identity may be conceived as a special limiting case of equivalence. For instance in arithmetic we write, $2 + 3 = 3 + 2$. This means that, in so far as the total number of objects mentioned, $2 + 3$ and $3 + 2$ come to the same number, namely 5. But $2 + 3$ and $3 + 2$ are not identical; the order of the symbols is different in the two combinations, and this difference of order directs different processes of thought. The importance of the equation arises from its assertion that these different processes of thought are identical as far as the total number of things thought of is concerned.

From this arithmetical point of view it is tempting to define equivalent things as being merely different ways of thinking of the same thing as it exists in the external world. Thus there is a certain aggregate, say of 5 things, which is thought of in different ways, as $2 + 3$ and as $3 + 2$. A sufficient objection to this definition is that the man who shall succeed in stating intelligibly the distinction between himself and the rest of the world will have solved the central problem of philosophy. As there is no universally accepted solution of this problem, it is obviously undesirable to assume this distinction as the basis of mathematical reasoning.

Thus from another point of view all things which for any purpose can be conceived as equivalent form the extension (in the logical sense) of some universal conception. And conversely the collection of objects which together form the extension of some universal conception can for some purpose be treated as equivalent. So $b = b'$ can be interpreted as symbolizing the fact that the two individual things $b$ and $b'$ are two individual cases of the same general conception $B$. For instance if $b$ stand for $2 + 3$ and $b'$ for $3 + 2$, both $b$ and $b'$ are individual instances of the general conception of a group of five things.

The sign $=$ as used in a calculus must be discriminated from the logical copula "is." Two things $b$ and $b'$ are connected in a calculus by the sign $=$, so that $b = b'$, when both $b$ and $b'$ possess the attribute $B$. But we may not translate this into the standard logical form, $b$ is $b'$. On the contrary, we say, $b$ is $B$, and $b'$ is $B$; and we may not translate these standard forms of formal logic into the symbolic form, $b = B$, $b' = B$; at least we may not do so, if the sign $=$ is to have the meaning which is assigned to it in a calculus.

It is to be observed that the proposition asserted by the equation, $b = b'$, consists of two elements; which for the sake of distinctness we will name, and will call respectively the "truism" and the "paradox." The truism is the partial identity of both $b$ and $b'$, their common $B$-ness. The paradox is the distinction between $b$ and $b'$, so that $b$ is one thing and $b'$ is another thing: and these things, as being different, must have in some relation diverse properties. In assertions of equivalence as contained in a calculus the truism is passed over with the slightest possible attention, the main stress being laid on the paradox. Thus in the equation $2 + 3 = 3 + 2$, the fact that both sides represent a common five-ness of number is not even mentioned explicitly. The sole direct statement is that the two *different* things $3 + 2$ and $2 + 3$ are in point of number equivalent.

The reason for this unequal distribution of attention is easy to understand. In order to discover new propositions asserting equivalence it is requisite to discover easy marks or tests of equivalent things. These tests are discovered by a careful discussion of the truism, of the common $B$-ness of $b$ and $b'$. But when once such tests have been elaborated, we may drop all thought of the essential nature of the attribute $B$, and simply apply the superficial test to $b$ and $b'$ in order to verify $b = b'$. Thus in order to verify that thirty-seven times fifty-six is equal to fifty-six times thirty-seven, we may use the entirely superficial test applicable to this case that the same factors are mentioned as multiplied, though in different order.

This discussion leads us at once to comprehend the essence of a calculus of substitutive signs. The signs are by convention to be considered equivalent when certain conditions hold. And these conditions when interpreted imply the fulfilment of the tests of equivalence.

Thus in the discussion of the laws of a calculus stress is laid on the truism, in the development of the consequences on the paradox.

4. *Operations.* Judgments of equivalence can be founded on direct perception, as when it is judged by direct perception that two different pieces of stuff match in colour. But the judgment may be founded on a knowledge of the respective derivations of the things judged to be equivalent from other things respectively either identical or equivalent. It is this process of derivation which is the special province of a calculus. The derivation of a thing $p$ from things $a$, $b$, $c$, . . . , can also be conceived

as an operation on the things $a, b, c, \ldots$, which produces the thing $p$. The idea of derivation includes that of a series of phenomenal occurrences. Thus two pieces of stuff may be judged to match in colour because they were dyed in the same dipping, or were cut from the same piece of stuff. But the idea is more general than that of phenomenal sequence of events: it includes purely logical activities of the mind, as when it is judged that an aggregate of five things has been presented to the mind by two aggregates of three things and of two things respectively. Another example of derivation is that of two propositions $a$ and $b$ which are both derived by strict deductive reasoning from the same propositions $c, d,$ and $e$. The two propositions are either both proved or both unproved according as $c, d,$ and $e$ are granted or disputed. Thus $a$ and $b$ are so far equivalent. In other words $a$ and $b$ may be considered as the equivalent results of two operations on $c, d$ and $e$.

The words operation, combination, derivation, and synthesis will be used to express the same general idea, of which each word suggests a somewhat specialized form. This general idea may be defined thus: A thing $a$ will be said to result from an operation on other things, $c, d, e$, etc., when $a$ is presented to the mind as the result of the presentations of $c, d$ and $e$, etc. under certain conditions; and these conditions are phenomenal events or mental activities which it is convenient to separate in idea into a group by themselves and to consider as defining the nature of the operation which is performed on $c, d, e$, etc.

Furthermore the fact that $c, d, e$, etc. are capable of undergoing a certain operation involving them all will be considered as constituting a relation between $c, d, e$, etc.

Also the fact that $c$ is capable of undergoing an operation of a certain general kind will be considered as a property of $c$. Any additional specialization of the kind of operation or of the nature of the result will be considered as a mode of that property.

5. *Substitutive Schemes.* Let $a, a'$, etc., $b, b'$, etc., $\ldots\ldots z, z'$, etc., denote any set of objects considered in relation to some common property which is symbolized by the use of the italic alphabet of letters. The common property may not be possessed in the same mode by different members of the set. Their equivalence, or identity in relation to this property, is symbolized by a literal identity. Thus the fact that the things $a$ and $m'$ are both symbolized by letters from the italic alphabet is here a sign that the things have some property in common, and the fact that the letters $a$ and $m'$ are different letters is a sign that the two things possess this

common property in different modes. On the other hand the two things $a$ and $a'$ possess the common property in the same mode, and as far as this property is concerned they are equivalent. Let the sign $=$ express equivalence in relation to this property, then $a = a'$, and $m = m'$.

Let a set of things such as that described above, considered in relation to their possession of a common property in equivalent or in non-equivalent modes, be called a *scheme* of things; and let the common property of which the possession by any object marks that object as belonging to the scheme be called the *determining property of the scheme*. Thus objects belonging to the same scheme are equivalent if they possess the determining property in the same mode.

Now relations must exist between non-equivalent things of the scheme which depend on the differences between the modes in which they possess the determining property of the scheme. In consequence of these relations from things $a$, $b$, $c$, etc. of the scheme another thing $m$ of the scheme can be derived by certain operations. The equivalence, $m = m'$, will exist between $m$ and $m'$, if $m$ and $m'$ are derived from other things of the scheme by operations which only differ in certain assigned modes. The modes in which processes of derivation of equivalent things $m$ and $m'$ from other things of the scheme can differ without destroying the equivalence of $m$ and $m'$ will be called the *characteristics* of the scheme.

Now it may happen that two schemes of things—with of course different determining properties—have the same characteristics. Also it may be possible to establish an unambiguous correspondence between the things of the two schemes, so that if $a$, $a'$, $b$, etc., belong to one scheme and $\alpha$, $\alpha'$, $\beta$, etc., belong to the other, then $a$ corresponds to $\alpha$, $a'$ to $\alpha'$, $b$ to $\beta$ and so on. The essential rule of the correspondence is that if in one scheme two things, say $a$ and $a'$, are equivalent, then in the other scheme their corresponding things $\alpha$ and $\alpha'$ are equivalent. Accordingly to any process of derivation in the italic alphabet by which $m$ is derived from $a$, $b$, etc. there must correspond a process of derivation in the Greek alphabet by which $\mu$ is derived from $\alpha$, $\beta$, etc.

In such a case instead of reasoning with respect to the properties of one scheme in order to deduce equivalences, we may substitute the other scheme, or conversely; and then transpose at the end of the argument. This device of reasoning, which is almost universal in mathematics, we will call the method of substitutive schemes, or more briefly, the method of substitution.

These substituted things belonging to another scheme are nothing else than substitutive signs. For in the use of substituted schemes we cease to think of the original scheme. The rule of reasoning is to confine thought to those properties, previously determined, which are shared in common with the original scheme, and to interpret the results from one set of things into the other at the end of the argument.

An instance of this process of reasoning by substitution is to be found in the theory of quantity. Quantities are measured by their ratio to an arbitrarily assumed quantity of the same kind, called the unit. Any set of quantities of one kind can be represented by a corresponding set of quantities of any other kind merely in so far as their numerical ratios to their unit are concerned. For the representative set have only to bear the same ratios to their unit as do the original set to their unit.

6. *Conventional Schemes.* The use of a calculus of substitutive signs in reasoning can now be explained.

Besides using substitutive schemes with naturally suitable properties, we may by convention assign to arbitrary marks laws of equivalence which are identical with the laws of equivalence of the originals about which we desire to reason. The set of marks may then be considered as a scheme of things with properties assigned by convention. The determining property of the scheme is that the marks are of certain assigned sorts arranged in certain types of sequence. The characteristics of the scheme are the conventional laws by which certain arrangements of the marks in sequence on paper are to be taken as equivalent. As long as the marks are treated as mutually determined by their conventional properties, reasoning concerning the marks will hold good concerning the originals for which the marks are substitutive signs. For instance in the employment of the marks $x$, $y$, $+$, the equation, $x + y = y + x$, asserts that a certain union on paper of $x$ and $y$ possesses the conventional quality that the order of $x$ and $y$ is indifferent. Therefore any union of two things with a result independent of any precedence of one thing before the other possesses so far properties identical with those of the union above set down between $x$ and $y$. Not only can the reasoning be transferred from the originals to the substitutive signs, but the imaginative thought itself can in a large measure be avoided. For whereas combinations of the original things are possible only in thought and by an act of the imagination, the combinations of the conventional substitutive signs of a calculus are physically made on paper. The mind has simply to attend to the rules for transformation and to use its experience and imagination to suggest likely methods of procedure. The rest is merely physical actual interchange of the signs instead of thought about the originals.

A calculus avoids the necessity of inference and replaces it by an external demonstration, where inference and external demonstration are to be taken in the senses assigned to them by F. H. Bradley.[3] In this connection a demonstration is to be defined as a process of combining a complex of facts, the data, into a whole so that some new fact is evident. Inference is an ideal combination or construction within the mind of the reasoner which results in the intuitive evidence of a new fact or relation between the data. But in the use of a calculus this process of combination is externally performed by the combination of the concrete symbols, with the result of a new fact respecting the symbols which arises for sensuous perception.[4] When this new fact is treated as a symbol carrying a meaning, it is found to mean the fact which would have been intuitively evident in the process of inference.

7. *Uninterpretable Forms.* The logical difficulty involved in the use of a calculus only partially interpretable can now be explained. The discussion of this great problem in its application to the special case of $(-1)^{\frac{1}{2}}$ engaged the attention of the leading mathematicians of the first half of this century, and led to the development on the one hand of the Theory of Functions of a Complex Variable, and on the other hand of the science here called Universal Algebra.

The difficulty is this: the symbol $(-1)^{\frac{1}{2}}$ is absolutely without meaning when it is endeavoured to interpret it as a number; but algebraic transformations which involve the use of complex quantities of the form $a + bi$, where $a$ and $b$ are numbers and $i$ stands for the above symbol, yield propositions which do relate purely to number. As a matter of fact the propositions thus discovered were found to be true propositions. The method therefore was trusted, before any explanation was forthcoming why algebraic reasoning which had no intelligible interpretation in arithmetic should give true arithmetical results.

The difficulty was solved by observing that Algebra does not depend on Arithmetic for the validity of its laws of transformation. If there were such a dependence, it is obvious that as soon as algebraic expressions are arithmetically unintelligible all laws respecting them must lose their validity. But the laws of Algebra, though suggested by Arithmetic, do not depend on it. They depend entirely on the convention by which it is stated that certain modes of grouping the symbols are to be considered as

---

3. Cf. Bradley, *Principles of Logic*, Bk ii. Pt i. Ch. iii.
4. Cf. C. S. Peirce, *Amer. Journ. of Math.* Vol. vii. p. 182: "As for algebra, the very idea of the art is that it presents formulae which can be manipulated, and that by observing the effects of such manipulation we find properties not otherwise to be discovered."

identical. This assigns certain properties to the marks which form the symbols of Algebra. The laws regulating the manipulation of the algebraic symbols are identical with those of Arithmetic. It follows that no algebraic theorem can ever contradict any result which could be arrived at by Arithmetic; for the reasoning in both cases merely applies the same general laws to different classes of things. If an algebraic theorem is interpretable in Arithmetic, the corresponding arithmetical theorem is therefore true. In short when once Algebra is conceived as an independent science dealing with the relations of certain marks conditioned by the observance of certain conventional laws, the difficulty vanishes. If the laws be identical, the theorems of the one science can only give results conditioned by the laws which also hold good for the other science; and therefore these results, when interpretable, are true.

It will be observed that the explanation of the legitimacy of the use of a partially interpretable calculus does not depend upon the fact that in another field of thought the calculus is entirely interpretable. The discovery of an interpretation undoubtedly gave the clue by means of which the true solution was arrived at. For the fact that the processes of the calculus were interpretable in a science so independent of Arithmetic as is Geometry at once showed that the laws of the calculus might have been defined in reference to geometrical processes. But it was a paradox to assert that a science like Algebra, which had been studied for centuries without reference to Geometry, was after all dependent upon Geometry for its first principles. The step to the true explanation was then easily taken.

But the importance of the assistance given to the study of Algebra by the discovery of a complete interpretation of its processes cannot be over-estimated. It is natural to think of the substitutive set of things as assisting the study of the properties of the originals. Especially is this the case with a calculus of which the interest almost entirely depends upon its relation to the originals. But it must be remembered that conversely the originals give immense aid to the study of the substitutive things or symbols.

The whole of Mathematics consists in the organization of a series of aids to the imagination in the process of reasoning; and for this purpose device is piled upon device. No sooner has a substitutive scheme been devised to assist in the investigation of any originals, than the imagination begins to use the originals to assist in the investigation of the substitutive scheme. In some connections it would be better to abandon the conception of originals studied by the aid of substitutive schemes, and to conceive of two sets of interrelated things studied together, each scheme exemplifying the operation of the same general laws. The discovery therefore of the geometrical representation of the algebraical complex quantity, though unessential to the logic of Algebra, has been quite essential to the modern developments of the science.

---

*The foregoing consists of Chapter I*
*from Whitehead's* A TREATISE ON UNIVERSAL ALGEBRA.

# Bertrand Russell

## 1872–

Russell began worrying about the foundations of mathematics at the age of eleven. He was studying Euclid at that time and was disappointed to learn that he was expected to accept some things without proof. It seemed a little slipshod to him. He wanted everything proved. He never lost this desire for clarity and certainty; it led him to attempt to establish the logical basis for all mathematics.

Bertrand Russell, British philosopher and mathematician, was born at Trelleck, in Monmouthshire, in 1872. Both parents died before he was four years old and he was brought up by his grandmother, Countess Russell. A woman of strong religious beliefs, she instilled in Russell the ideas that he must be of service to mankind and that he should always have the courage to follow his own conscience. Russell was profoundly influenced by his grandmother. Although he rejected her religious teachings at an early age, he has used his immense talent in humane and liberal causes for over half a century. He has publicly and courageously committed himself on many controversial issues; more than once this has meant going to prison.

Russell was tutored at home until he was eighteen. Then he entered Cambridge. Until this time his life had been rather solitary, but now a new world opened. At Cambridge he found a group of contemporaries with whom he could have endless discussions on everything. The mental adventure began. It has never ended. On his eightieth birthday Russell recommended, for longevity, a "habit of hilarious Olympian controversy."

One of the most productive and brilliant thinkers of our age, Russell has expressed himself vividly on many aspects of our culture —education, politics, history, manners, morals, war, and peace. A partial list of his writings includes: *Mysticism and Logic, and Other Essays* (1918), *Introduction to Mathematical Philosophy* (1919), *An Outline of Philosophy* (1927), *Marriage and Morals* (1929), *The Scientific Outlook* (1931), *An Inquiry into Meaning and Truth* (1940), *History of Western Philosophy* (1945), and, in collaboration with Alfred North Whitehead, *Principia Mathematica* (1910–13). He won the Nobel Prize for literature in 1950.

Logic is central in Russell's philosophy. His views on many things have changed profoundly in the course of his life, but these changes all proceeded from successively deeper applications of his logical method. This method dates from the year 1900, which Russell calls the most important year of his intellectual life. It was then, at the International Congress of Philosophy in Paris, which Russell attended with Whitehead, that Giuseppe Peano introduced a method for reasoning in symbols. Russell saw that it could extend the region of mathematical precision backward into areas that hitherto had been given over to vague speculation. The project of deducing mathematics from logic also appealed to Whitehead, and they began a remarkable intellectual collaboration. The result is the famous *Principia Mathematica*.

The first two of the following three selections are taken from *Mysticism and Logic*. In *The Study of Mathematics*, mathematics is conceived as a purely formal science. It is not derived from experience. And therein, for Russell, lies its beauty. Life can be a pretty muddled affair, "but the world of pure reason knows no compromise, no practical limitations, no barrier to the creative activity. . . ." Russell takes a critical look at educational methods that become so bogged down acquiring the first elements of the subject that the goal is never reached, or even glimpsed. This goal is Plato's world of "divine necessity," the world of purely intellectual

---

*Notes from the artist: ". . . a 'ball of yarn' technique— with a liberal sprinkling of mathematical formulas—was employed to express the restlessness and the constant searching and probing that is so much a part of the character of Russell. The quotation is from* Human Knowledge.*"*

Bertrand Russell

The relation of physical laws to experience is not altogether simple. Broadly speaking, laws can be disproved by experience, but not proved by it.

activity. Russell's passionate belief in it is contagious. He does not actually lead you inside the temple (he comes out on the steps to talk to you), but he leaves no doubt that the temple is there.

In *Mathematics and the Metaphysicians,* Russell makes the assertion that mathematics is the same thing as formal logic, as founded by Aristotle. But modern logic has gone beyond Aristotle; it has become symbolic. Words have been replaced by symbols that have no reference to the world of things. Why has this been so important in examining the foundations of mathematics? The answer seems paradoxical. Symbolism is useful because it makes things difficult (but only in the beginning).

Suspend your common sense when you read this article. You will be asked to believe that there is no such thing as the next moment; that when a thing moves, it is not in a state of motion; that there are just as many even numbers as there are numbers altogether; that the number of days in all time is no greater than the number of years. Russell intends to take the mystery out of mathematics. He does not hesitate to use shock treatment.

Traditional mathematics suffered a crisis in the nineteenth century. A vast superstructure of knowledge had been erected without sufficient thought of the foundation. Cracks appeared, hasty repairs were made, but repairs were really not enough. What was needed was a complete reconstruction of the foundation. The following selection is part of this project.

*Definition of Number* is taken from *Introduction to Mathematical Philosophy,* written during World War I. Russell was in jail when he wrote it. He had been imprisoned for several months because he had written a pamphlet accusing the American Army of "intimidating strikes at home." This was regarded as likely to impair the relationship between Great Britain and America. (The governor of the prison was required to read the manuscript for possible seditious tendencies.)

A definition of an idea usually expresses the idea in concepts which are more familiar to us. When the idea is as familiar as "number," what we say in explanation of it is likely to seem stranger than the thing itself. Thus, a definition of number might seem at first glance to be an arduous and needless task. The predicament of the centipede who was getting along very well until asked which leg came after which seems applicable. However, there is a reason for presenting the familiar in unfamiliar terms. It puts us at a distance from something which, otherwise, is too close to be seen.

The habit of mind that is developed in defining the obvious will stand you in very good stead when you enter the world of abstract thought. Your definitions will be your only landmarks.

# The Study of Mathematics

In regard to every form of human activity it is necessary that the question should be asked from time to time, What is its purpose and ideal? In what way does it contribute to the beauty of human existence? As respects those pursuits which contribute only remotely, by providing the mechanism of life, it is well to be reminded that not the mere fact of living is to be desired, but the art of living in the contemplation of great things. Still more in regard to those avocations which have no end outside themselves, which are to be justified, if at all, as actually adding to the sum of the world's permanent possessions, it is necessary to keep alive a knowledge of their aims, a clear prefiguring vision of the temple in which creative imagination is to be embodied.

The fulfilment of this need, in what concerns the studies forming the material upon which custom has decided to train the youthful mind, is indeed sadly remote—so remote as to make the mere statement of such a claim appear preposterous. Great men, fully alive to the beauty of the contemplations to whose service their lives are devoted, desiring that others may share in their joys, persuade mankind to impart to the successive generations the mechanical knowledge without which it is impossible to cross the threshold. Dry pedants possess themselves of the privilege of instilling this knowledge: they forget that it is to serve but as a key to open the doors of the temple; though they spend their lives on the steps leading up to those sacred doors, they turn their backs upon the temple so resolutely that its very existence is forgotten, and the eager youth, who would press forward to be initiated to its domes and arches, is bidden to turn back and count the steps.

Mathematics, perhaps more even than the study of Greece and Rome, has suffered from this oblivion of its due place in civilization. Although tradition has decreed that the great bulk of educated men shall know at least the elements of the subject, the reasons for which the tradition arose are forgotten, buried beneath a great rubbish-heap of pedantries and trivialities. To those who inquire as to the purpose of mathematics, the usual answer will be that it facilitates the making of machines, the travelling from place to place, and the victory over foreign nations, whether in war or commerce. If it be objected that these ends—all of which are of doubtful value—are not furthered by the merely elementary study imposed upon those who do not become expert mathematicians, the reply, it is true, will probably be that mathematics trains the reasoning faculties. Yet the very men who make this reply are, for the most part, unwilling to abandon the teaching of definite fallacies, known to be such, and instinctively rejected by the unsophisticated mind of every intelligent learner. And the reasoning faculty itself is generally conceived, by those who urge its cultivation, as merely a means for the avoidance of pitfalls and a help in the discovery of rules for the guidance of practical life. All these are undeniably important achievements to the credit of mathematics; yet it is none of these that entitles mathematics to a place in every liberal education. Plato, we know, regarded the contemplation of mathematical truths as worthy of the Deity; and Plato realized, more perhaps than any other single man, what those elements are in human life which merit a place in heaven. There is in mathematics, he says, "something which is *necessary* and cannot be set aside . . . and, if I mistake not, of divine necessity; for as to the human necessities of which the Many talk in this connection, nothing can be more ridiculous than such an application of the words. *Cleinias.* And what are these necessities of knowledge, Stranger, which are divine and not human? *Athenian.* Those things without some use or knowledge of which a man cannot become a God to the world, nor a spirit, nor yet a hero, nor able earnestly to think and care for man." [1] Such was Plato's judgment of mathematics; but the mathematicians do not read Plato, while those who read him know no mathematics, and regard his opinion upon this question as merely a curious aberration.

Mathematics, rightly viewed, possesses not only truth, but supreme beauty—a beauty cold and austere, like that of sculpture, without appeal to any part of our weaker nature, without the gorgeous trappings of painting or music, yet sublimely pure, and capable of a stern perfection such as only the greatest art can show. The true spirit of delight, the exaltation, the sense of being more than man, which is the touchstone of the highest excellence, is to be found in mathematics as surely as in poetry. What is best in mathematics deserves not merely to be learnt as a task, but to be assimilated as a part of daily thought, and brought again and again before the mind with ever-renewed encouragement.

---

1. This passage was pointed out to me by Professor Gilbert Murray.

Real life is, to most men, a long second-best, a perpetual compromise between the ideal and the possible; but the world of pure reason knows no compromise, no practical limitations, no barrier to the creative activity embodying in splendid edifices the passionate aspiration after the perfect from which all great work springs. Remote from human passions, remote even from the pitiful facts of nature, the generations have gradually created an ordered cosmos, where pure thought can dwell as in its natural home, and where one, at least, of our nobler impulses can escape from the dreary exile of the actual world.

So little, however, have mathematicians aimed at beauty, that hardly anything in their work has had this conscious purpose. Much, owing to irrepressible instincts, which were better than avowed beliefs, has been moulded by an unconscious taste; but much also has been spoilt by false notions of what was fitting. The characteristic excellence of mathematics is only to be found where the reasoning is rigidly logical: the rules of logic are to mathematics what those of structure are to architecture. In the most beautiful work, a chain of argument is presented in which every link is important on its own account, in which there is an air of ease and lucidity throughout, and the premises achieve more than would have been thought possible, by means which appear natural and inevitable. Literature embodies what is general in particular circumstances whose universal significance shines through their individual dress; but mathematics endeavours to present whatever is most general in its purity, without any irrelevant trappings.

How should the teaching of mathematics be conducted so as to communicate to the learner as much as possible of this high ideal? Here experience must, in a great measure, be our guide, but some maxims may result from our consideration of the ultimate purpose to be achieved.

One of the chief ends served by mathematics, when rightly taught, is to awaken the learner's belief in reason, his confidence in the truth of what has been demonstrated, and in the value of demonstration. This purpose is not served by existing instruction; but it is easy to see ways in which it might be served. At present, in what concerns arithmetic, the boy or girl is given a set of rules, which present themselves as neither true nor false, but as merely the will of the teacher, the way in which, for some unfathomable reason, the teacher prefers to have the game played. To some degree, in a study of such definite practical utility, this is no doubt unavoidable; but as soon as possible, the reasons of rules should be set forth by whatever means most readily appeal to the childish mind. In geometry, instead of the tedious apparatus of fallacious proofs for obvious truisms which constitutes the beginning of Euclid, the learner should be allowed at first to assume the truth of everything obvious, and should be instructed in the demonstrations of theorems which are at once startling and easily verifiable by actual drawing, such as those in which it is shown that three or more lines meet in a point. In this way belief is generated; it is seen that reasoning may lead to startling conclusions, which nevertheless the facts will verify; and thus the instinctive distrust of whatever is abstract or rational is gradually overcome. Where theorems are difficult, they should be first taught as exercises in geometrical drawing, until the figure has become thoroughly familiar; it will then be an agreeable advance to be taught the logical connections of the various lines or circles that occur. It is desirable also that the figure illustrating a theorem should be drawn in all possible cases and shapes, that so the abstract relations with which geometry is concerned may of themselves emerge as the residue of similarity amid such great apparent diversity. In this way the abstract demonstrations should form but a small part of the instruction, and should be given when, by familiarity with concrete illustrations, they have come to be felt as the natural embodiment of visible fact. In this early stage proofs should not be given with pedantic fullness; definitely fallacious methods, such as that of superposition, should be rigidly excluded from the first, but where, without such methods, the proof would be very difficult, the result should be rendered acceptable by arguments and illustrations which are explicitly contrasted with demonstrations.

In the beginning of algebra, even the most intelligent child finds, as a rule, very great difficulty. The use of letters is a mystery, which seems to have no purpose except mystification. It is almost impossible, at first, not to think that every letter stands for some particular number, if only the teacher would reveal *what* number it stands for. The fact is that in algebra the mind is first taught to consider general truths, truths which are not asserted to hold only of this or that particular thing, but of any one of a whole group of things. It is in the power of understanding and discovering such truths that the mastery of the intellect over the whole world of things actual and possible resides; and ability to deal with the general as such is one of the gifts that a mathematical education should bestow. But how little, as a rule, is the teacher of algebra able to explain the chasm which divides it from arithmetic, and how little is the learner assisted in his groping efforts at comprehension! Usually the method that has been adopted in arithmetic is continued: rules are set forth, with no adequate explanation of their grounds; the pupil learns to use the rules blindly, and presently, when he is able to obtain the answer that the teacher desires, he feels that he has mastered the difficulties of the subject. But of inner comprehension of the processes employed he has probably acquired almost nothing.

When algebra has been learnt, all goes smoothly until we reach those studies in which the notion of infinity is employed—the infinitesimal calculus and the whole of higher mathematics. The solution of the difficulties which formerly surrounded the mathematical infinite is probably the greatest achievement of which our own age has to boast. Since the beginnings of Greek thought these difficulties have been known; in every age the finest intellects have vainly endeavoured to answer the apparently unanswerable questions that had been asked by Zeno the Eleatic. At last Georg Cantor has found the answer, and has conquered for the intellect a new and vast province which had been given over to Chaos and old Night. It was assumed as self-evident, until Cantor and Dedekind established the opposite, that if, from any collection of things, some were taken away, the number of things left must always be less than the original number of things. This assumption, as a matter of fact, holds only of finite collections; and the rejection of it, where the infinite is concerned, has been shown to remove all the difficulties that had hitherto baffled human reason in this matter, and to render possible the creation of an exact science of the infinite. This stupendous fact ought to produce a revolution in the higher teaching of mathematics; it has itself added immeasurably to the educational value of the subject, and it has at last given the means of treating with logical precision many studies which, until lately, were wrapped in fallacy and obscurity. By those who were educated on the old lines, the new work is considered to be appallingly difficult, abstruse, and obscure; and it must be confessed that the discoverer, as is so often the case, has hardly himself emerged from the mists which the light of his intellect is dispelling. But inherently, the new doctrine of the infinite, to all candid and inquiring minds, has facilitated the mastery of higher mathematics; for hitherto, it has been necessary to learn, by a long process of sophistication, to give assent to arguments which, on first acquaintance, were rightly judged to be confused and erroneous. So far from producing a fearless belief in reason, a bold rejection of whatever failed to fulfil the strictest requirements of logic, a mathematical training, during the past two centuries, encouraged the belief that many things, which a rigid inquiry would reject as fallacious, must yet be accepted because they work in what the mathematician calls "practice." By this means, a timid, compromising spirit, or else a sacerdotal belief in mysteries not intelligible to the profane, has been bred where reason alone should have ruled. All this it is now time to sweep away; let those who wish to penetrate into the arcana of mathematics be taught at once the true theory in all its logical purity, and in the concatenation established by the very essence of the entities concerned.

If we are considering mathematics as an end in itself, and not as a technical training for engineers, it is very desirable to preserve the purity and strictness of its reasoning. Accordingly those who have attained a sufficient familiarity with its easier portions should be led backward from propositions to which they have assented as self-evident to more and more fundamental principles from which what had previously appeared as premises can be deduced. They should be taught—what the theory of infinity very aptly illustrates—that many propositions seem self-evident to the untrained mind which, nevertheless, a nearer scrutiny shows to be false. By this means they will be led to a sceptical inquiry into first principles, an examination of the foundations upon which the whole edifice of reasoning is built, or, to take perhaps a more fitting metaphor, the great trunk from which the spreading branches spring. At this stage, it is well to study afresh the elementary portions of mathematics, asking no longer merely whether a given proposition is true, but also how it grows out of the central principles of logic. Questions of this nature can now be answered with a precision and certainty which were formerly quite impossible; and in the chains of reasoning that the answer requires the unity of all mathematical studies at last unfolds itself.

In the great majority of mathematical text-books there is a total lack of unity in method and of systematic development of a central theme. Propositions of very diverse kinds are proved by whatever means are thought most easily intelligible, and much space is devoted to mere curiosities which in no way contribute to the main argument. But in the greatest works, unity and inevitability are felt as in the unfolding of a drama; in the premisses a subject is proposed for consideration, and in every subsequent step some definite advance is made towards mastery of its nature. The love of system, of interconnection, which is perhaps the inmost essence of the intellectual impulse, can find free play in mathematics as nowhere else. The learner who feels this impulse must not be repelled by an array of meaningless examples or distracted by amusing oddities, but must be encouraged to dwell upon central principles, to become familiar with the structure of the various subjects which are put before him, to travel easily over the steps of the more important deductions. In this way a good tone of mind is cultivated, and selective attention is taught to dwell by preference upon what is weighty and essential.

When the separate studies into which mathematics is divided have each been viewed as a logical whole, as a natural growth from the propositions which constitute their principles, the learner will be able to understand the fundamental science which unifies and systematizes the whole of deductive reasoning. This is symbolic logic—a study which, though it owes its inception to Aristotle, is yet, in its wider developments, a product, almost wholly, of the nineteenth century, and is indeed, in the present day, still growing with great rapidity. The true method of discovery in symbolic logic, and probably also the best method for introducing the study to a learner acquainted with other parts of mathematics, is the analysis of actual examples of deductive reasoning, with a view to the discovery of the principles employed. These principles, for the most part, are so embedded in our ratiocinative instincts that they are employed quite unconsciously, and can be dragged to light only by much patient effort. But when at last they have been found, they are seen to be few in number, and to be the sole source of everything in pure mathematics. The discovery that all mathematics follows inevitably from a small collection of fundamental laws is one which immeasurably enhances the intellectual beauty of the whole; to those who have been oppressed by the fragmentary and incomplete nature of most existing chains of deduction this discovery comes with all the overwhelming force of a revelation; like a palace emerging from the autumn mist as the traveller ascends an Italian hill-side, the stately storeys of the mathematical edifice appear in their due order and proportion, with a new perfection in every part.

Until symbolic logic had acquired its present development, the principles upon which mathematics depends were always supposed to be philosophical, and discoverable only by the uncertain, unprogressive methods hitherto employed by philosophers. So long as this was thought, mathematics seemed to be not autonomous, but dependent upon a study which had quite other methods than its own. Moreover, since the nature of the postulates from which arithmetic, analysis, and geometry are to be deduced was wrapped in all the traditional obscurities of metaphysical discussion, the edifice built upon such dubious foundations began to be viewed as no better than a castle in the air. In this respect, the discovery that the true principles are as much a part of mathematics as any of their consequences has very greatly increased the intellectual satisfaction to be obtained. This satisfaction ought not to be refused to learners capable of enjoying it, for it is of a kind to increase our respect for human powers and our knowledge of the beauties belonging to the abstract world.

Philosophers have commonly held that the laws of logic, which under-lie mathematics, are laws of thought, laws regulating the operations of our minds. By this opinion the true dignity of reason is very greatly lowered; it ceases to be an investigation into the very heart and immu-table essence of all things actual and possible, becoming, instead, an in-quiry into something more or less human and subject to our limitations. The contemplation of what is non-human, the discovery that our minds are capable of dealing with material not created by them, above all, the realization that beauty belongs to the outer world as to the inner are the chief means of overcoming the terrible sense of impotence, of weakness, of exile amid hostile powers, which is too apt to result from acknowledg-ing the all but omnipotence of alien forces. To reconcile us, by the ex-hibition of its awful beauty, to the reign of Fate—which is merely the literary personification of these forces—is the task of tragedy. But mathe-matics takes us still further from what is human, into the region of abso-lute necessity, to which not only the actual world, but every possible world, must conform; and even here it builds a habitation, or rather finds a habitation eternally standing, where our ideals are fully satisfied and our best hopes are not thwarted. It is only when we thoroughly under-stand the entire independence of ourselves, which belongs to this world that reason finds, that we can adequately realize the profound importance of its beauty.

Not only is mathematics independent of us and our thoughts, but in another sense we and the whole universe of existing things are independ-ent of mathematics. The apprehension of this purely ideal character is indispensable, if we are to understand rightly the place of mathematics as one among the arts. It was formerly supposed that pure reason could decide, in some respects, as to the nature of the actual world: geometry, at least, was thought to deal with the space in which we live. But we now know that pure mathematics can never pronounce upon questions of actual existence: the world of reason, in a sense, controls the world of fact, but it is not at any point creative of fact, and in the application of its results to the world in time and space, its certainty and precision are lost among approximations and working hypotheses. The objects con-sidered by mathematicians have, in the past, been mainly of a kind sug-gested by phenomena; but from such restrictions the abstract imagination should be wholly free. A reciprocal liberty must thus be accorded: reason cannot dictate to the world of facts, but the facts cannot restrict reason's privilege of dealing with whatever objects its love of beauty may cause to seem worthy of consideration. Here, as elsewhere, we build up our own ideals out of the fragments to be found in the world; and in the end it is hard to say whether the result is a creation or a discovery.

It is very desirable, in instruction, not merely to persuade the student of the accuracy of important theorems, but to persuade him in the way which itself has, of all possible ways, the most beauty. The true interest of a demonstration is not, as traditional modes of exposition suggest, concentrated wholly in the result; where this does occur, it must be viewed as a defect, to be remedied, if possible, by so generalizing the steps of the proof that each becomes important in and for itself. An argument which serves only to prove a conclusion is like a story subordinated to some moral which it is meant to teach: for aesthetic perfection no part of the whole should be merely a means. A certain practical spirit, a desire for rapid progress, for conquest of new realms, is responsible for the undue emphasis upon results which prevails in mathematical instruction. The better way is to propose some theme for consideration—in geometry, a figure having important properties; in analysis, a function of which the study is illuminating, and so on. Whenever proofs depend upon some only of the marks by which we define the object to be studied, these marks should be isolated and investigated on their own account. For it is a defect, in an argument, to employ more premises than the conclusion demands: what mathematicians call elegance results from employing only the essential principles in virtue of which the thesis is true. It is a merit in Euclid that he advances as far as he is able to go without employing the axiom of parallels—not, as is often said, because this axiom is inherently objectionable, but because, in mathematics, every new axiom diminishes the generality of the resulting theorems, and the greatest possible generality is before all things to be sought.

Of the effects of mathematics outside its own sphere more has been written than on the subject of its own proper ideal. The effect upon philosophy has, in the past, been most notable, but most varied; in the seventeenth century, idealism and rationalism, in the eighteenth, materialism and sensationalism, seemed equally its offspring. Of the effect which it is likely to have in the future it would be very rash to say much; but in one respect a good result appears probable. Against that kind of scepticism which abandons the pursuit of ideals because the road is arduous and the goal not certainly attainable, mathematics, within its own sphere, is a complete answer. Too often it is said that there is no absolute truth, but only opinion and private judgment; that each of us is conditioned, in his view of the world, by his own peculiarities, his own taste and bias; that there is no external kingdom of truth to which, by patience and discipline, we may at last obtain admittance, but only truth for me, for you, for every separate person. By this habit of mind one of the chief ends of human effort is denied, and the supreme virtue of candour, of fearless acknowledgment of what is, disappears from our moral vision. Of such scepticism mathematics is a perpetual reproof; for its edifice of truths stands unshakeable and inexpugnable to all the weapons of doubting cynicism.

The effects of mathematics upon practical life, though they should not be regarded as the motive of our studies, may be used to answer a doubt to which the solitary student must always be liable. In a world so full of evil and suffering, retirement into the cloister of contemplation, to the enjoyment of delights which, however noble, must always be for the few only, cannot but appear as a somewhat selfish refusal to share the burden imposed upon others by accidents in which justice plays no part. Have any of us the right, we ask, to withdraw from present evils, to leave our fellow-men unaided, while we live a life which, though arduous and austere, is yet plainly good in its own nature? When these questions arise, the true answer is, no doubt, that some must keep alive the sacred fire, some must preserve, in every generation, the haunting vision which shadows forth the goal of so much striving. But when, as must sometimes occur, this answer seems too cold, when we are almost maddened by the spectacle of sorrows to which we bring no help, then we may reflect that indirectly the mathematician often does more for human happiness than any of his more practically active contemporaries. The history of science abundantly proves that a body of abstract propositions—even if, as in the case of conic sections, it remains two thousand years without effect upon daily life—may yet, at any moment, be used to cause a revolution in the habitual thoughts and occupations of every citizen. The use of steam and electricity—to take striking instances—is rendered possible only by mathematics. In the results of abstract thought the world possesses a capital of which the employment in enriching the common round has no hitherto discoverable limits. Nor does experience give any means of deciding what parts of mathematics will be found useful. Utility, therefore, can be only a consolation in moments of discouragement, not a guide in directing our studies.

For the health of the moral life, for ennobling the tone of an age or a nation, the austerer virtues have a strange power, exceeding the power of those not informed and purified by thought. Of these austerer virtues the love of truth is the chief, and in mathematics, more than elsewhere, the love of truth may find encouragement for waning faith. Every great study is not only an end in itself, but also a means of creating and sustaining a lofty habit of mind; and this purpose should be kept always in view throughout the teaching and learning of mathematics.

# Mathematics and
# the Metaphysicians

The nineteenth century, which prided itself upon the invention of steam and evolution, might have derived a more legitimate title to fame from the discovery of pure mathematics. This science, like most others, was baptised long before it was born; and thus we find writers before the nineteenth century alluding to what they called pure mathematics. But if they had been asked what this subject was, they would only have been able to say that it consisted of Arithmetic, Algebra, Geometry, and so on. As to what these studies had in common, and as to what distinguished them from applied mathematics, our ancestors were completely in the dark.

Pure mathematics was discovered by Boole, in a work which he called the *Laws of Thought* (1854). This work abounds in asseverations that it is not mathematical, the fact being that Boole was too modest to suppose his book the first ever written on mathematics. He was also mistaken in supposing that he was dealing with the laws of thought: the question how people actually think was quite irrelevant to him, and if his book had really contained the laws of thought, it was curious that no one should ever have thought in such a way before. His book was in fact concerned with formal logic, and this is the same thing as mathematics.

Pure mathematics consists entirely of assertions to the effect that, if such and such a proposition is true of *anything*, then such and such another proposition is true of that thing. It is essential not to discuss whether the first proposition is really true, and not to mention what the anything is, of which it is supposed to be true. Both these points would belong to applied mathematics. We start, in pure mathematics, from certain rules of inference, by which we can infer that *if* one proposition is true, then so is some other proposition. These rules of inference constitute the major part of the principles of formal logic. We then take any hypothesis that seems amusing, and deduce its consequences. *If our* hypothesis is about *anything,* and not about some one or more particular things, then our deductions constitute mathematics. Thus mathematics may be defined as the subject in which we never know what we are talking about, nor whether what we are saying is true. People who have been puzzled by the beginnings of mathematics will, I hope, find comfort in this definition, and will probably agree that it is accurate.

As one of the chief triumphs of modern mathematics consists in having discovered what mathematics really is, a few more words on this subject may not be amiss. It is common to start any branch of mathematics—for instance, Geometry—with a certain number of primitive ideas, supposed incapable of definition, and a certain number of primitive propositions or axioms, supposed incapable of proof. Now the fact is that, though there are indefinables and indemonstrables in every branch of applied mathematics, there are none in pure mathematics except such as belong to general logic. Logic, broadly speaking, is distinguished by the fact that its propositions can be put into a form in which they apply to anything whatever. All pure mathematics—Arithmetic, Analysis, and Geometry— is built up by combinations of the primitive ideas of logic, and its propositions are deduced from the general axioms of logic, such as the syllogism and the other rules of inference. And this is no longer a dream or an aspiration. On the contrary, over the greater and more difficult part of the domain of mathematics, it has been already accomplished; in the few remaining cases, there is no special difficulty, and it is now being rapidly achieved. Philosophers have disputed for ages whether such deduction was possible; mathematicians have sat down and made the deduction. For the philosophers there is now nothing left but graceful acknowledgments.

The subject of formal logic, which has thus at last shown itself to be identical with mathematics, was, as every one knows, invented by Aristotle, and formed the chief study (other than theology) of the Middle Ages. But Aristotle never got beyond the syllogism, which is a very small part of the subject, and the schoolmen never got beyond Aristotle. If any proof were required of our superiority to the mediaeval doctors, it might be found in this. Throughout the Middle Ages, almost all the best intellects devoted themselves to formal logic, whereas in the nineteenth century only an infinitesimal proportion of the world's thought went into this subject. Nevertheless, in each decade since 1850 more has been done to advance the subject than in the whole period from Aristotle to Leibniz. People have discovered how to make reasoning symbolic, as it is in Algebra, so that deductions are effected by mathematical rules. They have discovered many rules besides the syllogism, and a new branch of logic, called the Logic of Relatives,[1] has been invented to deal with topics that wholly surpassed the powers of the old logic, though they form the chief contents of mathematics.

It is not easy for the lay mind to realize the importance of symbolism in discussing the foundations of mathematics, and the explanation may perhaps seem strangely paradoxical. The fact is that symbolism is useful because it makes things difficult. (This is not true of the advanced parts of mathematics, but only of the beginnings.) What we wish to know is, what can be deduced from what. Now, in the beginnings, everything is self-evident; and it is very hard to see whether one self-evident proposition follows from another or not. Obviousness is always the enemy to correctness. Hence we invent some new and difficult symbolism, in which nothing seems obvious. Then we set up certain rules for operating on the symbols, and the whole thing becomes mechanical. In this way we find out what must be taken as premiss and what can be demonstrated or defined. For instance, the whole of Arithmetic and Algebra has been shown to require three indefinable notions and five indemonstrable propositions. But without a symbolism it would have been very hard to find this out. It is so obvious that two and two are four, that we can hardly make ourselves sufficiently sceptical to doubt whether it can be proved. And the same holds in other cases where self-evident things are to be proved.

But the proof of self-evident propositions may seem, to the uninitiated, a somewhat frivolous occupation. To this we might reply that it is often by no means self-evident that one obvious proposition follows from another obvious proposition; so that we are really discovering new truths when we prove what is evident by a method which is not evident. But a more interesting retort is that, since people have tried to prove obvious propositions, they have found that many of them are false. Self-evidence is often a mere will-o'-the-wisp, which is sure to lead us astray if we take it as our guide. For instance, nothing is plainer than that a whole always has more terms than a part, or that a number is increased by adding one to it. But these propositions are now known to be usually false. Most numbers are infinite, and if a number is infinite you may add ones to it as long as you like without disturbing it in the least. One of the merits of a proof is that it instils a certain doubt as to the result proved; and when what is obvious can be proved in some cases, but not in others, it becomes possible to suppose that in these other cases it is false.

---

1. This subject is due in the main to Mr. C. S. Peirce.

The great master of the art of formal reasoning, among the men of our own day, is an Italian, Professor Peano, of the University of Turin.[2] He has reduced the greater part of mathematics (and he or his followers will, in time, have reduced the whole) to strict symbolic form, in which there are no words at all. In the ordinary mathematical books, there are no doubt fewer words than most readers would wish. Still, little phrases occur, such as *therefore, let us assume, consider,* or *hence it follows.* All these, however, are a concession, and are swept away by Professor Peano. For instance, if we wish to learn the whole of Arithmetic, Algebra, the Calculus, and indeed all that is usually called pure mathematics (except Geometry), we must start with a dictionary of three words. One symbol stands for *zero,* another for *number,* and a third for *next after.* What these ideas mean, it is necessary to know if you wish to become an arithmetician. But after symbols have been invented for these three ideas, not another word is required in the whole development. All future symbols are symbolically explained by means of these three. Even these three can be explained by means of the notions of *relation* and *class;* but this requires the Logic of Relations, which Professor Peano has never taken up. It must be admitted that what a mathematician has to know to begin with is not much. There are at most a dozen notions out of which all the notions in all pure mathematics (including Geometry) are compounded. Professor Peano, who is assisted by a very able school of young Italian disciples, has shown how this may be done; and although the method which he has invented is capable of being carried a good deal further than he has carried it, the honour of the pioneer must belong to him.

Two hundred years ago, Leibniz foresaw the science which Peano has perfected, and endeavoured to create it. He was prevented from succeeding by respect for the authority of Aristotle, whom he could not believe guilty of definite, formal fallacies; but the subject which he desired to create now exists, in spite of the patronizing contempt with which his schemes have been treated by all superior persons. From this "Universal Characteristic," as he called it, he hoped for a solution of all problems, and an end to all disputes. "If controversies were to arise," he says, "there would be no more need of disputation between two philosophers than between two accountants. For it would suffice to take their pens in their hands, to sit down to their desks, and to say to each other (with a friend as witness, if they liked), 'Let us calculate.'" This optimism has now appeared to be somewhat excessive; there still are problems whose

---

2. I ought to have added Frege, but his writings were unknown to me when this article was written. [Note added in 1917.]

solution is doubtful, and disputes which calculation cannot decide. But over an enormous field of what was formerly controversial, Leibniz's dream has become sober fact. In the whole philosophy of mathematics, which used to be at least as full of doubt as any other part of philosophy, order and certainty have replaced the confusion and hesitation which formerly reigned. Philosophers, of course, have not yet discovered this fact, and continue to write on such subjects in the old way. But mathematicians, at least in Italy, have now the power of treating the principles of mathematics in an exact and masterly manner, by means of which the certainty of mathematics extends also to mathematical philosophy. Hence many of the topics which used to be placed among the great mysteries— for example, the natures of infinity, of continuity, of space, time and motion—are now no longer in any degree open to doubt or discussion. Those who wish to know the nature of these things need only read the works of such men as Peano or Georg Cantor; they will there find exact and indubitable expositions of all these quondam mysteries.

In this capricious world, nothing is more capricious than posthumous fame. One of the most notable examples of posterity's lack of judgment is the Eleatic Zeno. This man, who may be regarded as the founder of the philosophy of infinity, appears in Plato's Parmenides in the privileged position of instructor to Socrates. He invented four arguments, all immeasurably subtle and profound, to prove that motion is impossible, that Achilles can never overtake the tortoise, and that an arrow in flight is really at rest. After being refuted by Aristotle, and by every subsequent philosopher from that day to our own, these arguments were reinstated, and made the basis of a mathematical renaissance, by a German professor, who probably never dreamed of any connection between himself and Zeno. Weierstrass,[3] by strictly banishing from mathematics the use of infinitesimals, has at last shown that we live in an unchanging world, and that the arrow in its flight is truly at rest. Zeno's only error lay in inferring (if he did infer) that, because there is no such thing as a state of change, therefore the world is in the same state at any one time as at any other. This is a consequence which by no means follows; and in this respect, the German mathematician is more constructive than the ingenious Greek. Weierstrass has been able, by embodying his views in mathematics, where familiarity with truth eliminates the vulgar prejudices of common sense, to invest Zeno's paradoxes with the respectable air of platitudes; and if the result is less delightful to the lover of reason than Zeno's

---

3. Professor of mathematics in the University of Berlin. He died in 1897.

bold defiance, it is at any rate more calculated to appease the mass of academic mankind.

Zeno was concerned, as a matter of fact, with three problems, each presented by motion, but each more abstract than motion, and capable of a purely arithmetical treatment. These are the problems of the infinitesimal, the infinite, and continuity. To state clearly the difficulties involved was to accomplish perhaps the hardest part of the philosopher's task. This was done by Zeno. From him to our own day, the finest intellects of each generation in turn attacked the problems, but achieved, broadly speaking, nothing. In our own time, however, three men—Weierstrass, Dedekind, and Cantor—have not merely advanced the three problems, but have completely solved them. The solutions, for those acquainted with mathematics, are so clear as to leave no longer the slightest doubt or difficulty. This achievement is probably the greatest of which our age has to boast; and I know of no age (except perhaps the golden age of Greece) which has a more convincing proof to offer of the transcendent genius of its great men. Of the three problems, that of the infinitesimal was solved by Weierstrass; the solution of the other two was begun by Dedekind, and definitively accomplished by Cantor.

The infinitesimal played formerly a great part in mathematics. It was introduced by the Greeks, who regarded a circle as differing infinitesimally from a polygon with a very large number of very small equal sides. It gradually grew in importance, until, when Leibniz invented the Infinitesimal Calculus, it seemed to become the fundamental notion of all higher mathematics. Carlyle tells, in his *Frederick the Great*, how Leibniz used to discourse to Queen Sophia Charlotte of Prussia concerning the infinitely little, and how she would reply that on that subject she needed no instruction—the behaviour of courtiers had made her thoroughly familiar with it. But philosophers and mathematicians—who for the most part had less acquaintance with courts—continued to discuss this topic, though without making any advance. The Calculus required continuity, and continuity was supposed to require the infinitely little; but nobody could discover what the infinitely little might be. It was plainly not quite zero, because a sufficiently large number of infinitesimals, added together, were seen to make up a finite whole. But nobody could point out any fraction which was not zero, and yet not finite. Thus there was a deadlock. But at last Weierstrass discovered that the infinitesimal was not needed at all, and that everything could be accomplished without it. Thus there was no longer any need to suppose that there was such a thing. Nowadays, therefore, mathematicians are more dignified than

Leibniz: instead of talking about the infinitely small, they talk about the infinitely great—a subject which, however appropriate to monarchs, seems, unfortunately, to interest them even less than the infinitely little interested the monarchs to whom Leibniz discoursed.

The banishment of the infinitesimal has all sorts of odd consequences, to which one has to become gradually accustomed. For example, there is no such thing as the next moment. The interval between one moment and the next would have to be infinitesimal, since, if we take two moments with a finite interval between them, there are always other moments in the interval. Thus if there are to be no infinitesimals, no two moments are quite consecutive, but there are always other moments between any two. Hence there must be an infinite number of moments between any two; because if there were a finite number one would be nearest the first of the two moments, and therefore next to it. This might be thought to be a difficulty; but, as a matter of fact, it is here that the philosophy of the infinite comes in, and makes all straight.

The same sort of thing happens in space. If any piece of matter be cut in two, and then each part be halved, and so on, the bits will become smaller and smaller, and can theoretically be made as small as we please. However small they may be, they can still be cut up and made smaller still. But they will always have *some* finite size, however small they may be. We never reach the infinitesimal in this way, and no finite number of divisions will bring us to points. Nevertheless there *are* points, only these are not to be reached by successive divisions. Here again, the philosophy of the infinite shows us how this is possible, and why points are not infinitesimal lengths.

As regards motion and change, we get similarly curious results. People used to think that when a thing changes, it must be in a state of change, and that when a thing moves, it is in a state of motion. This is now known to be a mistake. When a body moves, all that can be said is that it is in one place at one time and in another at another. We must not say that it will be in a neighbouring place at the next instant, since there is no next instant. Philosophers often tell us that when a body is in motion, it changes its position within the instant. To this view Zeno long ago made the fatal retort that every body always is where it is; but a retort so simple and brief was not of the kind to which philosophers are accustomed to give weight, and they have continued down to our own day to repeat the same phrases which roused the Eleatic's destructive ardour. It was only recently that it became possible to explain motion in detail in accordance with Zeno's platitude, and in opposition to the philosopher's paradox. We may now at last indulge the comfortable belief that a body in motion is just as truly where it is as a body at rest. Motion consists merely in the fact that bodies are sometimes in one place and sometimes in another, and that they are at intermediate places at intermediate times. Only those who have waded through the quagmire of philosophic speculation on this subject can realize what a liberation from antique prejudices is involved in this simple and straightforward commonplace.

The philosophy of the infinitesimal, as we have just seen, is mainly negative. People used to believe in it, and now they have found out their mistake. The philosophy of the infinite, on the other hand, is wholly positive. It was formerly supposed that infinite numbers, and the mathematical infinite generally, were self-contradictory. But as it was obvious that there were infinities—for example, the number of numbers—the contradictions of infinity seemed unavoidable, and philosophy seemed to have wandered into a cul-de-sac. This difficulty led to Kant's antinomies, and hence, more or less indirectly, to much of Hegel's dialectic method. Almost all current philosophy is upset by the fact (of which very few philosophers are as yet aware) that all the ancient and respectable contradictions in the notion of the infinite have been once for all disposed of. The method by which this has been done is most interesting and instructive. In the first place, though people had talked glibly about infinity ever since the beginnings of Greek thought, nobody had ever thought of asking, What is infinity? If any philosopher had been asked for a definition of infinity, he might have produced some unintelligible rigmarole, but he would certainly not have been able to give a definition that had any meaning at all. Twenty years ago, roughly speaking, Dedekind and Cantor asked this question, and, what is more remarkable, they answered it. They found, that is to say, a perfectly precise definition of an infinite number or an infinite collection of things. This was the first and perhaps the greatest step. It then remained to examine the supposed contradictions in this notion. Here Cantor proceeded in the only proper way. He took pairs of contradictory propositions, in which both sides of the contradiction would be usually regarded as demonstrable, and he strictly examined the supposed proofs. He found that all proofs adverse to infinity involved a certain principle, at first sight obviously true, but destructive, in its consequences, of almost all mathematics. The proofs favourable to infinity, on the other hand, involved no principle that had evil consequences. It thus appeared that common sense had allowed itself to be taken in by a specious maxim, and that, when once this maxim was rejected, all went well.

The maxim in question is that, if one collection is part of another, the one which is a part has fewer terms than the one of which it is a part. This maxim is true of finite numbers. For example, Englishmen are only some among Europeans, and there are fewer Englishmen than Europeans. But when we come to infinite numbers, this is no longer true. This breakdown of the maxim gives us the precise definition of infinity. A collection of terms is infinite when it contains as parts other collections which have just as many terms as it has. If you can take away some of the terms of a collection without diminishing the number of terms, then there are an infinite number of terms in the collection. For example, there are just as many even numbers as there are numbers altogether, since every number can be doubled. This may be seen by putting odd and even numbers together in one row, and even numbers alone in a row below:

1, 2, 3, 4, 5, *ad infinitum.*
2, 4, 6, 8, 10, *ad infinitum.*

There are obviously just as many numbers in the row below as in the row above, because there is one below for each one above. This property, which was formerly thought to be a contradiction, is now transformed into a harmless definition of infinity, and shows, in the above case, that the number of finite numbers is infinite.

But the uninitiated may wonder how it is possible to deal with a number which cannot be counted. It is impossible to count up *all* the numbers, one by one, because, however many we may count, there are always more to follow. The fact is that counting is a very vulgar and elementary way of finding out how many terms there are in a collection. And in any case, counting gives us what mathematicians call the *ordinal* number of our terms; that is to say, it arranges our terms in an order or series, and its result tells us what type of series results from this arrangement. In other words, it is impossible to count things without counting some first and others afterwards, so that counting always has to do with order. Now when there are only a finite number of terms, we can count them in any order we like; but when there are an infinite number, what corresponds to counting will give us quite different results according to the way in which we carry out the operation. Thus the ordinal number, which results from what, in a general sense, may be called counting, depends not only upon how many terms we have, but also (where the number of terms is infinite) upon the way in which the terms are arranged.

The fundamental infinite numbers are not ordinal, but are what is called *cardinal*. They are not obtained by putting our terms in order and counting them, but by a different method, which tells us, to begin with, whether two collections have the same number of terms, or, if not, which is the greater.[4] It does not tell us, in the way in which counting does, *what* number of terms a collection has; but if we define a number as the number of terms in such and such a collection, then this method enables us to discover whether some other collection that may be mentioned has more or fewer terms. An illustration will show how this is done. If there existed some country in which, for one reason or another, it was impossible to take a census, but in which it was known that every man had a wife and every woman a husband, then (provided polygamy was not a national institution) we should know, without counting, that there were exactly as many men as there were women in that country, neither more nor less. This method can be applied generally. If there is some relation which, like marriage, connects the things in one collection each with one of the things in another collection, and vice versa, then the two collections have the same number of terms. This was the way in which we found that there are as many even numbers as there are numbers. Every number can be doubled, and every even number can be halved, and each process gives just one number corresponding to the one that is doubled or halved. And in this way we can find any number of collections each of which has just as many terms as there are finite numbers. If every term of a collection can be hooked on to a number, and all the finite numbers are used once, and only once, in the process, then our collection must have just as many terms as there are finite numbers. This is the general method by which the numbers of infinite collections are defined.

But it must not be supposed that all infinite numbers are equal. On the contrary, there are infinitely more infinite numbers than finite ones. There are more ways of arranging the finite numbers in different types of series than there are finite numbers. There are probably more points in space and more moments in time than there are finite numbers. There are exactly as many fractions as whole numbers, although there are an infinite number of fractions between any two whole numbers. But there are more irrational numbers than there are whole numbers or fractions. There are probably exactly as many points in space as there are irrational numbers, and exactly as many points on a line a millionth of an inch long as in the whole of infinite space. There is a greatest of all infinite numbers, which is the number of things altogether, of every sort and kind.

---

4. Although some infinite numbers are greater than some others, it cannot be proved that of any two infinite numbers one must be the greater. [Note added in 1917.]

It is obvious that there cannot be a greater number than this, because, if everything has been taken, there is nothing left to add. Cantor has a proof that there is no greatest number, and if this proof were valid, the contradictions of infinity would reappear in a sublimated form. But in this one point, the master has been guilty of a very subtle fallacy, which I hope to explain in some future work.[5]

We can now understand why Zeno believed that Achilles cannot overtake the tortoise and why as a matter of fact he can overtake it. We shall see that all the people who disagreed with Zeno had no right to do so, because they all accepted premisses from which his conclusion followed. The argument is this: Let Achilles and the tortoise start along a road at the same time, the tortoise (as is only fair) being allowed a handicap. Let Achilles go twice as fast as the tortoise, or ten times or a hundred times as fast. Then he will never reach the tortoise. For at every moment the tortoise is somewhere and Achilles is somewhere; and neither is ever twice in the same place while the race is going on. Thus the tortoise goes to just as many places as Achilles does, because each is in one place at one moment, and in another at any other moment. But if Achilles were to catch up with the tortoise, the places where the tortoise would have been would be only part of the places where Achilles would have been. Here, we must suppose, Zeno appealed to the maxim that the whole has more terms than the part.[6] Thus if Achilles were to overtake the tortoise, he would have been in more places than the tortoise; but we saw that he must, in any period, be in exactly as many places as the tortoise. Hence we infer that he can never catch the tortoise. This argument is strictly correct, if we allow the axiom that the whole has more terms than the part. As the conclusion is absurd, the axiom must be rejected, and then all goes well. But there is no good word to be said for the philosophers of the past two thousand years and more, who have all allowed the axiom and denied the conclusion.

The retention of this axiom leads to absolute contradictions, while its rejection leads only to oddities. Some of these oddities, it must be confessed, are very odd. One of them, which I call the paradox of Tristram

---

5. Cantor was not guilty of a fallacy on this point. His proof that there is no greatest number is valid. The solution of the puzzle is complicated and depends upon the theory of types, which is explained in *Principia Mathematica*, Vol. I (Cambridge University Press, 1910). [Note added in 1917.]

6. This must not be regarded as a historically correct account of what Zeno actually had in mind. It is a new argument for his conclusion, not the argument which influenced him. On this point, see e.g. C. D. Broad, "Note on Achilles and the Tortoise," *Mind*, N.S., Vol. XXII, pp. 318–19. Much valuable work on the interpretation of Zeno has been done since this article was written. [Note added in 1917.]

Shandy, is the converse of the Achilles, and shows that the tortoise, if you give him time, will go just as far as Achilles. Tristram Shandy, as we know, employed two years in chronicling the first two days of his life, and lamented that, at this rate, material would accumulate faster than he could deal with it, so that, as years went by, he would be farther and farther from the end of his history. Now I maintain that if he had lived for ever, and had not wearied of his task, then, even if his life had continued as eventfully as it began, no part of his biography would have remained unwritten. For consider: the hundredth day will be described in the hundredth year, the thousandth in the thousandth year, and so on. Whatever day we may choose as so far on that he cannot hope to reach it, that day will be described in the corresponding year. Thus any day that may be mentioned will be written up sooner or later, and therefore no part of the biography will remain permanently unwritten. This paradoxical but perfectly true proposition depends upon the fact that the number of days in all time is no greater than the number of years.

Thus on the subject of infinity it is impossible to avoid conclusions which at first sight appear paradoxical, and this is the reason why so many philosophers have supposed that there were inherent contradictions in the infinite. But a little practice enables one to grasp the true principles of Cantor's doctrine, and to acquire new and better instincts as to the true and the false. The oddities then become no odder than the people at the antipodes, who used to be thought impossible because they would find it so inconvenient to stand on their heads.

The solution of the problems concerning infinity has enabled Cantor to solve also the problems of continuity. Of this, as of infinity, he has given a perfectly precise definition, and has shown that there are no contradictions in the notion so defined. But this subject is so technical that it is impossible to give any account of it here.

The notion of continuity depends upon that of *order*, since continuity is merely a particular type of order. Mathematics has, in modern times, brought order into greater and greater prominence. In former days, it was supposed (and philosophers are still apt to suppose) that quantity was the fundamental notion of mathematics. But nowadays, quantity is banished altogether, except from one little corner of Geometry, while order more and more reigns supreme. The investigation of different kinds of series and their relations is now a very large part of mathematics, and it has been found that this investigation can be conducted without any reference to quantity, and, for the most part, without any reference to number. All types of series are capable of formal definition, and their properties can be deduced from the principles of symbolic logic by means of the Algebra of Relatives. The notion of a limit, which is fundamental in the greater part of higher mathematics, used to be defined by means of quantity, as a term to which the terms of some series approximate as nearly as we please. But nowadays the limit is defined quite differently, and the series which it limits may not approximate to it at all. This improvement also is due to Cantor, and it is one which has revolutionized mathematics. Only order is now relevant to limits. Thus, for instance, the smallest of the infinite integers is the limit of the finite integers, though all finite integers are at an infinite distance from it. The study of different types of series is a general subject of which the study of ordinal numbers (mentioned above) is a special and very interesting branch. But the unavoidable technicalities of this subject render it impossible to explain to any but professed mathematicians.

Geometry, like Arithmetic, has been subsumed, in recent times, under the general study of order. It was formerly supposed that Geometry was the study of the nature of the space in which we live, and accordingly it was urged, by those who held that what exists can only be known empirically, that Geometry should really be regarded as belonging to applied mathematics. But it has gradually appeared, by the increase of non-Euclidean systems, that Geometry throws no more light upon the nature of space than Arithmetic throws upon the population of the United States. Geometry is a whole collection of deductive sciences based on a corresponding collection of sets of axioms. One set of axioms is Euclid's; other equally good sets of axioms lead to other results. Whether Euclid's axioms are true is a question as to which the pure mathematician is indifferent; and, what is more, it is a question which it is theoretically impossible to answer with certainty in the affirmative. It might possibly be shown, by very careful measurements, that Euclid's axioms are false; but no measurements could ever assure us (owing to the errors of observation) that they are exactly true. Thus the geometer leaves to the man of science to decide, as best he may, what axioms are most nearly true in the actual world. The geometer takes any set of axioms that seem interesting, and deduces their consequences. What defines Geometry, in this sense, is that the axioms must give rise to a series of more than one dimension. And it is thus that Geometry becomes a department in the study of order.

In Geometry, as in other parts of mathematics, Peano and his disciples have done work of the very greatest merit as regards principles. Formerly, it was held by philosophers and mathematicians alike that the proofs in Geometry depended on the figure; nowadays, this is known to be false. In the best books there are no figures at all. The reasoning proceeds by the strict rules of formal logic from a set of axioms laid down to begin with. If a figure is used, all sorts of things seem obviously to follow, which no formal reasoning can prove from the explicit axioms, and which, as a matter of fact, are only accepted because they are obvious. By banishing the figure, it becomes possible to discover *all* the axioms that are needed; and in this way all sorts of possibilities, which would have otherwise remained undetected, are brought to light.

One great advance, from the point of view of correctness, has been made by introducing points as they are required, and not starting, as was formerly done, by assuming the whole of space. This method is due partly to Peano, partly to another Italian named Fano. To those unaccustomed to it, it has an air of somewhat wilful pedantry. In this way, we begin with the following axioms: (1) There is a class of entities called *points*. (2) There is at least one point. (3) If *a* be a point, there is at least one other point besides *a*. Then we bring in the straight line joining two points, and begin again with (4), namely, on the straight line joining *a* and *b*, there is at least one other point besides *a* and *b*. (5) There is at least one point not on the line *ab*. And so we go on, till we have the means of obtaining as many points as we require. But the word *space*, as Peano humorously remarks, is one for which Geometry has no use at all.

The rigid methods employed by modern geometers have deposed Euclid from his pinnacle of correctness. It was thought, until recent times, that, as Sir Henry Savile remarked in 1621, there were only two blemishes in Euclid, the theory of parallels and the theory of proportion. It is now known that these are almost the only points in which Euclid is free from blemish. Countless errors are involved in his first eight propositions. That is to say, not only is it doubtful whether his axioms are true, which is a comparatively trivial matter, but it is certain that his propositions do not follow from the axioms which he enunciates. A vastly greater number of axioms, which Euclid unconsciously employs, are required for the proof of his propositions. Even in the first proposition of all, where he constructs an equilateral triangle on a given base, he uses two circles which are assumed to intersect. But no explicit axiom assures us that they do so, and in some kinds of spaces they do not always intersect. It is quite doubtful whether our space belongs to one of these kinds or not. Thus Euclid fails entirely to prove his point in the very first proposition. As he is certainly not an easy author, and is terribly long-winded, he has no longer any but a historical interest. Under these circumstances, it is nothing less than a scandal that he should still be taught to boys in England.[7] A book should have either intelligibility or correctness; to combine the two is impossible, but to lack both is to be unworthy of such a place as Euclid has occupied in education.

The most remarkable result of modern methods in mathematics is the importance of symbolic logic and of rigid formalism. Mathematicians, under the influence of Weierstrass, have shown in modern times a care for accuracy, and an aversion to slipshod reasoning, such as had not been known among them previously since the time of the Greeks. The great inventions of the seventeenth century—Analytical Geometry and the Infinitesimal Calculus—were so fruitful in new results that mathematicians had neither time nor inclination to examine their foundations. Philosophers, who should have taken up the task, had too little mathematical ability to invent the new branches of mathematics which have now been found necessary for any adequate discussion. Thus mathematicians were only awakened from their "dogmatic slumbers" when Weierstrass and his followers showed that many of their most cherished propositions are in general false. Macaulay, contrasting the certainty of mathematics with the uncertainty of philosophy, asks who ever heard of a reaction against Taylor's theorem? If he had lived now, he himself might have heard of such a reaction, for this is precisely one of the theorems which modern investigations have overthrown. Such rude shocks to mathematical faith have produced that love of formalism which appears, to those who are ignorant of its motive, to be mere outrageous pedantry.

The proof that all pure mathematics, including Geometry, is nothing but formal logic, is a fatal blow to the Kantian philosophy. Kant, rightly perceiving that Euclid's propositions could not be deduced from Euclid's axioms without the help of the figures, invented a theory of knowledge to account for this fact; and it accounted so successfully that, when the fact is shown to be a mere defect in Euclid, and not a result of the nature of geometrical reasoning, Kant's theory also has to be abandoned. The whole doctrine of *a priori* intuitions, by which Kant explained the possibility of pure mathematics, is wholly inapplicable to mathematics in its present form. The Aristotelian doctrines of the schoolmen come nearer in spirit to the doctrines which modern mathematics inspire; but the schoolmen were hampered by the fact that their formal logic was very defective, and that the philosophical logic based upon the syllogism

---

7. Since the above was written, he has ceased to be used as a text-book. But I fear many of the books now used are so bad that the change is no great improvement. [Note added in 1917.]

showed a corresponding narrowness. What is now required is to give the greatest possible development to mathematical logic, to allow to the full the importance of relations, and then to found upon this secure basis a new philosophical logic, which may hope to borrow some of the exactitude and certainty of its mathematical foundation. If this can be successfully accomplished, there is every reason to hope that the near future will be as great an epoch in pure philosophy as the immediate past has been in the principles of mathematics. Great triumphs inspire great hopes; and pure thought may achieve, within our generation, such results as will place our time, in this respect, on a level with the greatest age of Greece.[8]

8. The greatest age of Greece was brought to an end by the Peloponnesian War. [Note added in 1917.]

---

*The foregoing consists of Chapters IV and V*
*from Russell's* MYSTICISM AND LOGIC, AND OTHER ESSAYS.

# Definition of Number

The question "What is a number?" is one which has been often asked, but has only been correctly answered in our own time. The answer was given by Frege in 1884, in his *Grundlagen der Arithmetik*. Although this book is quite short, not difficult, and of the very highest importance, it attracted almost no attention, and the definition of number which it contains remained practically unknown until it was rediscovered by the present author in 1901.

In seeking a definition of number, the first thing to be clear about is what we may call the grammar of our inquiry. Many philosophers, when attempting to define number, are really setting to work to define plurality, which is quite a different thing. *Number* is what is characteristic of numbers, as *man* is what is characteristic of men. A plurality is not an instance of number, but of some particular number. A trio of men, for example, is an instance of the number 3, and the number 3 is an instance of number; but the trio is not an instance of number. This point may seem elementary and scarcely worth mentioning; yet it has proved too subtle for the philosophers, with few exceptions.

A particular number is not identical with any collection of terms having that number: the number 3 is not identical with the trio consisting of Brown, Jones, and Robinson. The number 3 is something which all trios have in common, and which distinguishes them from other collections. A number is something that characterizes certain collections, namely, those that have that number.

Instead of speaking of a "collection," we shall as a rule speak of a "class," or sometimes a "set." Other words used in mathematics for the same thing are "aggregate" and "manifold." We shall have much to say later on about classes. For the present, we will say as little as possible. But there are some remarks that must be made immediately.

A class or collection may be defined in two ways that at first sight seem quite distinct. We may enumerate its members, as when we say,

111

"The collection I mean is Brown, Jones, and Robinson." Or we may mention a defining property, as when we speak of "mankind" or "the inhabitants of London." The definition which enumerates is called a definition by "extension," and the one which mentions a defining property is called a definition by "intension." Of these two kinds of definition, the one by intension is logically more fundamental. This is shown by two considerations: (1) that the extensional definition can always be reduced to an intensional one; (2) that the intensional one often cannot even theoretically be reduced to the extensional one. Each of these points needs a word of explanation.

(1) Brown, Jones, and Robinson all of them possess a certain property which is possessed by nothing else in the whole universe, namely, the property of being either Brown or Jones or Robinson. This property can be used to give a definition by intension of the class consisting of Brown and Jones and Robinson. Consider such a formula as "$x$ is Brown or $x$ is Jones or $x$ is Robinson." This formula will be true for just three $x$'s, namely, Brown and Jones and Robinson. In this respect it resembles a cubic equation with its three roots. It may be taken as assigning a property common to the members of the class consisting of these three men, and peculiar to them. A similar treatment can obviously be applied to any other class given in extension.

(2) It is obvious that in practice we can often know a great deal about a class without being able to enumerate its members. No one man could actually enumerate all men, or even all the inhabitants of London, yet a great deal is known about each of these classes. This is enough to show that definition by extension is not *necessary* to knowledge about a class. But when we come to consider infinite classes, we find that enumeration is not even theoretically possible for beings who only live for a finite time. We cannot enumerate all the natural numbers: they are 0, 1, 2, 3, *and so on*. At some point we must content ourselves with "and so on." We cannot enumerate all fractions or all irrational numbers, or all of any other infinite collection. Thus our knowledge in regard to all such collections can only be derived from a definition by intension.

These remarks are relevant, when we are seeking the definition of number, in three different ways. In the first place, numbers themselves form an infinite collection, and cannot therefore be defined by enumeration. In the second place, the collections having a given number of terms themselves presumably form an infinite collection: it is to be presumed, for example, that there are an infinite collection of trios in the world, for if this were not the case the total number of things in the world would be finite, which, though possible, seems unlikely. In the third place, we wish to define "number" in such a way that infinite numbers may be possible; thus we must be able to speak of the number of terms in an infinite collection, and such a collection must be defined by intension, *i.e.*, by a property common to all its members and peculiar to them.

For many purposes, a class and a defining characteristic of it are practically interchangeable. The vital difference between the two consists in the fact that there is only one class having a given set of members, whereas there are always many different characteristics by which a given class may be defined. Men may be defined as featherless bipeds, or as rational animals, or (more correctly) by the traits by which Swift delineates the Yahoos. It is this fact that a defining characteristic is never unique which makes classes useful; otherwise we could be content with the properties common and peculiar to their members. Any one of these properties can be used in place of the class whenever uniqueness is not important.

Returning now to the definition of number, it is clear that number is a way of bringing together certain collections, namely, those that have a given number of terms. We can suppose all couples in one bundle, all trios in another, and so on. In this way we obtain various bundles of collections, each bundle consisting of all the collections that have a certain number of terms. Each bundle is a class whose members are collections, *i.e.*, classes; thus each is a class of classes. The bundle consisting of all couples, for example, is a class of classes: each couple is a class with two members, and the whole bundle of couples is a class with an infinite number of members, each of which is a class of two members.

How shall we decide whether two collections are to belong to the same bundle? The answer that suggests itself is: "Find out how many members each has, and put them in the same bundle if they have the same number of members." But this presupposes that we have defined numbers, and that we know how to discover how many terms a collection has. We are so used to the operation of counting that such a presupposition might easily pass unnoticed. In fact, however, counting, though familiar, is logically a very complex operation; moreover it is only available, as a means of discovering how many terms a collection has, when the collection is finite. Our definition of number must not assume in advance that all numbers are finite; and we cannot in any case, without a vicious circle, use counting to define numbers, because numbers are used in counting. We need, therefore, some other method of deciding when two collections have the same number of terms.

In actual fact, it is simpler logically to find out whether two collections have the same number of terms than it is to define what that number is. An illustration will make this clear. If there were no polygamy or polyandry anywhere in the world, it is clear that the number of husbands living at any moment would be exactly the same as the number of wives. We do not need a census to assure us of this, nor do we need to know what is the actual number of husbands and of wives. We know the number must be the same in both collections, because each husband has one wife and each wife has one husband. The relation of husband and wife is what is called "one–one."

A relation is said to be "one–one" when, if $x$ has the relation in question to $y$, no other term $x'$ has the same relation to $y$, and $x$ does not have the same relation to any term $y'$ other than $y$. When only the first of these two conditions is fulfilled, the relation is called "one–many"; when only the second is fulfilled, it is called "many–one." It should be observed that the number 1 is not used in these definitions.

In Christian countries, the relation of husband to wife is one–one; in Mohammedan countries it is one–many; in Tibet it is many–one. The relation of father to son is one–many; that of son to father is many–one, but that of eldest son to father is one–one. If $n$ is any number, the relation of $n$ to $n + 1$ is one–one; so is the relation of $n$ to $2n$ or to $3n$. When we are considering only positive numbers, the relation of $n$ to $n^2$ is one–one; but when negative numbers are admitted, it becomes two–one, since $n$ and $-n$ have the same square. These instances should suffice to make clear the notions of one–one, one–many, and many–one relations, which play a great part in the principles of mathematics, not only in relation to the definition of numbers, but in many other connections.

Two classes are said to be "similar" when there is a one–one relation which correlates the terms of the one class each with one term of the other class, in the same manner in which the relation of marriage correlates husbands with wives. A few preliminary definitions will help us to state this definition more precisely. The class of those terms that have a given relation to something or other is called the *domain* of that relation: thus fathers are the domain of the relation of father to child, husbands are the domain of the relation of husband to wife, wives are the domain of the relation of wife to husband, and husbands and wives together are the domain of the relation of marriage. The relation of wife to husband is called the *converse* of the relation of husband to wife. Similarly *less* is the converse of *greater, later* is the converse of *earlier,* and so on. Generally, the converse of a given relation is that relation which holds between $y$ and $x$ whenever the given relation holds between $x$ and $y$. The *converse domain* of a relation is the domain of its converse: thus the class of wives is the converse domain of the relation of husband to wife. We may now state our definition of similarity as follows:

*One class is said to be "similar" to another when there is a one–one relation of which the one class is the domain, while the other is the converse domain.*

It is easy to prove (1) that every class is similar to itself, (2) that if a class $a$ is similar to a class $\beta$, then $\beta$ is similar to $a$, (3) that if $a$ is similar to $\beta$ and $\beta$ to $\gamma$, then $a$ is similar to $\gamma$. A relation is said to be *reflexive* when it possesses the first of these properties, *symmetrical* when it possesses the second, and *transitive* when it possesses the third. It is obvious that a relation which is symmetrical and transitive must be reflexive throughout its domain. Relations which possess these properties are an important kind, and it is worth while to note that similarity is one of this kind of relations.

It is obvious to common sense that two finite classes have the same number of terms if they are similar, but not otherwise. The act of counting consists in establishing a one–one correlation between the set of objects counted and the natural numbers (excluding 0) that are used up in the process. Accordingly common sense concludes that there are as many objects in the set to be counted as there are numbers up to the last number used in the counting. And we also know that, so long as we confine ourselves to finite numbers, there are just $n$ numbers from 1 up to $n$. Hence it follows that the last number used in counting a collection is the number of terms in the collection, provided the collection is finite. But this result, besides being only applicable to finite collections, depends upon and assumes the fact that two classes which are similar have the same number of terms; for what we do when we count (say) 10 objects is to show that the set of these objects is similar to the set of numbers 1 to 10. The notion of similarity is logically presupposed in the operation of counting, and is logically simpler though less familiar. In counting, it is necessary to take the objects counted in a certain order, as first, second, third, etc., but order is not of the essence of number: it is an irrelevant addition, an unnecessary complication from the logical point of view. The notion of similarity does not demand an order: for example, we saw that the number of husbands is the same as the number of wives, without having to establish an order of precedence among them. The notion of similarity also does not require that the classes which are similar should be finite. Take, for example, the natural numbers (excluding 0) on the one hand, and the fractions which have 1 for their numerator on the other hand: it is obvious that we can correlate 2 with ½, 3 with ⅓, and so on, thus proving that the two classes are similar.

We may thus use the notion of "similarity" to decide when two collections are to belong to the same bundle, in the sense in which we were asking this question earlier in this chapter. We want to make one bundle containing the class that has no members: this will be for the number o. Then we want a bundle of all the classes that have one member: this will be for the number 1. Then, for the number 2, we want a bundle consisting of all couples; then one of all trios; and so on. Given any collection, we can define the bundle it is to belong to as being the class of all those collections that are "similar" to it. It is very easy to see that if (for example) a collection has three members, the class of all those collections that are similar to it will be the class of trios. And whatever number of terms a collection may have, those collections that are "similar" to it will have the same number of terms. We may take this as a *definition* of "having the same number of terms." It is obvious that it gives results conformable to usage so long as we confine ourselves to finite collections.

So far we have not suggested anything in the slightest degree paradoxical. But when we come to the actual definition of numbers we cannot avoid what must at first sight seem a paradox, though this impression will soon wear off. We naturally think that the class of couples (for example) is something different from the number 2. But there is no doubt about the class of couples: it is indubitable and not difficult to define, whereas the number 2, in any other sense, is a metaphysical entity about which we can never feel sure that it exists or that we have tracked it down. It is therefore more prudent to content ourselves with the class of couples, which we are sure of, than to hunt for a problematical number 2 which must always remain elusive. Accordingly we set up the following definition:

*The number of a class is the class of all those classes that are similar to it.*

Thus the number of a couple will be the class of all couples. In fact, the class of all couples will *be* the number 2, according to our definition. At the expense of a little oddity, this definition secures definiteness and indubitableness; and it is not difficult to prove that numbers so defined have all the properties that we expect numbers to have.

We may now go on to define numbers in general as any one of the bundles into which similarity collects classes. A number will be a set of classes such as that any two are similar to each other, and none outside the set are similar to any inside the set. In other words, a number (in general) is any collection which is the number of one of its members; or, more simply still:

*A number is anything which is the number of some class.*

Such a definition has a verbal appearance of being circular, but in fact it is not. We define "the number of a given class" without using the notion of number in general; therefore we may define number in general in terms of "the number of a given class" without committing any logical error.

Definitions of this sort are in fact very common. The class of fathers, for example, would have to be defined by first defining what it is to be the father of somebody; then the class of fathers will be all those who are somebody's father. Similarly if we want to define square numbers (say), we must first define what we mean by saying that one number is the square of another, and then define square numbers as those that are the squares of other numbers. This kind of procedure is very common, and it is important to realize that it is legitimate and even often necessary.

---

*The foregoing consists of Chapter II
from Russell's* INTRODUCTION TO MATHEMATICAL PHILOSOPHY.

# Edward Kasner

## 1878–1955

# James R. Newman

## 1907–

Edward Kasner, born in New York City in 1878, was educated at the College of the City of New York, and at Columbia and Göttingen Universities. He was on the teaching staff at Columbia from 1900 until his retirement in 1949. In addition, he lectured at the New School for Social Research from 1938 until 1951. He died in 1955.

Kasner's specialty was higher geometry. On this subject he wrote *Geometry upon a Quadric Surface, The Problems of Geometry,* and *Differential Geometric Aspects of Dynamics.* He also wrote *Einstein's Theory of Gravitation.* (He was called "one of the twelve men who understood Einstein.")

Interested in the simplification of mathematical terminology, Kasner introduced such phrases and words as snowflake curve, anti-snowflake curve, googol, and googolplex.

Kasner was widely known for his skill as a teacher. His humor, fertile imagination, and exceptional ability as a lecturer made his courses among the most popular at Columbia. But his audience extended beyond college students; he also liked to give lectures on infinity, topology, and other difficult matters to children of kindergarten age. It was his theory that the way to interest children in mathematics was to begin at the top, and only gradually work down to the elementary concepts.

All of his students remembered their instruction under Professor Kasner as an intellectual delight. James Newman, who attended several of Kasner's courses as a graduate student, attributes his own interest in mathematics to this teacher.

James R. Newman was born in 1907 in New York City. He attended Columbia University, graduating from the School of Law.

He has served with several government agencies and helped write the key bill that placed atomic development under civilian control. A writer as well as a lawyer, Newman has been an editor of *Scientific American* and *New Republic*.

Newman's interest in mathematics began when he discovered that there was much in the study of philosophy that could not be understood without some mathematical knowledge. He does not regard himself as an original, creative mathematician. His contribution to mathematics has been to serve as guide and interpreter in a too-little traveled land.

In 1956 Newman published a four-volume anthology, *The World of Mathematics*. This work is a collection of writings about mathematics and mathematicians appealing to a wide range of tastes and capacities. It became a best seller.

With his teacher Edward Kasner, Newman collaborated on *Mathematics and the Imagination*, from which the following selections are taken.

N*ew Names for Old* discusses new words that have been added to mathematical language. New ideas and new ways of looking at old ideas need new forms of expression. Most of these terms are familiar but are given special meaning in mathematical usage. In discussing these special meanings, the authors give a short tour of modern mathematics.

Two words for large numbers, googol and googolplex, prepare the reader for a glimpse into the mathematical land that lies beyond intuition and beyond imagination. This is the realm of the infinite. The difference between an immensely large number and infinity is not a quantitative difference, it is qualitative. At infinity, you are not just farther out—you are in a different country. And this country shares no border with your ordinary concept of mathematics.

The second piece, *Beyond the Googol*, makes the leap that carries you beyond all sense experience. It begins by clarifying the idea of counting. This requires a precise definition of number.[1] The everyday understanding of number is not sufficient for the task ahead. You are going to count that which would seem to be uncountable—the infinitely large.

---

[1] For additional writings on the concept of number, see Russell, pp. 84–117, and Dantzig, pp. 165–189, Vol. 9, in this set.

The problems of the infinite have always been challenging. They have given rise to such paradoxical notions as "motion is impossible" and "Achilles will never be able to overtake the tortoise." Aristotle and others failed to dispose of these paradoxes. Has modern mathematics succeeded? The answer is startling. It carries you far beyond your power to imagine. You will need an adventurous spirit. Ignore your "common sense" but hold fast to logic.

# New Names for Old

For out of olde feldes, as men seith,
Cometh al this newe corn fro yeer to yere;
And out of olde bokes, in good feith,
Cometh al this newe science that men lere.

—*Chaucer*

Every once in a while there is house cleaning in mathematics. Some old names are discarded, some dusted off and refurbished; new theories, new additions to the household are assigned a place and name. So what our title really means is new *words* in mathematics; not new names, but new words, new terms which have in part come to represent new concepts and a reappraisal of old ones in more or less recent mathematics. There are surely plenty of words already in mathematics as well as in other subjects. Indeed, there are so many words that it is even easier than it used to be to speak a great deal and say nothing. It is mostly through words strung together like beads in a necklace that half the population of the world has been induced to believe mad things and to sanctify mad deeds. Frank Vizetelly, the great lexicographer, estimated that there are 800,000 words in use in the English language. But mathematicians, generally quite modest, are not satisfied with these 800,000; let us give them a few more.

We can get along without new names until, as we advance in science, we acquire new ideas and new forms. A peculiar thing about mathematics is that it does not use so many long and hard names as the other sciences. Besides, it is more conservative than the other sciences in that it clings tenaciously to old words. The terms used by Euclid in his *Elements* are current in geometry today. But an Ionian physicist would find the terminology of modern physics, to put it colloquially, pure Greek. In chemistry, substances no more complicated than sugar, starch, or alcohol have names like these: Methylpropylenedihydroxycinnamenylacrylic

acid, or, 0-anhydrosulfaminobenzoine, or, protocatechuicaldehydemeth-
ylene. It would be inconvenient if we had to use such terms in everyday
conversation. Who could imagine even the aristocrat of science at the
breakfast table asking, "Please pass the O-anhydrosulfaminobenzoic acid,"
when all he wanted was sugar for his coffee? Biology also has some
tantalizing tongue twisters. The purpose of these long words is not to
frighten the exoteric, but to describe with scientific curtness what the
literary man would take half a page to express.

In mathematics there are many easy words like "group," "family,"
"ring," "simple curve," "limit," etc. But these ordinary words are sometimes
given a very peculiar and technical meaning. In fact, here is a
booby-prize definition of mathematics: *Mathematics is the science which
uses easy words for hard ideas.* In this it differs from any other science.
There are 500,000 known species of insects and every one has a long Latin
name. In mathematics we are more modest. We talk about "fields,"
"groups," "families," "spaces," although much more meaning is attached to
these words than ordinary conversation implies. As its use becomes more
and more technical, nobody can guess the mathematical meaning of a
word any more than one could guess that a "drug store" is a place where
they sell ice-cream sodas and umbrellas. No one could guess the meaning
of the word "group" as it is used in mathematics. Yet it is so important that
whole courses are given on the theory of "groups," and hundreds of books
are written about it.

Because mathematicians get along with common words, many amusing
ambiguities arise. For instance, the word "function" probably expresses
the most important idea in the whole history of mathematics. Yet, most
people hearing it would think of a "function" as meaning an evening social
affair, while others, less socially minded, would think of their livers. The
word "function" has at least a dozen meanings, but few people suspect the
mathematical one. The mathematical meaning (which we shall elaborate
upon later) is expressed most simply by a *table*. Such a table gives the
relation between two variable quantities when the value of one variable
quantity is determined by the value of the other. Thus, one variable
quantity may express the years from 1800 to 1938, and the other, the
number of men in the United States wearing handle-bar mustaches; or
one variable may express in decibels the amount of noise made by a
political speaker, and the other, the blood pressure units of his listeners.
You could probably never guess the meaning of the word "ring" as it
has been used in mathematics. It was introduced into the newer algebra
within the last twenty years. The theory of rings is much more recent than

the theory of groups. It is now found in most of the new books on algebra, and has nothing to do with either matrimony or bells.

Other ordinary words used in mathematics in a peculiar sense are "domain," "integration," "differentiation." The uninitiated would not be able to guess what they represent; only mathematicians would know about them. The word "transcendental" in mathematics has not the meaning it has in philosophy. A mathematician would say: The number $\pi$, equal to 3.14159 . . . , is transcendental, because it is not the root of any algebraic equation with integer coefficients.

Transcendental is a very exalted name for a small number, but it was coined when it was thought that transcendental numbers were as rare as quintuplets. The work of Georg Cantor in the realm of the infinite has since proved that of all the numbers in mathematics, the transcendental ones are the most common, or, to use the word in a slightly different sense, the least transcendental. We shall talk of this later when we speak of another famous transcendental number, $e$, the base of the natural logarithms. Immanuel Kant's "transcendental epistemology" is what most educated people might think of when the word transcendental is used, but in that sense it has nothing to do with mathematics. Again, take the word "evolution," used in mathematics to denote the process most of us learned in elementary school, and promptly forgot, of extracting square roots, cube roots, etc. Spencer, in his philosophy, defines evolution as "an integration of matter, and a dissipation of motion from an indefinite, incoherent homogeneity to a definite, coherent heterogeneity," etc. But that, fortunately, has nothing to do with mathematical evolution either. Even in Tennessee, one may extract square roots without running afoul of the law.

As we see, mathematics uses simple words for complicated ideas. An example of a simple word used in a complicated way is the word "simple." "Simple curve" and "simple group" represent important ideas in higher mathematics.

The above is not a simple curve. A simple curve is a closed curve which does not cross itself and may look like the figure on page 124. There are many important theorems about such figures that make the word worth while. Later, we are going to talk about a queer kind of mathematics called "rubber-sheet geometry," and will have much more to say about simple curves and nonsimple ones. A French mathematician, Jordan, gave the fundamental theorem: every simple curve has one inside and one outside. That is, every simple curve divides the plane into two regions, one inside the curve, and one outside.

There are some groups in mathematics that are "simple" groups. The definition of "simple group" is really so hard that it cannot be given here. If we wanted to get a clear idea of what a simple group was, we should probably have to spend a long time looking into a great many books, and then, without an extensive mathematical background, we should probably miss the point. First of all, we should have to define the concept "group." Then we should have to give a definition of subgroups, and then of self-conjugate subgroups, and then we should be able to tell what a simple group is. A simple group is simply a group without any self-conjugate subgroups—simple, is it not?

Mathematics is often erroneously referred to as the science of common sense. Actually, it may transcend common sense and go beyond either imagination or intuition. It has become a very strange and perhaps frightening subject from the ordinary point of view, but anyone who penetrates into it will find a veritable fairyland, a fairyland which is strange, but makes sense, if not common sense. From the ordinary point of view mathematics deals with strange things. We shall show you that occasionally it does deal with strange things, but mostly it deals with familiar things in a strange way. If you look at yourself in an ordinary mirror, regardless of your physical attributes, you may find yourself amusing, but not strange; a subway ride to Coney Island, and a glance at yourself in one of the distorting mirrors will convince you that from another point of view you may be strange as well as amusing. It is largely a matter of what you are accustomed to. A Russian peasant came to Moscow for the first time and went to see the sights. He went to the zoo and saw the giraffes. You may find a moral in his reaction as plainly as in the fables of La Fontaine. "Look," he said, "at what the Bolsheviks have done to our horses." That is what modern mathematics has done to simple geometry and to simple arithmetic.

There are other words and expressions, not so familiar, which have been invented even more recently. Take, for instance, the word "turbine." Of course, that is already used in engineering, but it is an entirely new word in geometry. The mathematical name applies to a certain diagram. (Geometry, whatever others may think, is the study of different shapes,

*Turbines*

many of them very beautiful, having harmony, grace and symmetry. Of course, there are also fat books written on abstract geometry, and abstract space in which neither a diagram nor a shape appears. This is a very important branch of mathematics, but it is not the geometry studied by the Egyptians and the Greeks. Most of us, if we can play chess at all, are content to play it on a board with wooden chess pieces; but there are some who play the game blindfolded and without touching the board. It might be a fair analogy to say that abstract geometry is like blindfold chess—it is a game played without concrete objects.) Above you see a picture of a turbine, in fact, two of them.

A turbine consists of an infinite number of "elements" filled in continuously. An element is not merely a point; it is a point with an associated direction—like an iron filing. A turbine is composed of an infinite number of these elements, arranged in a peculiar way: the points must be arranged on a perfect circle, and the inclination of the iron filings must be at the same angle to the circle throughout. There are thus an infinite number of elements of equal inclination to the various tangents of the circle. In the special case where the angle between the direction of the element and the direction of the tangent is zero, what would happen? The turbine would be a circle. In other words, the theory of turbines is a generalization of the theory of the circle. If the angle is ninety degrees, the elements point toward the center of the circle. In that special case we have a normal turbine (see left-hand diagram).

There is a geometry of turbines, instead of a geometry of circles. It is a rather technical branch of mathematics which concerns itself with working out continuous groups of transformations connected with differential equations and differential geometry. The geometry connected with the turbine bears the rather odd name of "turns and slides."

The circle is one of the oldest figures in mathematics. The straight line is the simplest line, but the circle is the simplest nonstraight curve. It is often regarded as the limit of a polygon with an infinite number of sides. You can see for yourself that as a series of polygons is inscribed in a circle with each polygon having more sides than its predecessor, each polygon gets to look more and more like a circle.

The Greeks were already familiar with the idea that as a regular polygon increases in the number of its sides, it differs less and less from the circle in which it is inscribed. Indeed, it may well be that in the eyes of an

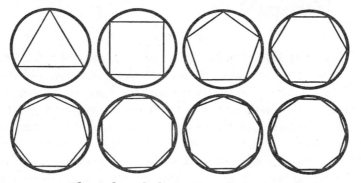

*The circle as the limit of inscribed polygons*

omniscient creature, the circle would look like a polygon with an infinite number of straight sides. However, in the absence of complete omniscience, we shall continue to regard a circle as being a nonstraight curve. There are some interesting generalizations of the circle when it is viewed in this way. There is, for example, the concept denoted by the word "cycle," which was introduced by a French mathematician, Laguerre. A cycle is a circle with an arrow on it, like this:

If you took the same circle and put an arrow on it in the opposite direction, it would become a different cycle.

The Greeks were specialists in the art of posing problems which neither they nor succeeding generations of mathematicians have ever been able to solve. The three most famous of these problems—the squaring of the circle, the duplication of the cube, and the trisection of an angle—we shall discuss later. Many well-meaning, self-appointed, and self-anointed mathematicians, and a motley assortment of lunatics and cranks, knowing neither history nor mathematics, supply an abundant crop of "solutions"

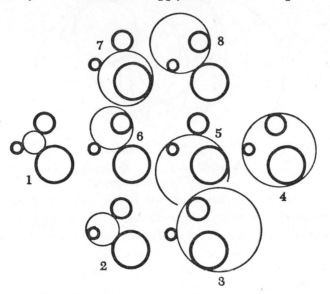

*The eight solutions of the problem of Apollonius.*
*Each lightly drawn circle is in contact with three heavily drawn ones.*

of these insoluble problems each year. However, some of the classical problems of antiquity have been solved. For example, the theory of cycles was used by Laguerre in solving the problem of Apollonius: given three fixed circles, to find a circle that touches them all. It turns out to be a matter of elementary high school geometry, although it involves ingenuity, and any brilliant high school student could work it out. It has eight answers, as shown in the diagram above.

They can all be constructed with ruler and compass, and many methods of solution have been found. Given three *circles*, there will be eight circles touching all of them. Given three *cycles*, however, there will be only one clockwise cycle that touches them all. (Two cycles are said to touch each other only if their arrows agree in direction at the point of contact.) Thus, by using the idea of cycles, we have one definite answer instead of eight. Laguerre made the idea of cycles the basis of an elegant theory.

Another variation of the circle introduced by the eminent American mathematician C. J. Keyser is obtained by taking a circle and removing one point.[1] This creates a serious change in conception. Keyser calls it "a pathocircle" (from pathological circle). He has used it in discussing the logic of axioms.

*The eight solutions of Appolonius*
*merged into one diagram*

We have made yet another change in the concept of circle, which introduces another word and a new diagram. Take a circle and instead of leaving one point out, simply emphasize one point as the initial point. This is to be called a "clock." It has been used in the theory of polygenic functions. "Polygenic" is a word recently introduced into the theory of complex functions—about 1927. There was an important word, "monogenic," introduced in the nineteenth century by the famous French mathematician Augustin Cauchy, and used in the classical theory of functions. It is used to denote functions that have a single derivative at a point, as in the differential calculus. But most functions, in the complex domain, have an infinite number of derivatives at a point. If a function is not monogenic, it can never be bigenic, or trigenic. Either the derivative has one value or an infinite number of values—either monogenic or polygenic, nothing intermediate. Monogenic means one rate of growth. Polygenic means many rates of growth. The complete derivative of a polygenic function is represented by a congruence (a double infinity) of clocks, all with different starting points, but with the same uniform rate of

1. This is a diagram which the reader will have to imagine, for it is beyond the capacity of any printer to make a circle with one point omitted. A point, having no dimensions, will, like many of the persons on the Lord High Executioner's list, never be missed. So the circle with one point missing is purely conceptual, not an idea which can be pictured.

rotation. It would be useless to attempt to give a simplified explanation of these concepts. (The neophyte will have to bear with us over a few intervals like this for the sake of the more experienced mathematical reader.)

*The parhexagon*

The going has been rather hard in the last paragraph, and if a few of the polygenic seas have swept you overboard, we shall throw you a hexagonal life preserver. We may consider a very simple word that has been introduced in elementary geometry to indicate a certain kind of hexagon. The word on which to fix your attention is "parhexagon." An ordinary hexagon has six arbitrary sides. A parhexagon is that kind of hexagon in which any side is both equal and parallel to the side opposite to it (as in the figure above).

If the opposite sides of a quadrilateral are equal and parallel, it is called a parallelogram. By the same reasoning that we use for the word parhexagon, a parallelogram might have been called a parquadrilateral.

Here is an example of a theorem about the parhexagon: take any irregular hexagon, not necessarily a parhexagon, ABCDEF. Draw the diagonals AC, BD, CE, DF, EA, and FB, forming the six triangles, ABC, BCD, CDE, DEF, EFA, and FAB. Find the six centers of gravity, A', B', C', D', E', and F' of these triangles. (The center of gravity of a

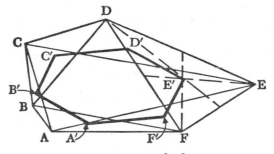

ABCDEF *is an irregular hexagon.*
A'B'C'D'E'F' *is a parhexagon.*

triangle is the point at which the triangle would balance if it were cut out of cardboard and supported only at that point; it coincides with the point of intersection of the medians.) Draw A'B', B'C', C'D', D'E', E'F', and F'A'. Then the new inner hexagon A'B'C'D'E'F' will always be a parhexagon.

The word radical, favorite call to arms among Republicans, Democrats, Communists, Socialists, Nazis, Fascists, Trotskyites, etc., has a less hortatory and bellicose character in mathematics. For one thing, everybody knows its meaning: *i.e.*, square root, cube root, fourth root, fifth root, etc. Combining a word previously defined with this one, we might say that the extraction of a root is the evolution of a radical. The square root of 9 is 3; the square root of 10 is greater than 3, and the most famous and the simplest of all square roots, the first incommensurable number discovered by the Greeks, the square root of 2, is 1.414. . . . There are also composite radicals—expressions like $\sqrt{7} + \sqrt[5]{10}$. The symbol for a radical is not the hammer and sickle, but a sign three or four centuries old, and the idea of the mathematical radical is even older than that. The concept of the "hyperradical," or "ultraradical," which means something higher than a radical, but lower than a transcendental, is of recent origin. It has a symbol which we shall see in a moment. First, we must say a few words about radicals in general. There are certain numbers and functions in mathematics which are not expressible in the language of radicals and which are generally not well understood. Many ideas for which there are no concrete or diagrammatic representations are difficult to explain. Most people find it impossible to think without words; it is necessary to give them a word and a symbol to pin their attention. Hyperradical or ultraradical, for which hitherto there have been neither words, nor symbols, fall into this category.

We first meet these ultraradicals, not in Mexico City, but in trying to solve equations of the fifth degree. The Egyptians solved equations of the first degree perhaps 4,000 years ago. That is, they found that the solution of the equation $ax + b = 0$, which is represented in geometry by a straight line, is $x = \dfrac{-b}{a}$. The quadratic equation $ax^2 + bx + c = 0$ was solved by the Hindus and the Arabs with the formula $x = \dfrac{-b \pm \sqrt{b^2 - 4ac}}{2a}$. The various conic sections, the circle, the ellipse, the parabola, and the hyperbola, are the geometric pictures of quadratic equations in two variables.

Then in the sixteenth century the Italians solved the equations of third and fourth degree, obtaining long formulas involving cube roots and square roots. So that by the year 1550, a few years before Shakespeare was born, the equation of the first, second, third, and fourth degrees had been solved. Then there was a delay of 250 years, because mathematicians were struggling with the equation of the fifth degree—the general quintic. Finally, at the beginning of the nineteenth century, Ruffini and Abel showed that equations of the fifth degree could not be solved with radicals. The general quintic is thus not like the general quadratic, cubic or biquadratic. Nevertheless, it presents a problem in algebra which theoretically can be solved by algebraic operations. Only, these operations are so hard that they cannot be expressed by the symbols for radicals. These new higher things are named "ultraradicals," and they too have their special symbols.

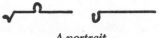

*A portrait of two ultraradicals*

With such symbols combined with radicals, we can solve equations of the fifth degree. For example, the solution of $x^5 + x = a$ may be written $x = \sqrt{a}$ or $x = \sqrt{a}$. The usefulness of the special symbol and name is apparent. Without them the solution of the quintic equation could not be compactly expressed.

We may now give a few ideas somewhat easier than those with which we have thus far occupied ourselves. These ideas were presented some time ago to a number of children in kindergarten. It was amazing how well they understood everything that was said to them. Indeed, it is a fair inference that kindergarten children can enjoy lectures on graduate mathematics as long as the mathematical concepts are clearly presented.

It was raining and the children were asked how many raindrops would fall on New York. The highest answer was 100. They had never counted higher than 100 and what they meant to imply when they used that number was merely something very, very big—as big as they could imagine. They were asked how many raindrops hit the roof, and how many hit New York, and how many single raindrops hit all of New York in 24 hours. They soon got a notion of the bigness of these numbers even though they did not know the symbols for them. They were certain in a little while that the number of raindrops was a great deal bigger than a hundred. They were asked to think of the number of grains of sand on the beach at Coney Island and decided that the number of grains of sand and the number of raindrops were about the same. But the important thing is that they realized that the number was *finite, not infinite.* In this respect they showed their distinct superiority over many scientists who to this day use the word infinite when they mean some big number, like a billion billion.

Counting, something such scientists evidently do not realize, is a precise operation.[2] It may be wonderful but there is nothing vague or mysterious about it. If you count something, the answer you get is either perfect or all wrong; there is no half way. It is very much like catching a train. You either catch it or you miss it, and if you miss it by a split second you might as well have come a week late. There is a famous quotation which illustrates this:

> Oh, the little more, and how much it is!
> And the little less, and what worlds away!

A big number is big, but it is definite and it is finite. Of course in poetry, the finite ends with about three thousand; any greater number is infinite. In many poems, the poet will talk to you about the infinite number of stars. But, if ever there was a hyperbole, this is it, for nobody, not even the poet, has ever seen more than three thousand stars on a clear night, without the aid of a telescope.

With the Hottentots, infinity begins at three.[3] Ask a Hottentot how many cows he owns, and if he has more than three he'll say "many." The number of raindrops falling on New York is also "many." It is a large finite number, but nowhere near infinity.

Now here is the name of a very large number: "Googol."[4] Most people would say, "A googol is so large that you cannot name it or talk about it; it is so large that it is infinite." Therefore, we shall talk about it, explain exactly what it is, and show that it belongs to the very same family as the number 1.

A googol is this number which one of the children in the kindergarten wrote on the blackboard: 100000000000000000000000000000000000000000 00000000000000000000000000000000000000000000000000000000000.

The definition of a googol is: 1 followed by a hundred zeros. It was decided, after careful mathematical researches in the kindergarten, that the number of raindrops falling on New York in 24 hours, or even in a year or in a century, is much less than a googol. Indeed, the googol is a number just larger than the largest numbers that are used in physics or astronomy. All those numbers require less than a hundred zeros. This

---

2. No one would say that 1 + 1 is "about equal to 2." It is just as silly to say that a billion billion is not a finite number, simply because it is big. Any number which can be named, or conceived of in terms of the integers is finite. *Infinite means something quite different*, as we shall see in the chapter on the googol.
3. Although, in all fairness, it must be pointed out that some of the tribes of the Belgian Congo can count to a million and beyond.
4. Not even approximately a Russian author.

information is, of course, available to everyone, but seems to be a great secret in many scientific quarters.

A very distinguished scientific publication recently came forth with the revelation that the number of snow crystals necessary to form the ice age was a billion to the billionth power. This is very startling and also very silly. A billion to the billionth power looks like this: $1000000000^{1000000000}$. A more reasonable estimate and a somewhat smaller number would be $10^{30}$. As a matter of fact, it has been estimated that if the entire universe, which you will concede is a trifle larger than the earth, were filled with protons and electrons, so that no vacant space remained, the total number of protons and electrons would be $10^{110}$ (*i.e.*, 1 with 110 zeros after it). Unfortunately, as soon as people talk about large numbers, they run amuck. They seem to be under the impression that since zero equals nothing, they can add as many zeros to a number as they please with practically no serious consequences. We shall have to be a little more careful than that in talking about big numbers.

To return to Coney Island, the number of grains of sand on the beach is about $10^{20}$, or more descriptively, 100000000000000000000. That is a large number, but not as large as the number mentioned by the divorcee in a recent divorce suit who had telephoned that she loved the man "a million billion billion times and eight times around the world." It was the largest number that she could conceive of, and shows the kind of thing that may be hatched in a love nest.

Though people do a great deal of talking, the total output since the beginning of gabble to the present day, including all baby talk, love songs, and Congressional debates, totals about $10^{16}$. This is ten million billion. Contrary to popular belief, this is a larger number of words than is spoken at the average afternoon bridge.

A great deal of the veneration for the authority of the printed word would vanish if one were to calculate the number of words which have been printed since the Gutenberg Bible appeared. It is a number somewhat larger than $10^{16}$. A recent popular historical novel alone accounts for the printing of several hundred billion words.

The largest number seen in finance (though new records are in the making) represents the amount of money in circulation in Germany at the peak of the inflation. It was less than a googol—merely 496, 585, 346, 000, 000, 000, 000. A distinguished economist vouches for the accuracy of this figure. The number of marks in circulation was very nearly equal to the number of grains of sand on Coney Island beach.

The number of atoms of oxygen in the average thimble is a good deal larger. It would be represented by perhaps 1000000000000000000000000 00000. The number of electrons, in size exceedingly smaller than the atoms, is much more enormous. The number of electrons which pass through the filament of an ordinary fifty-watt electric lamp in a minute equals the number of drops of water that flow over Niagara Falls in a century.

One may also calculate the number of electrons, not only in the average room, but over the whole earth, and out through the stars, the Milky Way, and all the nebulae. The reason for giving all these examples of very large numbers is to emphasize the fact that no matter how large the collection to be counted, a finite number will do the trick. We will have occasion later on to speak of infinite collections, but those encountered in nature, though sometimes very large, are all definitely finite. A celebrated scientist recently stated in all seriousness that he believed that the number of pores (through which leaves breathe) of all the leaves, of all the trees in all the world, would certainly be infinite. Needless to say, he was not a mathematician. The number of electrons in a single leaf is much bigger than the number of pores of all the leaves of all the trees of all the world. And still the number of all the electrons in the entire universe can be found by means of the physics of Einstein. It is a good deal less than a googol—perhaps one with seventy-nine zeros, $10^{79}$, as estimated by Eddington.

Words of wisdom are spoken by children at least as often as by scientists. The name "googol" was invented by a child (Dr. Kasner's nine-year-old nephew) who was asked to think up a name for a very big number, namely, 1 with a hundred zeros after it. He was very certain that this number was not infinite, and therefore equally certain that it had to have a name. At the same time that he suggested "googol" he gave a name for a still larger number: "Googolplex." A googolplex is much larger than a googol, but is still finite, as the inventor of the name was quick to point out. It was first suggested that a googolplex should be 1, followed by writing zeros until you got tired. This is a description of what would happen if one actually tried to write a googolplex, but different people get tired at different times and it would never do to have Carnera a better mathematician than Dr. Einstein, simply because he had more endurance. The googolplex then, is a specific finite number, with so many zeros after the 1 that the number of zeros is a googol. A googolplex is much bigger than a googol, much bigger even than a googol times a googol. A googol times a googol would be 1 with 200 zeros, whereas a googolplex is 1 with a googol of zeros. You will get some idea of the size of this very large but finite number from the fact that there would not be enough room to write it, if you went to the farthest star, touring all the nebulae and putting down zeros every inch of the way.

One might not believe that such a large number would ever really have any application; but one who felt that way would not be a mathematician. A number as large as the googolplex might be of real use in problems of combination. This would be the type of problem in which it might come up scientifically:

Consider this book which is made up of carbon and nitrogen and of other elements. The answer to the question, "How many atoms are there in this book?" would certainly be a finite number, even less than a googol. Now imagine that the book is held suspended by a string, the end of which you are holding. How long will it be necessary to wait before the book will jump up into your hand? Could it conceivably ever happen? One answer might be "No, it will never happen without some external force causing it to do so." But that is not correct. The right answer is that it will almost *certainly* happen *sometime* in less than a googolplex of years—perhaps tomorrow.

The explanation of this answer can be found in physical chemistry, statistical mechanics, the kinetic theory of gases, and the theory of probability. We cannot dispose of all these subjects in a few lines, but we will try. Molecules are always moving. Absolute rest of molecules would mean absolute zero degrees of temperature, and absolute zero degrees of temperature is not only nonexistent, but impossible to obtain. All the molecules of the surrounding air bombard the book. At present the bombardment from above and below is nearly the same and gravity keeps the book down. It is necessary to wait for the favorable moment when there happens to be an enormous number of molecules bombarding the book from below and very few from above. Then gravity will be overcome and the book will rise. It would be somewhat like the effect known in physics as the Brownian movement, which describes the behavior of small particles in a liquid as they dance about under the impact of molecules. It would be analogous to the Brownian movement on a vast scale.

But the probability that this will happen in the near future or, for that matter, on any specific occasion that we might mention, is between $\dfrac{1}{googol}$ and $\dfrac{1}{googolplex}$. To be reasonably sure that the book will rise, we should have to wait between a googol and a googolplex of years.

When working with electrons or with problems of combination like the one of the book, we need larger numbers than are usually talked about. It is for that reason that names like googol and googolplex, though they may appear to be mere jokes, have a real value. The names help to fix in our minds the fact that we are still dealing with finite numbers. To repeat, a googol is $10^{100}$; a googolplex is 10 to the googol power, which may be written $10^{10^{100}} = 10^{\text{googol}}$.

We have seen that the number of years that one would have to wait to see the miracle of the rising book would be less than a googolplex. In that number of years the earth may well have become a frozen planet as dead as the moon, or perhaps splintered to a number of meteors and comets. The real miracle is not that the book will rise, but that with the aid of mathematics, we can project ourselves into the future and predict with accuracy *when* it will probably rise, *i.e.*, some time between today and the year googolplex.

We have mentioned quite a few new names in mathematics—new names for old and new ideas. There is one more new name which it is proper to mention in conclusion. Watson Davis, the popular science reporter, has given us the name "mathescope." With the aid of the magnificent new microscopes and telescopes, man, midway between the stars and the atoms, has come a little closer to both. The mathescope is not a physical instrument; it is a purely intellectual instrument, the ever-increasing insight which mathematics gives into the fairyland which lies beyond intuition and beyond imagination. Mathematicians, unlike philosophers, say nothing about ultimate truth, but patiently, like the makers of the great microscopes, and the great telescopes, they grind their lenses. In this book, we shall let you see through the newer and greater lenses which the mathematicians have ground. Be prepared for strange sights through the mathescope!

# Beyond the Googol

If you do not expect the unexpected, you will not find it;
for it is hard to be sought out, and difficult.

*—Heraclitus*

Mathematics may well be a science of austere logical propositions in precise canonical form, but in its countless applications it serves as a tool and a language, the language of description, of number and size. It describes with economy and elegance the elliptic orbits of the planets as readily as the shape and dimensions of this page or a cornfield. The whirling dance of the electron can be seen by no one; the most powerful telescopes can reveal only a meager bit of the distant stars and nebulae and the cold far corners of space. But with the aid of mathematics and the imagination the very small, the very large—all things may be brought within man's domain.

To count is to talk the language of number. To count to a googol, or to count to ten is part of the same process; the googol is simply harder to pronounce. The essential thing to realize is that the googol and ten are kin, like the giant stars and the electron. Arithmetic—this counting language—makes the whole world kin, both in space and in time.

To grasp the meaning and importance of mathematics, to appreciate its beauty and its value, arithmetic must first be understood, for mostly, since its beginning, mathematics has been arithmetic in simple or elaborate attire. Arithmetic has been the queen and the handmaiden of the sciences from the days of the astrologers of Chaldea and the high priests of Egypt to the present days of relativity, quanta, and the adding machine. Historians may dispute the meaning of ancient papyri, theologians may wrangle over the exegesis of Scripture, philosophers may debate over

Pythagorean doctrine, but all will concede that the numbers in the papyri, in the Scriptures and in the writings of Pythagoras are the same as the numbers of today. As arithmetic, mathematics has helped man to cast horoscopes, to make calendars, to predict the risings of the Nile, to measure fields and the height of the Pyramids, to measure the speed of a stone as it fell from a tower in Pisa, the speed of an apple as it fell from a tree in Woolsthorpe, to weigh the stars and the atoms, to mark the passage of time, to find the curvature of space. And although mathematics is also the calculus, the theory of probability, the matrix algebra, the science of the infinite, it is still the art of counting.

Everyone who will read this book can count, and yet, what is counting? The dictionary definitions are about as helpful as Johnson's definition of a net: "A series of reticulated interstices." *Learning to compare is learning to count.* Numbers come much later; they are an artificiality, an abstraction. Counting, matching, comparing are almost as indigenous to man as his fingers. Without the faculty of comparing, and without his fingers, it is unlikely that he would have arrived at numbers.

One who knows nothing of the formal processes of counting is still able to compare two classes of objects, to determine which is the greater, which the less. Without knowing anything about numbers, one may ascertain whether two classes have the same number of elements; for example, barring prior mishaps, it is easy to show that we have the same number of fingers on both hands by simply matching finger with finger on each hand.

To describe the process of matching, which underlies counting, mathematicians use a picturesque name. They call it putting classes into a "one-to-one reciprocal correspondence" with each other. Indeed, that is all there is to the art of counting as practiced by primitive peoples, by us, or by Einstein. A few examples may serve to make this clear.

In a monogamous country it is unnecessary to count both the husbands and the wives in order to ascertain the number of married people. If allowances are made for the few gay Lotharios who do not conform to either custom or statute, it is sufficient to count either the husbands or the wives. There are just as many in one class as in the other. The correspondence between the two classes is one-to-one.

There are more useful illustrations. Many people are gathered in a large hall where seats are to be provided. The question is, are there enough chairs to go around? It would be quite a job to count both the people and the chairs, and in this case unnecessary. In kindergarten children play a game called "Going to Jerusalem"; in a room full of children and chairs there is always one less chair than the number of children. At a signal, each child runs for a chair. The child left standing is "out." A chair is removed and the game continues. Here is the solution to our problem. It is only necessary to ask everyone in the hall to be seated. If everyone sits down and no chairs are left vacant, it is evident that there are as many chairs as people. In other words, without actually knowing the number of chairs or people, one does know that the number is the same. The two classes—chairs and people—have been shown to be equal in number by a one-to-one correspondence. To each person corresponds a chair, to each chair, a person.

In counting any class of objects, it is this method alone which is employed. One class contains the things to be counted; the other class is always at hand. It is the class of integers, or "natural numbers," which for convenience we regard as being given in serial order: 1, 2, 3, 4, 5, 6, 7. . . . Matching in one-to-one correspondence the elements of the first class with the integers, we experience a common, but none the less wonderful phenomenon—the last integer necessary to complete the pairings denotes *how many* elements there are.

In clarifying the idea of counting, we made the unwarranted assumption that the concept of number was understood by everyone. The number concept may seem intuitively clear, but a precise definition is required. While the definition may seem worse than the disease, it is not as difficult as appears at first glance. Read it carefully and you will find that it is both explicit and economical.

Given a class $C$ containing certain elements, it is possible to find other classes, such that the elements of each may be matched one to one with the elements of $C$. (Each of these classes is thus called "equivalent to $C$.") All such classes, including $C$, whatever the character of their elements, share one property in common: all of them have the same *cardinal number*, which is called the *cardinal number* of the class $C$.[1]

The cardinal number of the class $C$ is thus seen to be the *symbol* representing the set of all classes that can be put into one-to-one correspondence with $C$. For example, the number 5 is simply the name, or

---

1. We distinguish cardinal from *ordinal numbers*, which denote the relation of an element in a class to the others, with reference to some system of order. Thus, we speak of the *first* Pharaoh of Egypt, or of the *fourth* integer, in their customary order, or of the *third* day of the week, etc. These are examples of ordinals.

symbol, attached to the set of all the classes, each of which can be put into one-to-one correspondence with the fingers of one hand.

Hereafter we may refer without ambiguity to the number of elements in a class as the cardinal number of that class or, briefly, as "its cardinality." The question, "How many letters are there in the word *mathematics?*" is the same as the question, "What is the cardinality of the class whose elements are the letters in the word *mathematics?*" Employing the method of one-to-one correspondence, the following graphic device answers the question, and illustrates the method:

| M | A | T | H | E | M | A | T | I | C | S |
|---|---|---|---|---|---|---|---|---|---|---|
| ↕ | ↕ | ↕ | ↕ | ↕ | ↕ | ↕ | ↕ | ↕ | ↕ | ↕ |
| 1 | 2 | 3 | 4 | 5 | 6 | 7 | 8 | 9 | 10 | 11 |

It must now be evident that this method is neither strange nor esoteric; it was not invented by mathematicians to make something natural and easy seem unnatural and hard. It is the method employed when we count our change or our chickens; it is the proper method for counting any class, no matter how large, from ten to a googolplex—and beyond.

Soon we shall speak of the "beyond" when we turn to classes which are not finite. Indeed, we shall try *to measure our measuring class*—the integers. One-to-one correspondence should, therefore, be thoroughly understood, for an amazing revelation awaits us: Infinite classes can also be counted, and by the very same means. But before we try to count them, let us practice on some very big numbers—big, but not infinite.

"Googol" is already in our vocabulary: It is a big number—one, with a hundred zeros after it. Even bigger is the googolplex: 1 with a googol zeros after it. Most numbers encountered in the description of nature are much smaller, though a few are larger.

Enormous numbers occur frequently in modern science. Sir Arthur Eddington claims that there are, not approximately, but exactly $136 \cdot 2^{256}$ protons,[2] and an equal number of electrons, in the universe. Though not easy to visualize, this number, as a symbol on paper, takes up little room. Not quite as large as the googol, it is completely dwarfed by the googolplex. None the less, Eddington's number, the googol, and the googolplex are finite.

---

2. Let no one suppose that Sir Arthur has counted them. But he does have a theory to justify his claim. Anyone with a better theory may challenge Sir Arthur, for who can be referee? Here is his number written out: 15,747,724,136,275,002,577,605,-653,961,181,555,468,044,717,914,527,116,709,366,231,425,076,185,631,031,296— accurate, he says, to the last digit.

A veritable giant is Skewes' number, even bigger than a googolplex. It gives information about the distribution of primes and looks like this:

$$10^{10^{10^{34}}}$$

Or, for example, the total possible number of moves in a game of chess is:

$$10^{10^{50}}$$

And speaking of chess, as the eminent English mathematician G. H. Hardy pointed out—if we imagine the entire universe as a chessboard, and the protons in it as chessmen, and if we agree to call any interchange in the position of two protons a "move" in this cosmic game, then the total number of possible moves, of all odd coincidences, would be Skewes' number:

$$10^{10^{10^{34}}}$$

No doubt most people believe that such numbers are part of the marvelous advance of science, and that a few generations ago, to say nothing of centuries back, no one in dream or fancy could have conceived of them.

There is some truth in that idea. For one thing, the ancient cumbersome methods of mathematical notation made the writing of big numbers difficult, if not actually impossible. For another, the average citizen of today encounters such huge sums, representing armament expenditures and stellar distances, that he is quite conversant with, and immune to, big numbers.

But there were clever people in ancient times. Poets in every age may have sung of the stars as infinite in number, when all they saw was, perhaps, three thousand. But to Archimedes, a number as large as a googol, or even larger, was not disconcerting. He says as much in an introductory passage in *The Sand Reckoner*, realizing that a number is not infinite merely because it is enormous.

> There are some, King Gelon, who think that the number of the sand is infinite in multitude; and I mean by the sand, not only that which exists about Syracuse and the rest of Sicily, but also that which is found in every region whether inhabited or uninhabited. Again there are some who, without regarding it as infinite, yet think that no number has been named which is great enough to exceed its multitude. And it is clear that they who hold this view, if they imagined a mass made up of sand in other respects as large as the mass of the earth, including in it all the

seas and the hollows of the earth filled up to a height equal to that of the highest of the mountains, would be many times further still from recognizing that any number could be expressed which exceeded the multitude of the sand so taken. But I will try to show you by means of geometrical proofs, which you will be able to follow, that, of the numbers named by me and given in the work which I sent to Zeuxippus, some exceed not only the number of the mass of sand equal in magnitude to the earth filled up in the way described, but also that of a mass equal in magnitude to the universe.

The Greeks had very definite ideas about the infinite. Just as we are indebted to them for much of our wit and our learning, so are we indebted to them for much of our sophistication about the infinite. Indeed, had we always retained their clear-sightedness, many of the problems and paradoxes connected with the infinite would never have arisen.

Above everything, we must realize that "very big" and "infinite" are entirely different.[3] By using the method of one-to-one correspondence, the protons and electrons in the universe can theoretically be counted as easily as the buttons on a vest. Sufficient and more than sufficient for that task, or for the task of counting any finite collection, are the integers. But measuring the *totality of integers* is another problem. To measure such a class demands a lofty viewpoint. Besides being, as the German mathematician Kronecker thought, the work of God, which requires courage to appraise, the class of integers is infinite—which is a great deal more inconvenient. It is worse than heresy to measure our own endless measuring rod!

The problems of the infinite have challenged man's mind and have fired his imagination as no other single problem in the history of thought. The infinite appears both strange and familiar, at times beyond our grasp, at times natural and easy to understand. In conquering it, man broke the fetters that bound him to earth. All his faculties were required for this conquest—his reasoning powers, his poetic fancy, his desire to know.

To establish the science of the infinite involves the principle of *mathematical induction*. This principle affirms the power of reasoning by recurrence. It typifies almost all mathematical thinking, all that we do when we construct complex aggregates out of simple elements. It is, as

---

3. There is no point where the very big starts to merge into the infinite. You may write a number as big as you please; it will be no nearer the infinite than the number 1 or the number 7. Make sure that you keep this distinction very clear and you will have mastered many of the subtleties of the transfinite.

Poincaré remarked, "at once necessary to the mathematician and irreducible to logic." His statement of the principle is: "If a property be true of the number one, and if we establish that it is true of $n + 1$,[4] provided it be of $n$, it will be true of all the whole numbers." Mathematical induction is not derived from experience, rather is it an inherent, intuitive, almost instinctive property of the mind. *What we have once done we can do again.*

If we can construct numbers to ten, to a million, to a googol, we are led to believe that there is no stopping, no end. Convinced of this, we need not go on forever; the mind grasps that which it has never experienced—the infinite itself. Without any sense of discontinuity, without transgressing the canons of logic, the mathematician and philosopher have bridged in one stroke the gulf between the finite and the infinite. The mathematics of the infinite is a sheer affirmation of the inherent power of reasoning by recurrence.

In the sense that "infinite" means "without end, without bound," simply "not finite," probably everyone understands its meaning. No difficulty arises where no precise definition is required. Nevertheless, in spite of the famous epigram that mathematics is the science in which we do not know what we are talking about, at least we shall have to agree to talk about the same thing. Apparently, even those of scientific temper can argue bitterly to the point of mutual vilification on subjects ranging from Marxism and dialectical materialism to group theory and the uncertainty principle, only to find, on the verge of exhaustion and collapse, that they are on the same side of the fence. Such arguments are generally the results of vague terminology; to assume that everyone is familiar with the precise mathematical definition of "infinite" is to build a new Tower of Babel.

Before undertaking a definition, we might do well to glance backwards to see how mathematicians and philosophers of other times dealt with the problem.

The infinite has a double aspect—the infinitely large, and the infinitely small. Repeated arguments and demonstrations, of apparently apodictic force, were advanced, overwhelmed, and once more resuscitated to prove or disprove its existence. Few of the arguments were ever refuted—each was buried under an avalanche of others. The happy result was that the problem never became any clearer.[5]

The warfare began in antiquity with the paradoxes of Zeno; it has never

---

4. Where $n$ is any integer.
5. No one has written more brilliantly or more wittily on this subject than Bertrand Russell. See particularly his essays in the volume *Mysticism and Logic*.

ceased. Fine points were debated with a fervor worthy of the earliest Christian martyrs, but without a tenth part of the acumen of medieval theologians. Today, some mathematicians think the infinite has been reduced to a state of vassalage. Others are still wondering what it is.

Zeno's puzzles may help to bring the problem into sharper focus. Zeno of Elea, it will be recalled, said some disquieting things about motion, with reference to an arrow, Achilles, and a tortoise. This strange company was employed on behalf of the tenet of Eleatic philosophy—that all motion is an illusion. It has been suggested, probably by "baffled critics," that "Zeno had his tongue in cheek when he made his puzzles." Regardless of motive, they are immeasurably subtle, and perhaps still defy solution.[6]

One paradox—the Dichotomy—states that it is impossible to cover any given distance. The argument: First, half the distance must be traversed, then half of the remaining distance, then again half of what remains, and so on. It follows that some portion of the distance to be covered always remains, and therefore motion is impossible! A solution of this paradox reads:

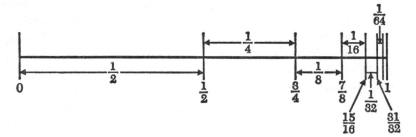

The successive distances to be covered form an infinite geometric series:

$$\frac{1}{2} + \frac{1}{4} + \frac{1}{8} + \frac{1}{16} + \frac{1}{32} + \cdots$$

each term of which is half of the one before. Although this series has an infinite number of terms, its sum is *finite* and equals 1. Herein, it is said, lies the flaw of the Dichotomy. Zeno assumed that any totality composed of an infinite number of parts must, itself, be infinite, whereas we have just seen an infinite number of elements which make up the finite totality—1.

6. To be sure, a variety of explanations have been given for the paradoxes. In the last analysis, the explanations for the riddles rest upon the interpretation of the foundations of mathematics. Mathematicians like Brouwer, who reject the infinite, would probably not accept any of the solutions given.

The paradox of the tortoise states that Achilles, running to overtake the tortoise, must first reach the place where it started:—but the tortoise has already departed. This comedy, however, is repeated indefinitely. As Achilles arrives at each new point in the race, the tortoise having been there, has already left. Achilles is as unlikely to catch him as a rider on a carrousel the rider ahead.

Finally: the arrow in flight must be moving every instant of time. But at every instant it must be *somewhere* in space. However, if the arrow must always be in some one place, it cannot at every instant also be in transit, for to be in transit is to be *nowhere*.

Aristotle and lesser saints in almost every age tried to demolish these paradoxes, but not very creditably. Three German professors succeeded where the saints had failed. At the end of the nineteenth century, it seemed that Bolzano, Weierstrass and Cantor had laid the infinite to rest, and Zeno's paradoxes as well.

The modern method of disposing of the paradoxes is not to dismiss them as mere sophisms unworthy of serious attention. The history of mathematics, in fact, recounts a poetic vindication of Zeno's stand. Zeno was, at one time, as Bertrand Russell has said, "A notable victim of posterity's lack of judgment." That wrong has been righted. In disposing of the infinitely small, Weierstrass showed that the moving arrow *is* really always at rest, and that we live in Zeno's changeless world. The work of Georg Cantor, which we shall soon encounter, showed that if we are to believe that Achilles *can* catch the tortoise, we shall have to be prepared to swallow a bigger paradox than any Zeno ever conceived of: THE WHOLE IS NO GREATER THAN MANY OF ITS PARTS!

The infinitely small had been a nuisance for more than two thousand years. At best, the innumerable opinions it evoked deserved the laconic verdict of Scotch juries: "Not proven." Until Weierstrass appeared, the total advance was a confirmation of Zeno's argument against motion. Even the jokes were better. Leibniz, according to Carlyle, made the mistake of trying to explain the infinitesimal to a Queen—Sophie Charlotte of Prussia. She informed him that the behavior of her courtiers made her so familiar with the infinitely small, that she needed no mathematical tutor to explain it. But philosophers and mathematicians, according to Russell, "having less acquaintance with the courts, continued to discuss this topic, though without making any advance."

Berkeley, with the subtlety and humor necessary for an Irish bishop, made some pointed attacks on the infinitesimal, during the adolescent period of the calculus, that had the very best, sharp-witted, scholastic sting. One could perhaps speak, if only with poetic fervor, of the infinitely large, but what, pray, was the infinitely small? The Greeks, with less than their customary sagacity, introduced it in regarding a circle as differing infinitesimally from a polygon with a large number of equal sides. Leibniz used it as the bricks for the infinitesimal calculus. Still, no one knew what it was. The infinitesimal had wondrous properties. It was not zero, yet smaller than any quantity. It could be assigned no quantity or size, yet a sizable number of infinitesimals made a very definite quantity. Unable to discover its nature, happily able to dispense with it, Weierstrass interred it alongside of the phlogiston and other once-cherished errors.

The infinitely large offered more stubborn resistance. Whatever it is, it is a doughty weed. The subject of reams of nonsense, sacred and profane, it was first discussed fully, logically, and without benefit of clergy-like prejudices by Bernhard Bolzano. *Die Paradoxien des Unendlichen,* a remarkable little volume, appeared posthumously in 1851. Like the work of another Austrian priest, Gregor Mendel, whose distinguished treatise on the principles of heredity escaped oblivion only by chance, this important book, charmingly written, made no great impression on Bolzano's contemporaries. It is the creation of a clear, forceful, penetrating intelligence. For the first time in twenty centuries the infinite was treated as a problem in science, and not as a problem in theology.

Both Cantor and Dedekind are indebted to Bolzano for the foundations of the mathematical treatment of the infinite. Among the many paradoxes he gathered and explained, one, dating from Galileo, illustrates a typical source of confusion:

Construct a square—*ABCD*. About the point *A* as center, with one side as radius, describe a quarter-circle, intersecting the square at *B* and *D*. Draw *PR* parallel to *AD*, cutting *AB* at *P*, *CD* at *R*, the diagonal *AC* at *N*, and the quarter-circle at *M*.

By a well-known geometrical theorem, it can be shown that if *PN*, *PM* and *PR* are radii, the following relationship exists:

$$\pi\overline{PN}^2 = \pi\overline{PR}^2 - \pi\overline{PM}^2 \tag{1}$$

Permit *PR* to approach *AD*. Then the circle with *PN* as radius becomes smaller, and the ring between the circles with *PM* and *PR* as radii becomes correspondingly smaller. Finally, when *PR* becomes identical with *AD*, the radius *PN* vanishes, leaving the point *A*, while the ring between the two circles *PM* and *PR* contracts into one periphery with *AD* as radius. From equation (1) it may be concluded that the *point A* takes up as much area as the *circumference* of the circle with *AD* as radius.

Bolzano realized that there is only an *appearance* of a paradox. The two classes of points, one composed of a single member, the point *A*, the other of the points in the circumference of the circle with *AB* as radius, take up

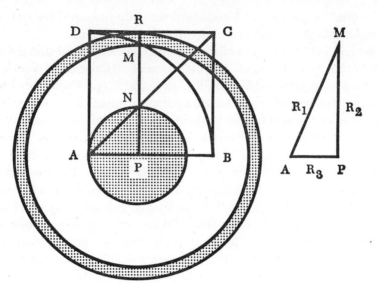

*Extract triangle APM from the figure.*
*It is not hard to see that its three sides equal respectively*
*the radii of the three circles.*

Thus

$$R_1{}^2 - R_2{}^2 = R_3{}^2$$

or,

$$\pi R_1{}^2 - \pi R_2{}^2 = \pi R_3{}^2$$
*or, the two shaded areas are equal.*

exactly the same amount of area. The area of both is zero! The paradox springs from the erroneous conception that the number of points in a given configuration is an indication of the area which it occupies. Points, finite or infinite in number, have no dimensions and can therefore occupy no area.

Through the centuries such paradoxes had piled up. Born of the union of vague ideas and vague philosophical reflections, they were nurtured on sloppy thinking. Bolzano cleared away most of the muddle, preparing the way for Cantor. It is to Cantor that the mathematics of the infinitely large owes its coming of age.

Georg Cantor was born in St. Petersburg in 1845, six years before Bolzano's book appeared. Though born in Russia, he lived the greater part of his life in Germany, where he taught at the University of Halle. While Weierstrass was busy disposing of the infinitesimal, Cantor set himself the apparently more formidable task at the other pole. The infinitely small might be laughed out of existence, but who dared laugh at the infinitely large? Certainly not Cantor! Theological curiosity prompted his task, but the mathematical interest came to subsume every other.

In dealing with the science of the infinite, Cantor realized that the first requisite was to define terms. His definition of "infinite class" which we shall paraphrase, rests upon a paradox. AN INFINITE CLASS HAS THE UNIQUE PROPERTY THAT THE WHOLE IS NO GREATER THAN SOME OF ITS PARTS. That statement is as essential for the mathematics of the infinite as THE WHOLE IS GREATER THAN ANY OF ITS PARTS is for finite arithmetic. When we recall that two classes are equal if their elements can be put into one-to-one correspondence, the latter statement becomes obvious. Zeno would not have challenged it, in spite of his scepticism about the obvious. But what is obvious for the finite is false for the infinite; our extensive experience with finite classes is misleading. Since, for example, the class of men and the class of mathematicians are both finite, anyone realizing that some men are not mathematicians would correctly conclude that the class of men is the larger of the two. He might also conclude that the number of integers, even and odd, is greater than the number of even integers. But we see from the following pairing that he would be mistaken:

$$1 \quad 2 \quad 3 \quad 4 \quad 5 \quad 6 \quad 7 \ldots$$
$$\updownarrow \quad \updownarrow \quad \updownarrow \quad \updownarrow \quad \updownarrow \quad \updownarrow \quad \updownarrow$$
$$2 \quad 4 \quad 6 \quad 8 \quad 10 \quad 12 \quad 14 \ldots$$

Under every integer, odd or even, we may write its double—an even integer. That is, we place each of the elements of the class of all the integers, odd and even, into a one-to-one correspondence with the elements of the class composed solely of even integers. This process may be continued to the googolplex and beyond.

Now, the class of integers is infinite. No integer, no matter how great, can describe its cardinality (or numerosity). Yet, since it is possible to establish a one-to-one correspondence between the class of even numbers and the class of integers, we have succeeded in counting the class of even numbers just as we count a finite collection. The two classes being perfectly matched, we must conclude that they have the same cardinality.

That their cardinality is the same we *know,* just as we knew that the chairs and the people in the hall were equal in number when every chair was occupied and no one was left standing. Thus, we arrive at the fundamental paradox of all infinite classes:—There exist component parts of an infinite class which are just as great as the class itself. THE WHOLE IS NO GREATER THAN SOME OF ITS PARTS!

The class composed of the even integers *is thinned out* as compared with the class of all integers, but evidently "thinning out" has not the slightest effect on its cardinality. Moreover, there is almost no limit to the number of times this process can be repeated. For instance, there are as many square numbers and cube numbers as there are integers. The appropriate pairings are:

$$
\begin{array}{cccccc}
1 & 2 & 3 & 4 & 5 & 6 \ldots \\
\updownarrow & \updownarrow & \updownarrow & \updownarrow & \updownarrow & \updownarrow \\
1 & 4 & 9 & 16 & 25 & 36 \ldots \\
1^2 & 2^2 & 3^2 & 4^2 & 5^2 & 6^2
\end{array}
\qquad
\begin{array}{cccccc}
1 & 2 & 3 & 4 & 5 & 6 \ldots \\
\updownarrow & \updownarrow & \updownarrow & \updownarrow & \updownarrow & \updownarrow \\
1 & 8 & 27 & 64 & 125 & 216 \ldots \\
1^3 & 2^3 & 3^3 & 4^3 & 5^3 & 6^3
\end{array}
$$

Indeed, from any denumerable class there can always be removed a denumerably infinite number of denumerably infinite classes without affecting the cardinality of the original class.

Infinite classes which can be put into one-to-one correspondence with the integers, and thus "counted," Cantor called *countable,* or *denumerably infinite.* Since all finite sets are countable, and we can assign to each one a number, it is natural to try to extend this notion and assign to the class of all integers a number representing its cardinality. Yet, it is obvious from our description of "infinite class" that no ordinary integer would be adequate to describe the cardinality of the whole class of integers. In effect, it would be asking a snake to swallow itself entirely. Thus, the first of the transfinite numbers was created to describe the cardinality of countable infinite classes. Etymologically old, mathematically new, $\aleph$ (aleph), the first letter of the Hebrew alphabet, was suggested. However, Cantor finally decided to use the compound symbol $\aleph_0$ (Aleph-Null). If asked, "How many integers are there?" it would be correct to reply, "There are $\aleph_0$ integers."

Because he suspected that there were other transfinite numbers, in fact an infinite number of transfinites, and the cardinality of the integers the smallest, Cantor affixed to the first $\aleph$ a small zero as subscript. The cardinality of a denumerably infinite class is therefore referred to as $\aleph_0$ (Aleph-

Null). The anticipated transfinite numbers form a hierarchy of alephs: $\aleph_0$, $\aleph_1$, $\aleph_2$, $\aleph_3$ . . .

All this may seem very strange, and it is quite excusable for the reader by now to be thoroughly bewildered. Yet, if you have followed the previous reasoning step by step, and will go to the trouble of rereading, you will see that nothing which has been said is repugnant to straight thinking. Having established what is meant by counting in the finite domain, and what is meant by number, we decided to extend the counting process to infinite classes. As for our right to follow such a procedure, we have the same right, for example, as those who decided that man had crawled on the surface of the earth long enough and that it was about time for him to fly. It is our right to venture forth in the world of ideas as it is our right to extend our horizons in the physical universe. One restraint alone is laid upon us in these adventures of ideas: that we abide by the rules of logic.

Upon extending the counting process it was evident at once that no finite number could adequately describe an infinite class. If any number of ordinary arithmetic describes the cardinality of a class, that class must be finite, even though there were not enough ink or enough space or enough time to write the number out. We shall then require an entirely new kind of number, nowhere to be found in finite arithmetic, to describe the cardinality of an infinite class. Accordingly, the totality of integers was assigned the cardinality "aleph." Suspecting that there were *other* infinite classes with a cardinality *greater* than that of the totality of integers, we supposed a whole hierarchy of alephs, of which the cardinal number of the totality of integers was named Aleph-Null to indicate it was the smallest of the transfinites.

Having had an interlude in the form of a summary, let us turn once more to scrutinize the alephs, to find if, upon closer acquaintance, they may not become easier to understand.

The arithmetic of the alephs bears little resemblance to that of the finite integers. The immodest behavior of $\aleph_0$ is typical.

A simple problem in addition looks like this:

$$\aleph_0 + 1 = \aleph_0$$
$$\aleph_0 + \text{googol} = \aleph_0$$
$$\aleph_0 + \aleph_0 = \aleph_0$$

The multiplication table would be easy to teach, easier to learn:

$$1 \times \aleph_0 = \aleph_0$$
$$2 \times \aleph_0 = \aleph_0$$
$$3 \times \aleph_0 = \aleph_0$$
$$n \times \aleph_0 = \aleph_0$$

where $n$ represents any finite number.
Also,

$$(\aleph_0)^2 = \aleph_0 \times \aleph_0$$
$$= \aleph_0$$

And thus,

$$(\aleph_0)^n = \aleph_0$$

when $n$ is a finite integer.

There seems to be no variation of the theme; the monotony appears inescapable. But it is all very deceptive and treacherous. We go along obtaining the same result, no matter what we do to $\aleph_0$, when suddenly we try:

$$(\aleph_0)^{\aleph_0}$$

This operation, at last, creates a new transfinite. But before considering it, there is more to be said about countable classes.

Common sense says that there are many more fractions than integers, for between any two integers there is an infinite number of fractions. Alas—common sense is amidst alien corn in the land of the infinite. Cantor discovered a simple but elegant proof that the rational fractions form a denumerably infinite sequence equivalent to the class of integers. Whence, this sequence must have the same cardinality.[7]

The set of all rational fractions is arranged, not in order of increasing

---

7. It has been suggested that at this point the tired reader puts the book down with a sigh—and goes to the movies. We can only offer in mitigation that this proof, like the one which follows on the noncountability of the real numbers, is tough and no bones about it. You may grit your teeth and try to get what you can out of them, or conveniently omit them. The essential thing to come away with is that Cantor found that the rational fractions are countable but that the set of real numbers is not. Thus, in spite of what common sense tells you, there are no more fractions than there are integers and there are more real numbers between 0 and 1 than there are elements in the whole class of integers.

magnitude, but in order of ascending numerators and denominators in an array:

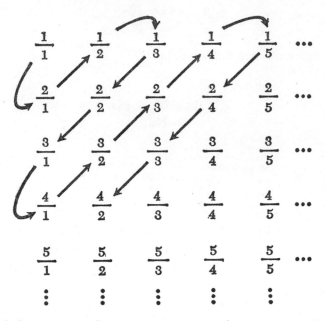

Since each fraction may be written as a pair of integers, *i.e.*, ⅔ as (3,4), the familiar one-to-one correspondence with the integers may be effected. This is illustrated in the above array by the arrows.

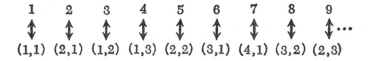

Cantor also found, by means of a proof (too technical to concern us here) based on the "height" of algebraic equations, that the class of all algebraic numbers, numbers which are the solutions of algebraic equations with integer coefficients, of the form:

$$a_0 x^n + a_1 x^{n-1} + \ldots + a_{n-1} x + a_n = 0$$

is denumerably infinite.

But Cantor felt that there were other transfinites, that there were classes which were not countable, which could not be put into one-to-one correspondence with the integers. And one of his greatest triumphs came when he succeeded in showing that there are classes with a cardinality greater than $\aleph_0$.

The class of real numbers composed of the rational and irrational numbers [8] is such a class. It contains those irrationals which are algebraic as well as those which are not. The latter are called *transcendental* *numbers*.[9]

Two important transcendental numbers were known to exist in Cantor's time: $\pi$, the ratio of the circumference of a circle to its diameter, and $e$, the base of the natural logarithms. Little more was known about the class of transcendentals: it was an enigma. What Cantor had to prove, in order to show that the class of real numbers was nondenumerable (*i.e.*, too big to be counted by the class of integers), was the unlikely fact that the class of transcendentals was nondenumerable. Since the rational and the algebraic numbers were known to be denumerable, and the sum of any denumerable number of denumerable classes is also a denumerable class, the sole remaining class which could make the totality of real numbers nondenumerable was the class of transcendentals.

He was able to devise such a proof. If it can be shown that the class of real numbers between 0 and 1 is nondenumerable, it will follow a fortiori that all the real numbers are nondenumerable. Employing a device often used in advanced mathematics, the *reductio ad absurdum*, Cantor assumed that to be true which he suspected was false, and then showed that this assumption led to a contradiction. He assumed that the real numbers between 0 and 1 were countable and could, therefore, be paired with the integers. Having proved that this assumption led to a contradiction, it followed that its opposite, namely, that the real numbers could *not* be paired with the integers (and were therefore not countable), was true.

To count the real numbers betwen 0 and 1, it is required that they all be expressed in a uniform way and a method of writing them down in order be devised so that they can be paired one to one with the integers. The first requirement can be fulfilled, for it is possible to express every real number as a nonterminating decimal. Thus, for example: [10]

$$\frac{1}{3} = .3333 \cdots \qquad\qquad \frac{3}{14} = .21428571428571 \cdots$$

$$\frac{1}{9} = .1111111 \cdots \qquad\qquad \frac{\sqrt{2}}{2} = \frac{1.414 \cdots}{2} = .707 \cdots$$

Now, the second requirement confronts us. *How shall we make the*

---

8. Irrational numbers are numbers which *cannot* be expressed as rational fractions. For Example, $\sqrt{2}$, $\sqrt{3}$, $e$, $\pi$. The class of real numbers is made up of rationals like 1, 2, 3, $\frac{1}{4}$, $1\frac{7}{32}$, and irrationals as above.

9. A transcendental number is one which is not the root of an algebraic equation with integer coefficients.

10. Any terminating decimal, such as .4, has a nonterminating form .3999 $\cdots$

*pairings?* What system may be devised to ensure the appearance of *every* decimal? We did find a method for ensuring the appearance of every rational fraction. Of course, we could not actually write them all, any more than we could actually write all the integers; but the method of increasing numerators and denominators was so explicit that, if we had had an infinite time in which to do it, we could actually have set down all the fractions and have been certain that we had not omitted any. Or, to put it another way: It was always certain and determinate after a fraction had been paired with an integer, what the next fraction would be, and the next, and the next, and so on.

On the other hand, when a real number, expressed as a nonterminating decimal, is paired with an integer, what method is there for determining what the next decimal in order should be? You have only to ask yourself, which shall be the *first* of the nonterminating decimals to pair with the integer 1, and you have an inkling of the difficulty of the problem. Cantor however *assumed* that such a pairing does exist, without attempting to give its explicit form. His scheme was: With the integer 1 pair the decimal $.a_1 a_2 a_3 \ldots$, with the integer 2, $.b_1 b_2 b_3 \ldots$, etc. Each of the letters represents a digit of the nonterminating decimal in which it appears. The determinate array of pairing between the decimals and the integers would then be:

$$1 \leftrightarrow 0. \ a_1 \ a_2 \ a_3 \ a_4 \ a_5 \ \ldots$$
$$2 \leftrightarrow 0. \ b_1 \ b_2 \ b_3 \ b_4 \ b_5 \ \ldots$$
$$3 \leftrightarrow 0. \ c_1 \ c_2 \ c_3 \ c_4 \ c_5 \ \ldots$$
$$4 \leftrightarrow 0. \ d_1 \ d_2 \ d_3 \ d_4 \ d_5 \ \ldots$$
$$. \quad . \quad . \quad . \quad . \quad . \quad .$$
$$. \quad . \quad . \quad . \quad . \quad . \quad .$$
$$. \quad . \quad . \quad . \quad . \quad . \quad .$$

That was Cantor's array. But at once it was evident that it glaringly exhibited the very contradiction for which he had been seeking. And in this defeat lay his triumph. For no matter *how* the decimals are arranged, by whatever system, by whatever scheme, it is always possible to construct an infinity of others which are not present in the array. The point is worth repeating: having contrived a general form for an array which we believed would include *every* decimal, we find, in spite of all our efforts, that *some* decimals are bound to be omitted. This, Cantor showed by his famous "diagonal proof." The conditions for determining a decimal omitted from the array are simple. It must differ from the first decimal in the array in its first place, from the second decimal in the array in its second place, from the third decimal in its third place, and so on. But then, *it must differ from every decimal in the entire array in* at least one place. If (as illustrated in the figure) we draw a diagonal line through our model array and write a new decimal, each digit of which shall differ from every digit intercepted by the diagonal, this new decimal cannot be found in the array.

$$1 \leftrightarrow 0.\ a_1\ a_2\ a_3\ a_4\ a_5 \ldots$$
$$2 \leftrightarrow 0.\ b_1\ b_2\ b_3\ b_4\ b_5 \ldots$$
$$3 \leftrightarrow 0.\ c_1\ c_2\ c_3\ c_4\ c_5 \ldots$$
$$4 \leftrightarrow 0.\ d_1\ d_2\ d_3\ d_4\ d_5 \ldots$$
$$5 \leftrightarrow 0.\ e_1\ e_2\ e_3\ e_4\ e_5 \ldots$$

The new decimal may be written:

$$0.\ a_1\ a_2\ a_3\ a_4\ a_5 \ldots ;$$

where $a_1$ differs from $a_1$, $a_2$ differs from $b_2$, $a_3$ from $c_3$, $a_4$ from $d_4$, $a_5$ from $e_5$, etc. Accordingly, it will differ from each decimal in at least one place, from the $n$th decimal in at least its $n$th place. This proves conclusively that there is no way of including all the decimals in any possible array, no way of pairing them off with the integers. Therefore, as Cantor set out to prove:

1. The class of transcendental numbers is not only infinite, but also not countable, *i.e.*, nondenumerably infinite.
2. The real numbers between 0 and 1 are infinite and not countable.
3. A fortiori, the class of all real numbers is nondenumerable.

To the noncountable class of real numbers, Cantor assigned a new transfinite cardinal. It was one of the alephs, but which one remains unsolved to this day. It is suspected that this transfinite, called the "cardinal of the continuum," which is represented by $c$ or $C$, is identical with $\aleph_1$. But a proof acceptable to most mathematicians has yet to be devised.

The arithmetic of $C$ is much the same as that of $\aleph_0$. The multiplication table has the same dependable monotone quality. But when $C$ is combined with $\aleph_0$, it swallows it completely. Thus:

$$C + \aleph_0 = C \qquad\qquad C - \aleph_0 = C$$
$$C \times \aleph_0 = C \text{ and even } C \times C = C$$

Again, we hope for a variation of the theme when we come to the process of involution. Yet, for the moment, we are disappointed, for $C^{\aleph_0} = C$. But just as $(\aleph_0)^{\aleph_0}$ does not equal $\aleph_0$, so $C^o$ does not equal $C$.

We are now in a position to solve our earlier problem in involution, for actually Cantor found that $(\aleph_0)^{\aleph_0} = C$. Likewise $C^o$ gives rise to a new transfinite, greater than $C$. This transfinite represents the cardinality of the class of all one-valued functions. It is also one of the $\aleph$'s, but again, which one is unknown. It is often designated by the letter $F$.[11] In general, the process of involution, when repeated, continues to generate higher transfinites.

Just as the integers served as a measuring rod for classes with the cardinality $\aleph_0$, the class of real numbers serves as a measuring rod for classes with the cardinality $C$. Indeed, there are classes of geometric elements which can be measured in no other way except by the class of real numbers.

From the geometric notion of a point, the idea is evolved that on any given line segment there are an infinite number of points. The points on a line segment are also, as mathematicians say, "everywhere dense." This means that between any two points there is an infinitude of others. The concept of two immediately adjoining points is, therefore, meaningless. This property of being "everywhere dense," constitutes one of the essential characteristics of a *continuum*. Cantor, in referring to the "cardinality of the continuum," recognized that it applies alike to the class of real numbers and the class of points on a line segment. Both are everywhere dense, and both have the same cardinality, $C$. In other words, it is possible to pair the points on a line segment with the real numbers.

Classes with the cardinality $C$ possess a property similar to classes with the cardinality $\aleph_0$: they may be thinned out without in any way affecting their cardinality. In this connection, we see in very striking fashion another illustration of the principle of transfinite arithmetic, that the whole is no greater than many of its parts. For instance, it can be proved that there are as many points on a line one foot long as there are on a line one yard long. The line segment $AB$ in the figure below is [about] three times as long as the line $A'B'$. Nevertheless, it is possible to put the class of all points on the segment $AB$ into a one-to-one correspondence with the class of points on the segment $A'B'$.

---

11. A simple geometric interpretation of the class of all one-valued functions $F$ is the following: With each point of a line segment, associate a color of the spectrum. The class $F$ is then composed of all possible combinations of colors and points that can be conceived.

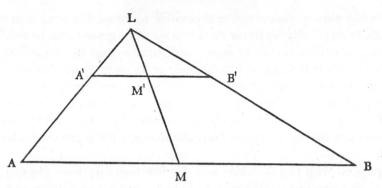

Let $L$ be the intersection of the lines $AA'$ and $BB'$. If then to any point $M$ of $AB$, there corresponds a point $M'$ of $A'B'$, which is on the line $LM$, we have established the desired correspondence between the class of points on $A'B'$ and those on $AB$. It is easy to see intuitively and to prove geometrically that this is always possible, and that, therefore, the cardinality of the two classes of points is the same. Thus, since $A'B'$ is smaller than $AB$, it may be considered a proper part of $AB$, and we have again established that an infinite class may contain as proper parts, subclasses equivalent to it.

There are more startling examples in geometry which illustrate the power of the continuum. Although the statement that a line one inch in length contains as many points as a line stretching around the equator, or as a line stretching from the earth to the most distant stars, is startling enough, it is fantastic to think that a line segment one-millionth of an inch long has as many points as there are in all three-dimensional space in the entire universe. Nevertheless, this is true. Once the principles of Cantor's theory of transfinites is understood, such statements cease to sound like the extravagances of a mathematical madman. The oddities, as Russell has said, "then become no odder than the people at the antipodes who used to be thought impossible because they would find it so inconvenient to stand on their heads." Even conceding that the treatment of the infinite is a form of mathematical madness, one is forced to admit, as does the Duke in *Measure for Measure:*

> If she be mad—as I believe no other—
> Her madness hath the oddest frame of sense,
> Such a dependency of thing on thing,
> As e'er I heard in madness.

Until now we have deliberately avoided a definition of "infinite class."

But at last our equipment makes it possible to do so. We have seen that an infinite class, whether its cardinality is $\aleph_0$, $C$, or greater, can be thinned out in a countless variety of ways, without affecting its cardinality. In short, the whole is no greater than many of its parts. Now, this property does not belong to finite classes at all; it belongs only to infinite classes. Hence, it is a unique method of determining whether a class is finite or infinite. Thus, our definition reads: *An infinite class is one which can be put into one-to-one reciprocal correspondence with a proper subset of itself.*

Equipped with this definition and the few ideas we have gleaned we may re-examine some of the paradoxes of Zeno. That of Achilles and the tortoise may be expressed as follows: Achilles and the tortoise, running the same course, must each occupy the same number of distinct positions during their race. However, if Achilles is to catch his more leisurely and determined opponent, he will have to occupy *more* positions than the tortoise, in the same elapsed period of time. Since this is manifestly impossible, you may put your money on the tortoise.

But don't be too hasty. There are better ways of saving money than merely counting change. In fact, you had best bet on Achilles after all, for he is likely to win the race. Even though we may not have realized it, we have just finished proving that he could overtake the tortoise by showing that a line a millionth of an inch long has just as many points as a line stretching from the earth to the farthest star. In other words, the points on the tiny line segment can be placed into one-to-one correspondence with the points on the great line, for there is no relation between the number of points on a line and its length. But this reveals the error in thinking that Achilles cannot catch the tortoise. The statement that Achilles must occupy as many distinct positions as the tortoise is correct. So is the statement that he must travel a greater distance than the tortoise in the same time. The only incorrect statement is the inference that since he must occupy the same number of positions as the tortoise he cannot travel further while doing so. Even though the classes of points on each line, which correspond to the several positions of both Achilles and the tortoise are equivalent, the line representing the path of Achilles is much longer than that representing the path of the tortoise. Achilles may travel much further than the tortoise without successively touching more points.

The solution of the paradox involving the arrow in flight requires a word about another type of continuum. It is convenient and certainly familiar to regard time as a continuum. The time continuum has the same properties as the space continuum: the successive instants in any elapsed portion of time, just as the points on a line, may be put into one-to-one correspondence with the class of real numbers; between any two instants of time an infinity of others may be interpolated; time also has the mathematical property mentioned before—it is everywhere dense.

Zeno's argument stated that at every instant of time the arrow was somewhere, in some place or position, and therefore, could not at any instant be in motion. Although the statement that the arrow had at every moment to be in some place is true, the conclusion that, therefore, it could not be moving is absurd. Our natural tendency to accept this absurdity as true springs from our firm conviction that motion is entirely different from rest. We are not confused about the position of a body when it is at rest—we feel there is no mystery about the state of rest. We should feel the same when we consider a body in motion.

When a body is at rest, it is in one position at one instant of time and at a later instant it is still in the same position. When a body is in motion, there is a one-to-one correspondence between every instant of time and

|  | REST |  | MOTION |
|---|---|---|---|

| On Liberty Island | 9 A.M. | In the city |
|---|---|---|

| On Liberty Island | 11 A.M. | Over the river |
|---|---|---|

| On Liberty Island | 3 P.M. | In the mountains |
|---|---|---|

*At the times shown,*
*the Statue of Liberty is at the point shown,*
*while the taxi's passengers see the different scenes shown at the right.*

every new position. To make this clear we may construct two tables: One will describe a body at rest, the other, a body in motion. The "rest" table will tell the life history and the life geography of the Statue of Liberty, while the "motion" table will describe the odyssey of an automobile.

The tables indicate that to every instant of time there corresponds a position of the Statue of Liberty and of the taxi. There is a one-to-one space-time correspondence for rest as well as for motion.

No paradox is concealed in the puzzle of the arrow when we look at our table. Indeed, it would be strange if there were gaps in the table; if it were impossible, at any instant, to determine exactly what the position of the arrow is.

Most of us would swear by the existence of motion, but we are not accustomed to think of it as something which makes an object occupy different positions at different instants of time. We are apt to think that motion endows an object with the strange property of being continually nowhere. Impeded by the limitations of our senses which prevent us from perceiving that an object in motion simply occupies one position after another and does so rather quickly, we foster an illusion about the nature of motion and weave it into a fairy tale. Mathematics helps us to analyze and clarify what we perceive, to a point where we are forced to acknowledge, if we no longer wish to be guided by fairy tales, that we live either in Mr. Russell's changeless world or in a world where motion is but a form of rest. The story of motion is the same as the story of rest. It is the same story told at a quicker tempo. The story of rest is: "It is here." The story of motion is: "It is here, it is there." Because, in this respect, it resembles Hamlet's father's ghost is no reason to doubt its existence. Most of our beliefs are chained to less substantial phantoms. Motion is perhaps not easy for our senses to grasp, but with the aid of mathematics, its essence may first be properly understood.

At the beginning of the twentieth century it was generally conceded that Cantor's work had clarified the concept of the infinite so that it could be talked of and treated like any other respectable mathematical concept. The controversy which arises wherever mathematical philosophers meet, on paper, or in person, shows that this was a mistaken view. In its simplest terms this controversy, so far as it concerns the infinite, centers about the questions: Does the infinite exist? Is there such a thing as an infinite class? Such questions can have little meaning unless the term mathematical "existence" is first explained.

In his famous "Agony in Eight Fits," Lewis Carroll hunted the snark. Nobody was acquainted with the snark or knew much about it except that it existed and that it was best to keep away from a boojum. The infinite may be a boojum, too, but its existence in any form is a matter of considerable doubt. Boojum or garden variety, the infinite certainly does not exist in the same sense that we say, "There are fish in the sea." For that matter, the statement, "There is a number called 7," refers to something which has a different existence from the fish in the sea. "Existence" in the mathematical sense is wholly different from the existence of objects in the physical world. A billiard ball may have as one of its properties, in addition to whiteness, roundness, hardness, etc., a relation of circumference to diameter involving the number $\pi$. We may agree that the billiard ball and $\pi$ both exist; we must also agree that the billiard ball and $\pi$ lead different kinds of lives.

There have been as many views on the problem of existence since Euclid and Aristotle as there have been philosophers. In modern times, the various schools of mathematical philosophy, the Logistic school, Formalists, and Intuitionists, have all disputed the somewhat less than glassy essence of mathematical being. All these disputes are beyond our ken, our scope, or our intention. A stranger company even than the tortoise, Achilles, and the arrow, have defended the existence of infinite classes—defended it in the same sense that they would defend the existence of the number 7. The Formalists, who think mathematics is a meaningless game, but play it with no less gusto, and the Logistic school, which considers that mathematics is a branch of logic—both have taken Cantor's part and have defended the alephs. The defense rests on the notion of self-consistency. "Existence" is a metaphysical expression tied up with notions of being and other bugaboos worse even than boojums. But the expression, "self-consistent proposition" sounds like the language of logic and has its odor of sanctity. A proposition which is not self-contradictory is, according to the Logistic school, a true existence statement. From this standpoint the greater part of Cantor's mathematics of the infinite is unassailable.

New problems and new paradoxes, however, have been discovered arising out of parts of Cantor's structure because of certain difficulties already inherent in classical logic. They center about the use of the word "all." The paradoxes encountered in ordinary parlance, such as "All generalities are false including this one," constitute a real problem in the foundations of logic, just as did the Epimenides paradox whence they sprang. In the Epimenides, a Cretan is made to say that all Cretans are liars, which, if true, makes the speaker a liar for telling the truth. To dispose of this type of paradox the Logistic school invented a "Theory of Types." The theory of types and the axiom of reducibility on which it is based must be accepted as axioms to avoid paradoxes of this kind. In order to accomplish this a reform of classical logic is required which has already been undertaken. Like most reforms it is not wholly satisfactory—even to the reformers—but by means of their theory of types the last vestige of inconsistency has been driven out of the house that Cantor built. The theory of transfinites may still be so much nonsense to many mathematicians, but it is certainly consistent. The serious charge Henri Poincaré expressed in his aphorism, *La logistique n'est plus stérile: elle engendre la contradiction* [Logic is sterile no longer: it is engendering contradiction], has been successfully rebutted by the logistic doctrine so far as the infinite is concerned.

To Cantor's alephs then, we may ascribe the same existence as to the number 7. An existence statement free from self-contradiction may be made relative to either. For that matter, there is no valid reason to trust in the finite any more than in the infinite. It is as permissible to discard the infinite as it is to reject the impressions of one's senses. It is neither more, nor less scientific to do so. In the final analysis, this is a matter of faith and taste, but *not* on a par with rejecting the belief in Santa Claus. Infinite classes, judged by finite standards, generate paradoxes much more absurd and a great deal less pleasing than the belief in Santa Claus; but when they are judged by the appropriate standards, they lose their odd appearance, behave as predictably as any finite integer.

At last in its proper setting, the infinite has assumed a respectable place next to the finite, just as real and just as dependable, even though wholly different in character. Whatever the infinite may be, it is no longer a purple cow.

---

*The foregoing consists of Chapters I and II*
*from Kasner and Newman's* MATHEMATICS AND THE IMAGINATION.

# Tobias Dantzig

## 1884–1956

Tobias Dantzig was born in Russia in 1884. As a young man he studied in Paris under several great French mathematicians, among them Henri Poincaré. At an early age he decided that mathematics should be acquired by study of the works of the masters. This conviction led him to pursue his studies back through the medieval ages to the Greeks and their discoveries in science.

Dantzig went to the United States in 1910. After taking his doctorate at the University of Indiana, he taught at Columbia and at the University of Maryland. At various times he served as mathematical consultant for industry. This acquaintance with industrial problems gave him a lifelong interest in the applications of mathematics. After his retirement from university teaching, he continued to write and to give courses in the history of mathematics. He died in 1956.

A lover of stories, Dantzig never forgot a tale. This vast reservoir was put to good use in the classroom and in his writings. He was intensely interested in mathematicians as people, and his writings are spiced with colorful anecdotes about famous scientific personalities. Among his works are *The Story of Geometry, Aspects of Science, The Bequest of the Greeks,* and *Number: The Language of Science.*

The last-named book was praised by Albert Einstein as the best book on the evolution of mathematics that had come into his hands. This work broke a new path. It was the first attempt to bring mathematics to the public in a manner suited to the mathematically untrained. The following two selections are taken from this pioneering effort. They both deal with the evolution of the number concept.

*Fingerprints* shows man at a very early stage in his attempt to gain understanding and power over the world. Whatever is counted is somehow captured, as in a net. When primitive man fashioned this net, its design was almost inevitably determined by the fact that he had ten fingers. Before he had words or written symbols for numbers, he possessed on his own hands the tools for counting. Through the ages the net has become larger and more intricate. It has been cast beyond the world into the universe. But it still carries the imprint of man's physical make-up. We count by tens.

"Has the concept [of number] been born of experience, or has experience merely served to render explicit what was already latent in the primitive mind?" Dantzig asks a question on which there is a long history of speculation. Various and conflicting answers are found in the writings of Plato, Aristotle, Kant, Russell, and James.

*The Empty Column* is the story of how mathematics was stymied for centuries for want of a symbol—our modern zero. Everyday calculations remained in the hands of the experts long after commerce and industry cried out for an arithmetic that could be understood by everyone.

Why did this notation come so late? Alfred North Whitehead says: "The point about zero is that we do not need to use it in the operations of daily life. No one goes out to buy zero fish. It is in a way the most civilized of all the cardinals, and its use is only forced on us by the needs of cultivated modes of thought."

To this story of the growth of our modern number system, Dantzig brings a lively sense of the human qualities involved. "It is not a story of brilliant achievement, heroic deeds, or noble sacrifice. It is a story of blind stumbling and chance discovery, of groping in the dark and refusing to admit the light. It is a story replete with obscurantism and prejudice, of sound judgment often eclipsed by loyalty to tradition, and of reason long held subservient to custom. In short, it is a human story."

# *Fingerprints*

M

an, even in the lower stages of development, possesses a faculty which, for want of a better name, I shall call *number sense*. This faculty permits him to recognize that something has changed in a small collection when, without his direct knowledge, an object has been removed from or added to the collection.

Number sense should not be confused with counting, which is probably of a much later vintage, and involves, as we shall see, a rather intricate mental process. Counting, so far as we know, is an attribute exclusively human, whereas some brute species seem to possess a rudimentary number sense akin to our own. At least, such is the opinion of competent observers of animal behavior, and the theory is supported by a weighty mass of evidence.

Many birds, for instance, possess such a number sense. If a nest contains four eggs one can safely be taken, but when two are removed the bird generally deserts. In some unaccountable way the bird can distinguish two from three. But this faculty is by no means confined to birds. In fact the most striking instance we know is that of the insect called the "solitary wasp." The mother wasp lays her eggs in individual cells and provides each egg with a number of live caterpillars on which the young feed when hatched. Now, the number of victims is remarkably constant for a given species of wasp: some species provide 5, others 12, others again as high as 24 caterpillars per cell. But most remarkable is the case of the *Genus Eumenus*, a variety in which the male is much smaller than the female. In some mysterious way the mother knows whether the egg will produce a male or a female grub and apportions the quantity of food accordingly; she does not change the species or size of the prey, but if the egg is male she supplies it with five victims, if female with ten.

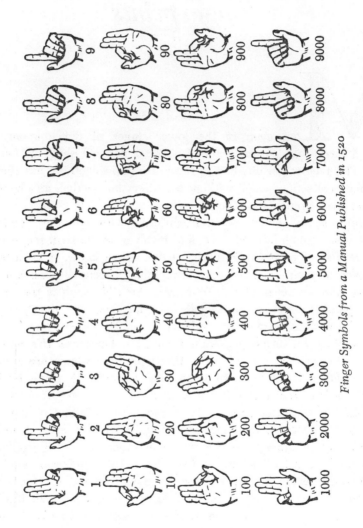

*Finger Symbols from a Manual Published in 1520*

The regularity in the action of the wasp and the fact that this action is connected with a fundamental function in the life of the insect make this last case less convincing than the one which follows. Here the action of the bird seems to border on the conscious:

A squire was determined to shoot a crow which made its nest in the watchtower of his estate. Repeatedly he had tried to surprise the bird, but in vain: at the approach of man the crow would leave its nest. From a distant tree it would watchfully wait until the man had left the tower and then return to its nest. One day the squire hit upon a ruse: two men entered the tower, one remained within, the other came out and went on. But the bird was not deceived: it kept away until the man within came out. The experiment was repeated on the succeeding days with two, three, then four men, yet without success. Finally, five men were sent: as before, all entered the tower, and one remained while the other four came out and went away. Here the crow lost count. Unable to distinguish between four and five it promptly returned to its nest.

2. Two arguments may be raised against such evidence. The first is that the species possessing such a number sense are exceedingly few, that no such faculty has been found among mammals, and that even the monkeys seem to lack it. The second argument is that in all known cases the number sense of animals is so limited in scope as to be ignored.

Now the first point is well taken. It is indeed a remarkable fact that the faculty of perceiving number, in one form or another, seems to be confined to some insects and birds and to men. Observation and experiments on dogs, horses and other domestic animals have failed to reveal any number sense.

As to the second argument, it is of little value, because the scope of the human number sense is also quite limited. In every practical case where civilized man is called upon to discern number, he is consciously or unconsciously aiding his direct number sense with such artifices as symmetric pattern reading, mental grouping or counting. *Counting* especially has become such an integral part of our mental equipment that psychological tests on our number perception are fraught with great difficulties. Nevertheless some progress has been made; carefully conducted experiments lead to the inevitable conclusion that the direct *visual* number sense of the average civilized man rarely extends beyond four, and that the *tactile* sense is still more limited in scope.

Anthropological studies on primitive peoples corroborate these results to a remarkable degree. They reveal that those savages *who have not reached the stage of finger counting* are almost completely deprived of all perception of number. Such is the case among numerous tribes in Australia, the South Sea Islands, South America, and Africa. Curr, who has made an extensive study of primitive Australia, holds that but few of the natives are able to discern four, and that no Australian in his wild state can perceive seven. The Bushmen of South Africa have no number words beyond *one, two* and *many,* and these words are so inarticulate that it may be doubted whether the natives attach a clear meaning to them.

We have no reasons to believe and many reasons to doubt that our own remote ancestors were better equipped, since practically all European languages bear traces of such early limitations. The English *thrice,* just like the Latin *ter,* has the double meaning: three times, and many. There is a plausible connection between the Latin *tres,* three, and *trans,* beyond; the same can be said regarding the French *très,* very, and *trois,* three.

The genesis of number is hidden behind the impenetrable veil of countless prehistoric ages. Has the concept been born of experience, or has experience merely served to render explicit what was already latent in the primitive mind? Here is a fascinating subject for metaphysical speculation, but for this very reason beyond the scope of this study.

If we are to judge of the development of our own remote ancestors by the mental state of contemporary tribes we cannot escape the conclusion that the beginnings were extremely modest. A rudimentary number sense, not greater in scope than that possessed by birds, was the nucleus from which the number concept grew. And there is little doubt that, left to this direct number perception, man would have advanced no further in the art of reckoning than the birds did. But through a series of remarkable circumstances man has learned to aid his exceedingly limited perception of number by an artifice which was destined to exert a tremendous influence on his future life. This artifice is counting, and it is to *counting* that we owe the extraordinary progress which we have made in expressing our universe in terms of number.

3. There are primitive languages which have words for every color of the rainbow but have no word for color; there are others which have all number words but no word for number. The same is true of other conceptions. The English language is very rich in native expressions for particular types of collections: *flock, herd, set, lot* and *bunch* apply to

special cases; yet the words *collection* and *aggregate* are of foreign extraction.

The concrete preceded the abstract. "It must have required many ages to discover," says Bertrand Russell, "that a brace of pheasants and a couple of days were both instances of the number two." To this day we have quite a few ways of expressing the idea *two:* pair, couple, set, team, twin, brace, etc., etc.

A striking example of this extreme concreteness of the early number concept is the Thimshian language of a British Columbia tribe. There we find seven distinct sets of number words: one for flat objects and animals; one for round objects and time; one for counting men; one for long objects and trees; one for canoes; one for measures; one for counting when no definite object is referred to. The last is probably a later development; the others must be relics of the earliest days when the tribesmen had not yet learned to count.

It is counting that consolidated the concrete and therefore hetero-geneous notion of plurality, so characteristic of primitive man, into the *homogeneous abstract number concept,* which made mathematics pos-sible.

4. Yet, strange though it may seem, it is possible to arrive at a logical, clear-cut number concept without bringing in the artifices of counting.

We enter a hall. Before us are two collections: the seats of the auditorium, and the audience. *Without counting* we can ascertain whether the two collections are equal and, if not equal, which is the greater. For if every seat is taken and no man is standing, *we know without counting* that the two collections are equal. If every seat is taken and some in the audience are standing, *we know without counting* that there are more people than seats.

We derive this knowledge through a process which dominates all mathematics and which has received the name of *one-to-one correspond-ence.* It consists in assigning to every object of one collection an object of the other, the process being continued until one of the collections, or both, are exhausted.

The number technique of many primitive peoples is confined to just such a matching or tallying. They keep the record of their herds and armies by means of notches cut in a tree or pebbles gathered in a pile. That our own ancestors were adept in such methods is evidenced by the etymology of the words *tally* and *calculate,* of which the first comes from the Latin *talea,* cutting, and the second from the Latin *calculus,* pebble.

It would seem at first that the process of correspondence gives only a means for comparing two collections, but is incapable of creating number in the absolute sense of the word. Yet the transition from relative number to absolute is not difficult. It is necessary only to create *model collections,* each typifying a possible collection. Estimating any given collection is then reduced to the selection among the available models of one which can be matched with the given collection member by member.

Primitive man finds such models in his immediate environment: the wings of a bird may symbolize the number two, clover-leaves three, the legs of an animal four, the fingers on his own hand five. Evidence of this origin of number words can be found in many a primitive language. Of course, once the number word has been created and adopted, it becomes as good a model as the object it originally represented. The necessity of discriminating between the name of the borrowed object and the number symbol itself would naturally tend to bring about a change in sound, until in the course of time the very connection between the two is lost to memory. As man learns to rely more and more on his language, the sounds supersede the images for which they stood, and the originally concrete models take the abstract form of number words. Memory and habit lend concreteness to these abstract forms, and so mere words become measures of plurality.

5. The concept I just described is called *cardinal* number. The cardinal number rests on the principle of correspondence: it implies *no counting.* To create a counting process it is not enough to have a motley array of models, comprehensive though this latter may be. We must devise a number *system:* our set of models must be arranged in an ordered sequence, a sequence which progresses in the sense of growing magnitude, the *natural sequence:* one, two, three. . . . Once this system is created, *counting a collection* means assigning to every member a term in the natural sequence in *ordered succession* until the collection is exhausted. The term of the natural sequence assigned to the *last* member of the collection is called the *ordinal number* of the collection.

The ordinal system may take the concrete form of a rosary, but this, of course, is not essential. The *ordinal* system acquires existence when the first few number words have been committed to memory in their *ordered succession,* and a phonetic scheme has been devised to pass from any larger number to its *successor.*

We have learned to pass with such facility from cardinal to ordinal number that the two aspects appear to us as one. To determine the plurality of a collection, *i.e.*, its cardinal number, we do not bother any more to find a model collection with which we can match it—we *count* it. And to the fact that we have learned to identify the two aspects of number is due our progress in mathematics. For whereas in practice we are really interested in the cardinal number, this latter is incapable of creating an arithmetic. The operations of arithmetic are based on the tacit assumption that *we can always pass from any number to its successor*, and this is the essence of the ordinal concept.

And so matching by itself is incapable of creating an art of reckoning. Without our ability to arrange things in ordered succession little progress could have been made. Correspondence and succession, the two principles which permeate all mathematics—nay, all realms of exact thought—are woven into the very fabric of our number system.

6. It is natural to inquire at this point whether this subtle distinction between cardinal and ordinal number had any part in the early history of the number concept. One is tempted to surmise that the cardinal number, based on matching only, preceded the ordinal number, which requires both matching and ordering. Yet the most careful investigations into primitive culture and philology fail to reveal any such precedence. Wherever any number technique exists at all, both aspects of number are found.

But, also, wherever a counting technique, worthy of the name, exists at all, *finger counting* has been found to either precede it or accompany it. And in his fingers man possesses a device which permits him to pass imperceptibly from cardinal to ordinal number. Should he want to indicate that a certain collection contains four objects he will raise or turn down four fingers *simultaneously;* should he want to count the same collection he will raise or turn down these fingers *in succession.* In the first case he is using his fingers as a cardinal model, in the second as an ordinal system. Unmistakable traces of this origin of counting are found in practically every primitive language. In most of these tongues the number "five" is expressed by "hand," the number "ten" by "two hands," or sometimes by "man." Furthermore, in many primitive languages the number words up to four are identical with the names given to the four fingers.

The more civilized languages underwent a process of attrition which obliterated the original meaning of the words. Yet here too "fingerprints" are not lacking. Compare the Sanskrit *panca*, five, with the related

Persian *pentcha*, hand; the Russian *piat*, five, with *piast*, the outstretched hand.

It is to his articulate ten fingers that man owes his success in calculation. It is these fingers which have taught him to count and thus extend the scope of number indefinitely. Without this device the number technique of man could not have advanced far beyond the rudimentary number sense. And it is reasonable to conjecture that without our fingers the development of number, and consequently that of the exact sciences, to which we owe our material and intellectual progress, would have been hopelessly dwarfed.

7. And yet, except that our children still learn to count on their fingers and that we ourselves sometimes resort to it as a gesture of emphasis, finger counting is a lost art among modern civilized people. The advent of writing, simplified numeration, and universal schooling have rendered the art obsolete and superfluous. Under the circumstances it is only natural for us to underestimate the role that finger counting has played in the history of reckoning. Only a few hundred years ago finger counting was such a widespread custom in Western Europe that no manual of arithmetic was complete unless it gave full instructions in the method. (See figure on page 166.)

The art of using his fingers in counting and in performing the simple operations of arithmetic was then one of the accomplishments of an educated man. The greatest ingenuity was displayed in devising rules for adding and multiplying numbers on one's fingers. Thus, to this day, the peasant of central France (Auvergne) uses a curious method for multiplying numbers above 5. If he wishes to multiply $9 \times 8$, he bends down 4 fingers on his left hand (4 being the excess of 9 over 5), and 3 fingers on his right hand ($8 - 5 = 3$). Then the number of the bent-down fingers gives him the tens of the result ($4 + 3 = 7$), while the product of the unbent fingers gives him the units ($1 \times 2 = 2$).

Artifices of the same nature have been observed in widely separated places, such as Bessarabia, Serbia and Syria. Their striking similarity and the fact that these countries were all at one time parts of the great Roman Empire lead one to suspect the Roman origin of these devices. Yet, it may be maintained with equal plausibility that these methods evolved independently, similar conditions bringing about similar results.

Even today the greater portion of humanity is counting on fingers: to primitive man, we must remember, this is the only means of performing the simple calculations of his daily life.

8. How old is our number language? It is impossible to indicate the exact period in which number words originated, yet there is unmistakable evidence that it preceded written history by many thousands of years. One fact we have mentioned already: all traces of the original meaning of the number words in European languages, with the possible exception of *five*, are lost. And this is the more remarkable, since, as a rule, number words possess an extraordinary stability. While time has wrought radical changes in all other aspects we find that the number vocabulary has been practically unaffected. In fact this stability is utilized by philologists to trace kinships between apparently remote language groups. The reader is invited to examine the table at the end of the chapter where the number words of the standard Indo-European languages are compared.

Why is it then that in spite of this stability no trace of the original meaning is found? A plausible conjecture is that while number words have remained unchanged since the days when they originated, the names of the concrete objects from which the number words were borrowed have undergone a complete metamorphosis.

9. As to the structure of the number language, philological researches disclose an almost universal uniformity. Everywhere the ten fingers of man have left their permanent imprint.

Indeed, there is no mistaking the influence of our ten fingers on the "selection" of the base of our number system. In all Indo-European languages, as well as Semitic, Mongolian, and most primitive languages, the base of numeration is ten, *i.e.*, there are independent number words up to ten, beyond which some compounding principle is used until 100 is reached. All these languages have independent words for 100 and 1000, and some languages for even higher decimal units. There are apparent exceptions, such as the English *eleven* and *twelve*, or the German *elf* and *zwölf*, but these have been traced to *ein-lif* and *zwo-lif; lif* being old German for *ten*.

It is true that in addition to the decimal system, two other bases are reasonably widespread, but their character confirms to a remarkable degree the *anthropomorphic* nature of our counting scheme. These two other systems are the quinary, base 5, and the vigesimal, base 20.

In the *quinary* system there are independent number words up to *five*, and the compounding begins thereafter. (See table on pages 176 and 177.) It evidently originated among people who had the habit of counting on one hand. But why should man confine himself to one hand? A plausible explanation is that primitive man rarely goes about unarmed. If he wants to count, he tucks his weapon under his arm, the left arm as a rule, and counts on his left hand, using his right hand as check-off. This may explain why the left hand is almost universally used by right-handed people for counting.

Many languages still bear the traces of a quinary system, and it is reasonable to believe that some decimal systems passed through the quinary stage. Some philologists claim that even the Indo-European number languages are of a quinary origin. They point to the Greek word *pempazein,* to count by fives, and also to the unquestionably quinary character of the Roman numerals. However, there is no other evidence of this sort, and it is much more probable that our group of languages passed through a preliminary *vigesimal stage.*

This latter probably originated among the primitive tribes who counted on their toes as well as on their fingers. A most striking example of such a system is that used by the Maya Indians of Central America. Of the same general character was the system of the ancient Aztecs. The day of the Aztecs was divided into 20 hours; a division of the army contained 8000 soldiers ($8000 = 20 \times 20 \times 20$).

While pure vigesimal systems are rare, there are numerous languages where the decimal and the vigesimal systems have merged. We have the English *score, twoscore,* and *threescore;* the French *vingt* (20) and *quatre-vingt* ($4 \times 20$). The old French used this form still more frequently; a hospital in Paris originally built for 300 blind veterans bears the quaint name of *Quinze-Vingt* (Fifteenscore); the name *Onze-Vingt* (Elevenscore) was given to a corps of police sergeants comprising 220 men.

10. There exists among the most primitive tribes of Australia and Africa a system of numeration which has neither 5, 10, nor 20 for base. It is a *binary* system, *i.e.,* of base two. These savages have not yet reached finger counting. They have independent numbers for one and two, and composite numbers up to six. Beyond six everything is denoted by "heap."

Curr, whom we have already quoted in connection with the Australian tribes, claims that most of these count by pairs. So strong, indeed, is this habit of the native that he will rarely notice that two pins have been removed from a row of seven; he will, however, become immediately aware if one pin is missing. His sense of *parity* is stronger than his number sense.

Curiously enough, this most primitive of bases had an eminent advocate in relatively recent times in no less a person than Leibnitz. A binary numeration requires but two symbols, 0 and 1, by means of which all other numbers are expressed, as shown in the following table:

| Decimal | 1 | 2 | 3 | 4 | 5 | 6 | 7 | 8 |
|---|---|---|---|---|---|---|---|---|
| Binary | 1 | 10 | 11 | 100 | 101 | 110 | 111 | 1000 |
| Decimal | 9 | 10 | 11 | 12 | 13 | 14 | 15 | 16 |
| Binary | 1001 | 1010 | 1011 | 1100 | 1101 | 1110 | 1111 | 10000 |

The advantages of the *base two* are economy of symbols and tremendous simplicity in operations. It must be remembered that every system requires that tables of addition and multiplication be committed to memory. For the binary system these reduce to $1 + 1 = 10$ and $1 \times 1 = 1$; whereas for the decimal, each table has 100 entries. Yet this advantage is more than offset by lack of compactness: thus the decimal number $4096 = 2^{12}$ would be expressed in the binary system by 1,000,000,000,000.

It is the mystic elegance of the binary system that made Leibnitz exclaim: *Omnibus ex nihil ducendis sufficit unum.* (One suffices to derive all out of nothing.) Says Laplace:

> Leibnitz saw in his binary arithmetic the image of Creation. . . . He imagined that Unity represented God, and Zero the void; that the Supreme Being drew all beings from the void, just as unity and zero express all numbers in his system of numeration. This conception was so pleasing to Leibnitz that he communicated it to the Jesuit, Grimaldi, president of the Chinese tribunal for mathematics, in the hope that this emblem of creation would convert the Emperor of China, who was very fond of the sciences. I mention this merely to show how the prejudices of childhood may cloud the vision even of the greatest men!

11. It is interesting to speculate what turn the history of culture would have taken if instead of flexible fingers man had had just two "inarticulate" stumps. If any system of numeration could at all have developed under such circumstances, it would have probably been of the binary type.

That mankind adopted the decimal system is a *physiological accident*. Those who see the hand of Providence in everything will have to admit that Providence is a poor mathematician. For outside its physiological merit the decimal base has little to commend itself. Almost any other base, with the possible exception of *nine*, would have done as well and probably better.

Indeed, if the choice of a base were left to a group of experts, we should probably witness a conflict between the practical man, who would insist on a base with the greatest number of divisors, such as *twelve,* and the mathematician, who would want a prime number, such as *seven* or *eleven,* for a base. As a matter of fact, late in the eighteenth century the great naturalist Buffon proposed that the duodecimal system (base 12) be universally adopted. He pointed to the fact that 12 has 4 divisors, while 10 has only 2, and maintained that throughout the ages this inadequacy of our decimal system had been so keenly felt that, in spite of 10 being the universal base, most measures had 12 secondary units.

On the other hand the great mathematician Lagrange claimed that a prime base is far more advantageous. He pointed to the fact that with a prime base every systematic fraction would be irreducible and would therefore represent the number in a unique way. In our present numeration, for instance, the decimal fraction .36 stands really for many fractions: $^{36}\!/_{100}$, $^{18}\!/_{50}$, and $^9\!/_{25}$. . . . Such an ambiguity would be considerably lessened if a prime base, such as eleven, were adopted.

But whether the enlightened group to whom we would entrust the selection of the base decided on a prime or a composite base, we may rest assured that the number *ten* would not even be considered, for it is neither prime nor has it a sufficient number of divisors.

In our own age, when calculating devices have largely supplanted mental arithmetic, nobody would take either proposal seriously. The advantages gained are so slight, and the tradition of counting by tens so firm, that the challenge seems ridiculous.

From the standpoint of the history of culture a change of base, even if practicable, would be highly undesirable. As long as man counts by tens, his ten fingers will remind him of the human origin of this most important phase of his mental life. So may the decimal system stand as a living monument to the proposition: *Man is the measure of all things.*

### Number Words of Some Indo-European Languages Showing the Extraordinary Stability of Number Words

| | Sanskrit | Ancient Greek | Latin | German | English | French | Russian |
|---|---|---|---|---|---|---|---|
| 1 | eka | en | unus | eins | one | un | odyn |
| 2 | dva | duo | duo | zwei | two | deux | dva |
| 3 | tri | tri | tres | drei | three | trois | tri |
| 4 | catur | tetra | quatuor | vier | four | quatre | chetyre |
| 5 | panca | pente | quinque | fünf | five | cinq | piat |
| 6 | sas | hex | sex | sechs | six | six | shest |
| 7 | sapta | hepta | septem | sieben | seven | sept | sem |
| 8 | asta | octo | octo | acht | eight | huit | vosem |
| 9 | nava | ennea | novem | neun | nine | neuf | deviat |
| 10 | daca | deca | decem | zehn | ten | dix | desiat |
| 100 | cata | ecaton | centum | hundert | hundred | cent | sto |
| 1000 | sehastre | xilia | mille | tausend | thousand | mille | tysiaca |

## A Typical Quinary System: The Api Language of the New Hebrides

| | Word | Meaning |
|---|---|---|
| 1 | tai | |
| 2 | lua | |
| 3 | tolu | |
| 4 | vari | |
| 5 | luna | hand |
| 6 | otai | other one |
| 7 | olua | " two |
| 8 | otolu | " three |
| 9 | ovair | " four |
| 10 | lua luna | two hands |

## A Typical Vigesimal System: The Maya Language of Central America

| 1 | hun | 1 |
|---|---|---|
| 20 | kal | 20 |
| $20^2$ | bak | 400 |
| $20^3$ | pic | 8000 |
| $20^4$ | calab | 160,000 |
| $20^5$ | kinchel | 3,200,000 |
| $20^6$ | alce | 64,000,000 |

## A Typical Binary System: A Western Tribe of Torres Straits

| 1 | urapun |
|---|---|
| 2 | okosa |
| 3 | okosa-urapun |
| 4 | okosa-okosa |
| 5 | okosa-okosa-urapun |
| 6 | okosa-okosa-okosa |

# The Empty Column

**1.**

As I am writing these lines there rings in my ears the old refrain:

>Reading, 'Riting, 'Rithmetic,
>Taught to the tune of a hickory-stick!

In this chapter I propose to tell the story of one of three R's, the one, which, though oldest, came hardest to mankind.

It is not a story of brilliant achievement, heroic deeds, or noble sacrifice. It is a story of blind stumbling and chance discovery, of groping in the dark and refusing to admit the light. It is a story replete with obscurantism and prejudice, of sound judgment often eclipsed by loyalty to tradition, and of reason long held subservient to custom. In short, it is a human story.

**2.** Written numeration is probably as old as private property. There is little doubt that it originated in man's desire to keep a record of his flocks and other goods. Notches on a stick or tree, scratches on stones and rocks, marks in clay—these are the earliest forms of this endeavor to record numbers by written symbols. Archaeological researches trace such records to times immemorial, as they are found in the caves of prehistoric man in Europe, Africa and Asia. Numeration is at least as old as written language, and there is evidence that it preceded it. Perhaps, even, the recording of numbers had suggested the recording of sounds.

The oldest records indicating the systematic use of written numerals are those of the ancient Sumerians and Egyptians. They are all traced back to about the same epoch, around 3500 B.C. When we examine them we are struck with the great similarity in the principles used. There is, of course, the possibility that there was communication between these peoples in spite of the distances that separated them. However, it is more likely that they developed their numerations along the lines of least resistance, *i.e.*, that their numerations were but an outgrowth of the natural process of tallying. (See figure, page 180.)

Indeed, whether it be the cuneiform numerals of the ancient Babylonians, the hieroglyphics of the Egyptian papyri, or the queer figures of the early Chinese records, we find everywhere a distinctly *cardinal* principle. Each numeral up to nine is merely a collection of strokes. The same principle is used beyond nine, units of a higher class, such as tens, hundreds, etc., being represented by special symbols.

3. The English tally stick, of obscure but probably very ancient origin, also bears this unquestionably cardinal character. A schematic picture of the tally is shown in the accompanying figure. The small notches each represent a pound sterling, the larger ones 10 pounds, 100 pounds, etc.

It is curious that the English tally persisted for many centuries after the introduction of modern numeration made its use ridiculously obsolete. In fact it was responsible for an important episode in the history of Parliament. Charles Dickens described this episode with inimitable sarcasm in an address on administrative reform, which he delivered a few years after the incident occurred.

> Ages ago a savage mode of keeping accounts on notched sticks was introduced into the Court of Exchequer and the accounts were kept much as Robinson Crusoe kept his calendar on the desert island. A multitude of accountants, bookkeepers, and actuaries were born and died. . . . Still official routine inclined to those notched sticks as if they were pillars of the Constitution, and still the Exchequer accounts continued to be kept on certain splints of elm-wood called *tallies*. In the reign of George III an inquiry was made by some revolutionary spirit whether, pens, ink and paper, slates and pencils being in existence, this obstinate adherence to an obsolete custom ought to be continued, and whether a change ought not be effected. All the red tape in the country grew redder at the bare mention of this bold and original conception, and it took until 1826 to get these sticks abolished. In 1834 it was found that there was a considerable accumulation of them; and the question then arose, what was to be done with such worn-out, worm-eaten, rotten old bits of wood? The sticks were housed in Westminster, and it would naturally occur to any intelligent person that nothing could be easier than to allow them to be carried away for firewood by the miserable people who lived in that neighbourhood. However, they never had been useful, and official routine required that they should never be, and so the order went out that they were to be privately and confidentially burned. It came to pass that

| | 1 | 2 | 3 | 4 | 5 | 9 | 10 | 12 | 23 | 60 | 100 | 1000 | 10000 |
|---|---|---|---|---|---|---|---|---|---|---|---|---|---|
| SUMERIAN 3400 B.C. | 𒁹 | 𒐀 | 𒐁 | 𒐂 | 𒐅 | 𒐉 | 𒌋 | 𒌋𒁹𒁹 | 𒌋𒌋𒐂 | 𒐋 | 𒐏 | 𒌋𒐏 | 𒐏𒐏 |
| HIEROGLYPHICS 3400 B.C. | ∧ | ∧∧ | ∧∧∧ | ∧∧∧∧ | ∧∧∧∧∧ | ∧∧∧∧∧∧∧∧∧ | ∩ | ∩∧∧ | ∩∩∧∧∧ | ∩∩∩∩∩∩ | 𓍢 | 𓆼 | 𓂭 |
| GREEK | α' | β' | γ' | δ' | ε' | θ' | ι' | ιβ' | κγ' | ξ' | ρ' | ,α | ,ι |

ANCIENT NUMERATIONS

SCHEMATIC DRAWING OF ENGLISH TALLY STICK

they were burned in a stove in the House of Lords. The stove, over-gorged with these preposterous sticks, set fire to the panelling; the panelling set fire to the House of Commons; the two houses were reduced to ashes; architects were called in to build others; and we are now in the second million of the cost thereof.

4. As opposed to this purely cardinal character of the earliest records there is the ordinal numeration, in which the numbers are represented by the letters of an alphabet in their spoken succession.

The earliest evidence of this principle is that of the Phoenician numeration. It probably arose from the urge for compactness brought about by the complexities of a growing commerce. The Phoenician origin of both the Hebrew and the Greek numeration is unquestionable: the Phoenician system was adopted bodily, together with the alphabet, and even the sounds of the letters were retained.

On the other hand, the Roman numeration, which has survived to this day, shows a marked return to the earlier cardinal methods. Yet Greek influence is shown in the literal symbols adopted for certain units, such as X for ten, C for hundred, M for thousand. But the substitution of letters for the more picturesque symbols of the Chaldeans or the Egyptians does not constitute a departure from principle.

5. The evolution of the numerations of antiquity found its final expression in the ordinal system of the Greeks and the cardinal system of Rome. Which of the two was superior? The question would have significance if the only object of a numeration were a compact recording of quantity. But this is not the main issue. A far more important question is: how well is the system adapted to arithmetical operations, and what ease does it lend to calculations?

In this respect there is hardly any choice between the two methods: neither was capable of creating an arithmetic which could be used by a man of average intelligence. This is why, from the beginning of history until the advent of our modern *positional* numeration, so little progress was made in the art of reckoning.

Not that there were no attempts to devise rules for operating on these numerals. How difficult these rules were can be gleaned from the great awe in which all reckoning was held in these days. A man skilled in the art was regarded as endowed with almost supernatural powers. This may explain why arithmetic from time immemorial was so assiduously cultivated by the priesthood. . . . Not only was this [relation of early mathematics to religious rites and mysteries] true of the ancient Orient, where science was built around religion, but even the enlightened Greeks never completely freed themselves from this mysticism of number and form.

And to a certain extent this awe persists to this day. The average man identifies mathematical ability with quickness in figures. "So you are a mathematician? Why, then you have no trouble with your income-tax return!" What mathematician has not at least once in his career been so addressed? There is, perhaps, unconscious irony in these words, for are not most professional mathematicians spared all trouble incident to excessive income?

6. There is a story of a German merchant of the fifteenth century, which I have not succeeded in authenticating, but it is so characteristic of the situation then existing that I cannot resist the temptation of telling it. It appears that the merchant had a son to whom he desired to give an advanced commercial education. He appealed to a prominent professor of a university for advice as to where he should send his son. The reply was that if the mathematical curriculum of the young man was to be confined to adding and subtracting, he perhaps could obtain the instruction in a German university; but the art of multiplying and dividing, he continued, had been greatly developed in Italy, which in his opinion was the only country where such advanced instruction could be obtained.

As a matter of fact, multiplication and division as practiced in those days had little in common with the modern operations bearing the same names. Multiplication, for instance, was a succession of *duplations*, which was the name given to the doubling of a number. In the same way division was reduced to *mediation, i.e.,* "halving" a number. A clearer insight into the status of reckoning in the Middle Ages can be obtained from an example. Using modern notations:

$$
\begin{array}{ll}
\text{Today} & \text{Thirteenth century} \\
46 & 46 \times 2 = 92 \\
13 & 46 \times 4 = 92 \times 2 = 184 \\
\hline
138 & 46 \times 8 = 184 \times 2 = 368 \\
46 & 368 + 184 + 46 = 598 \\
\hline
598 &
\end{array}
$$

We begin to understand why humanity so obstinately clung to such devices as the abacus or even the tally. Computations which a child can now perform required then the services of a specialist, and what is now only a matter of a few minutes meant in the twelfth century days of elaborate work.

The greatly increased facility with which the average man today manipulates number has been often taken as proof of the growth of the human intellect. The truth of the matter is that the difficulties then experienced were inherent in the numeration in use, a numeration not susceptible to simple, clear-cut rules. The discovery of the modern positional numeration did away with these obstacles and made arithmetic accessible even to the dullest mind.

7. The growing complexities of life, industry and commerce, of landed property and slave-holding, of taxation and military organization—all called for calculations more or less intricate, but beyond the scope of the finger technique. The rigid, unwieldy numeration was incapable of meeting the demand. How did man, in the five thousand years of his civilized existence which preceded modern numeration, counter these difficulties?

The answer is that from the very outset he had to resort to mechanical devices which vary in form with place and age but are all the same in principle. The scheme can be typified by the curious method of counting an army which has been found in Madagascar. The soldiers are made to file through a narrow passage, and one pebble is dropped for each. When 10 pebbles are counted, a pebble is cast into another pile representing tens, and the counting continues. When 10 pebbles are amassed in the second pile, a pebble is cast into a third pile representing hundreds, and so on until all the soldiers have been accounted for.

From this there is but one step to the *counting board* or *abacus* which in one form or another has been found in practically every country where a counting technique exists. The abacus in its general form consists of a flat board divided into a series of parallel columns, each column representing a distinct decimal class, such as units, tens, hundreds, etc. The board is provided with a set of counters which are used to indicate the number of units in each class. For instance, to represent 574 on the abacus, 4 counters are put on the last column, 7 counters on the next to the last and 5 on the third to the last column. (See figure on page 184.)

The many counting boards known differ merely in the construction of the columns and in the type of counters used. The Greek and Roman types had loose counters, while the Chinese Suan-Pan of today has perforated balls sliding on slender bamboo rods. The Russian Szczety, like the Chinese variety, consists of a wooden frame on which is mounted a

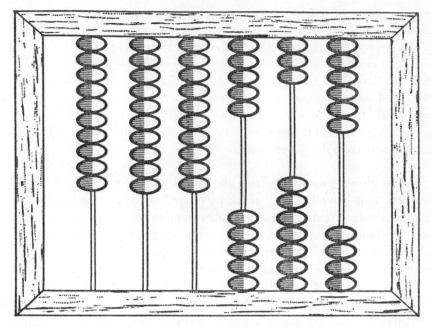

*A Schematic Drawing of a Counting Board*

series of wire rods with sliding buttons for counters. Finally, it is more than probable that the ancient Hindu dust board was also an abacus in principle, the part of the counters here being played by erasable marks written on sand.

The origin of the word abacus is not certain. Some trace it to the Semitic *abac*, dust; others believe that it came from the Greek *abax*, slab. The instrument was widely used in Greece, and we find references to it in Herodotus and Polybius. The latter, commenting on the court of Philip II of Macedonia in his *Historia*, makes this suggestive statement:

> Like counters on the abacus which at the pleasure of the calculator may at one moment be worth a talent and the next moment a chalcus, so are the courtiers at their King's nod at one moment at the height of prosperity and at the next objects of human pity.

To this day the counting board is in daily use in the rural districts of Russia and throughout China, where it persists in open competition with modern calculating devices. But in Western Europe and America the abacus survived as a mere curiosity which few people have seen except in pictures. Few realize how extensively the abacus was used in their own countries only a few hundred years ago, where after a fashion it managed to meet the difficulties which were beyond the power of a clumsy numeration.

8. One who reflects upon the history of reckoning up to the invention of the principle of position is struck by the paucity of achievement. This long period of nearly five thousand years saw the fall and rise of many a civilization, each leaving behind it a heritage of literature, art, philosophy and religion. But what was the net achievement in the field of reckoning, the earliest art practiced by man? An inflexible numeration so crude as to make progress well-nigh impossible, and a calculating device so limited in scope that even elementary calculations called for the services of an expert. And what is more, man used these devices for thousands of years without making a single worthwhile improvement in the instrument, without contributing a single important idea to the system!

This criticism may sound severe; after all it is not fair to judge the achievements of a remote age by the standards of our own time of accelerated progress and feverish activity. Yet, even when compared with the slow growth of ideas during the Dark Ages, the history of reckoning presents a peculiar picture of desolate stagnation.

When viewed in this light, the achievement of the unknown Hindu who sometime in the first centuries of our era discovered the principle of position assumes the proportions of a world event. Not only did this principle constitute a radical departure in method, but we know now that without it no progress in arithmetic was possible. And yet the principle is so simple that today the dullest schoolboy has no difficulty in grasping it. In a measure, it is suggested by the very structure of our number language. Indeed, it would appear that the first attempt to translate the action of the counting board into the language of numerals ought to have resulted in the discovery of the principle of position.

Particularly puzzling to us is the fact that the great mathematicians of classical Greece did not stumble on it. Is it that the Greeks had such a marked contempt for applied science, leaving even the instruction of their children to the slaves? But if so, how is it that the nation which gave us geometry and carried this science so far did not create even a rudimentary algebra? Is it not equally strange that algebra, that cornerstone of modern mathematics, also originated in India and at about the same time when positional numeration did?

9. A close examination of the anatomy of our modern numeration may shed light on these questions. The principle of position consists in giving

the numeral a value which depends not only on the member of the natural sequence it represents, but also on the position it occupies with respect to the other symbols of the group. Thus, the same digit 2 has different meanings in the three numbers 342, 725, 269: in the first case it stands for two; in the second for twenty; in the third for two hundred. As a matter of fact 342 is just an abbreviation for three hundred plus four tens plus two units.

But that is precisely the scheme of the counting board, where 342 is represented by

And, as I said before, it would seem that it is sufficient to translate this scheme into the language of numerals to obtain substantially what we have today.

True! But there is one difficulty. Any attempt to make a permanent record of a counting-board operation would meet the obstacle that such an entry as ≡ = may represent any one of several numbers: 32, 302, 320, 3,002, and 3,020 among others. In order to avoid this ambiguity it is essential to have some method of representing the gaps, *i.e.*, what is needed is a *symbol for an empty column*.

We see therefore that no progress was possible until a symbol was invented for an *empty* class, a symbol for *nothing*, our modern *zero*. The concrete mind of the ancient Greeks could not conceive the void as a number, let alone endow the void with a symbol.

And neither did the unknown Hindu see in zero the symbol of nothing. The Indian term for zero was *sunya*, which meant "empty" or "blank," but had no connotation of "void" or "nothing." And so, from all appearances, the discovery of zero was an accident brought about by an attempt to make an unambiguous permanent record of a counting-board operation.

10. How the Indian *sunya* became the zero of today constitutes one of the most interesting chapters in the history of culture. When the Arabs of the tenth century adopted the Indian numeration, they translated the Indian *sunya* by their own, *sifr*, which meant "empty" in Arabic. When the Indo-Arabic numeration was first introduced into Italy, *sifr* was latinized into *zephirum*. This happened at the beginning of the thirteenth century, and in the course of the next hundred years the word underwent a series of changes which culminated in the Italian *zero*.

About the same time Jordanus Nemerarius was introducing the Arabic system into Germany. He kept the Arabic word, changing it slightly to *cifra*. That for some time in the learned circles of Europe the word *cifra* and its derivatives denoted zero is shown by the fact that the great Gauss, the last of the mathematicians of the nineteenth century who wrote in Latin, still used *cifra* in this sense. In the English language the word *cifra* has become *cipher* and has retained its original meaning of zero.

The attitude of the common people toward this new numeration is reflected in the fact that soon after its introduction into Europe, the word *cifra* was used as a secret sign; but this connotation was altogether lost in the succeeding centuries. The verb *decipher* remains as a monument of these early days.

The next stage in this development saw the new art of reckoning spread more widely. It is significant that the essential part played by zero in this new system did not escape the notice of the masses. Indeed, they identified the whole system with its most striking feature, the *cifra*, and this explains how this word in its different forms, *ziffer, chiffre,* etc., came to receive the meaning of numeral, which it has in Europe today.

This double meaning, the popular *cifra* standing for numeral and the *cifra* of the learned signifying zero, caused considerable confusion. In vain did scholars attempt to revive the original meaning of the word: the popular meaning had taken deep root. The learned had to yield to popular usage, and the matter was eventually settled by adopting the Italian zero in the sense in which it is used today.

The same interest attaches to the word *algorithm*. As the term is used today, it applies to any mathematical procedure consisting of an indefinite number of steps, each step applying to the result of the one preceding it. But between the tenth and fifteenth centuries *algorithm* was synonymous with positional numeration. We now know that the word is merely a corruption of Al Kworesmi, the name of the Arabian mathematician of the ninth century whose book (in Latin translation) was the first work on this subject to reach Western Europe.

11. Today, when positional numeration has become a part of our daily life, it seems that the superiority of this method, the compactness of its notation, the ease and elegance it introduced in calculations, should have assured the rapid and sweeping acceptance of it. In reality, the transition, far from being immediate, extended over long centuries. The struggle between the Abacists, who defended the old traditions, and the Algorists, who advocated the reform, lasted from the eleventh to the fifteenth century and went through all the usual stages of obscurantism and reac-

tion. In some places Arabic numerals were banned from official documents; in others, the art was prohibited altogether. And, as usual, prohibition did not succeed in abolishing, but merely served to spread bootlegging, ample evidence of which is found in the thirteenth-century archives of Italy, where, it appears, merchants were using the Arabic numerals as a sort of secret code.

Yet, for a while reaction succeeded in arresting the progress and in hampering the development of the new system. Indeed, little of essential value or of lasting influence was contributed to the art of reckoning in these transition centuries. Only the outward appearance of the numerals went through a series of changes; not, however, from any desire for improvement, but because the manuals of these days were handwritten. In fact, the numerals did not assume a stable form until the introduction of printing. It can be added parenthetically that so great was the stabilizing influence of printing that the numerals of today have essentially the same appearance as those of the fifteenth century.

12. As to the final victory of the Algorists, no definite date can be set. We do know that at the beginning of the sixteenth century the supremacy of the new numeration was incontestable. Since then progress was unhampered, so that in the course of the next hundred years all the rules of operations, both on integers and on common and decimal fractions, reached practically the same scope and form in which they are taught today in our schools.

Another century, and the Abacists and all they stood for were so completely forgotten that various peoples of Europe began each to regard the positional numeration as its own national achievement. So, for instance, early in the nineteenth century we find that Arabic numerals were called in Germany *Deutsche* with a view to differentiating them from the Roman, which were recognized as of foreign origin.

As to the abacus itself, no traces of it are found in Western Europe during the eighteenth century. Its reappearance early in the nineteenth century occurred under very curious circumstances. The mathematician Poncelet, a general under Napoleon, was captured in the Russian campaign and spent many years in Russia as a prisoner of war. Upon returning to France he brought, among other curios, a Russian abacus. For many years to come, this importation of Poncelet's was regarded as a great curiosity of "barbaric" origin. Such examples of national amnesia abound in the history of culture. How many educated people even today know that only four hundred years ago finger counting was the average man's only means of calculating, while the counting board was accessible only to the professional calculators of the time?

13. Conceived in all probability as the symbol for an empty column on a counting board, the Indian *sunya* was destined to become the turning point in a development without which the progress of modern science, industry, or commerce is inconceivable. And the influence of this great discovery was by no means confined to arithmetic. By paving the way to a generalized number concept, it played just as fundamental a role in practically every branch of mathematics. In the history of culture the discovery of zero will always stand out as one of the greatest single achievements of the human race.

A great discovery! Yes. But, like so many other early discoveries, which have profoundly affected the life of the race—not the reward of painstaking research, but a gift from blind chance.

---

*The foregoing two selections consist*
*of Chapters I and II*
*from Dantzig's* NUMBER: THE LANGUAGE OF SCIENCE.

# Leonhard Euler

## 1707–1783

The story of mathematics during the eighteenth century is centered upon Leonhard Euler. He was the most prolific mathematical author of all time. It has been estimated that sixty to eighty large quarto volumes would be needed for his collected work. Not all of it, however, has stood the meticulous inspection of this century. Armed with the powerful tools invented by Descartes, Newton, and Leibniz, mathematicians of Euler's day were busy and optimistic, unhampered by the wary self-criticism of modern times.

Euler was born in 1707, at Basel in Switzerland. He received the degree of Master of Arts from the University of Basel at the age of seventeen. Three years later he was invited to join the Academy at St. Petersburg (Leningrad).

In those days mathematicians were frequently connected with a royal court. Euler held such posts successively under Catherine I of Russia, Frederick the Great of Prussia, and Catherine the Great of Russia. Royal patronage was not always predictable, but esteem for learning crossed national lines. When a Russian army invaded Germany in 1760 and pillaged a farm belonging to Euler, his losses were immediately made good by the Russian Empress.

---

*Notes from the artist: "A portrait of Euler against a background comprising three of his mathematical conclusions. At the top is his discovery of the formula expressing the relationship of e, π, and i, followed by eight, and part of the ninth, of the Eulerian numbers. Opposite his profile is a suggestion of a 'magic' square of the order of ten, representing an arrangement of numerical relationships that Euler believed could not exist. . . . He was not disproved until 1959."*

LEONHARD
EULER

Euler enriched mathematics in every department. He is considered one of the founders of modern analysis. Although his energy was as remarkable as his genius, he overtaxed himself. His last years were spent in total blindness. Despite this handicap he continued his labors, aided by his powerful memory. His productivity continued until his death in 1783.

Topology (*geometria situs*) has been called rubber-sheet geometry. It examines geometric properties that are unaffected when we stretch or twist or otherwise change an object's size and shape. Euler's memoir on the Königsberg bridges is one of the foundation stones of this branch of mathematics. *The Seven Bridges of Königsberg* resulted from what might be called mathematical recreation. But the small amusement of the Königsberg townsfolk disclosed an important scientific principle to Euler.

It is interesting to notice the importance of the symbols used in solving this problem. The symbols themselves suggest relationships between the bridges and the land areas that are not apparent from inspection of the picture. N. R. Campbell has written of this aspect of mathematical analysis.

Mathematical puzzles often lead to important discoveries, but they need no excuse beyond intellectual delight. You may want to stop at the end of paragraph fifteen and try to discover for yourself the simplification mentioned by Euler.

# The Seven Bridges
# of Königsberg

**1.**

The branch of geometry that deals with magnitudes has been zealously studied throughout the past, but there is another branch that has been almost unknown up to now; Leibniz spoke of it first, calling it the "geometry of position" (*geometria situs*). This branch of geometry deals with relations dependent on position alone, and investigates the properties of position; it does not take magnitudes into consideration, nor does it involve calculation with quantities. But as yet no satisfactory definition has been given of the problems that belong to this geometry of position or of the method to be used in solving them. Recently there was announced a problem that, while it certainly seemed to belong to geometry, was nevertheless so designed that it did not call for the determination of a magnitude, nor could it be solved by quantitative calculation; consequently I did not hesitate to assign it to the geometry of position, especially since the solution required only the consideration of position, calculation being of no use. In this paper I shall give an account of the method that I discovered for solving this type of problem, which may serve as an example of the geometry of position.

**2.** The problem, which I understand is quite well known, is stated as follows: In the town of Königsberg in Prussia there is an island A, called "Kneiphof," with the two branches of the river (Pregel) flowing around it, as shown in Fig. 1. There are seven bridges, a, b, c, d, e, f and g, crossing the two branches. The question is whether a person can plan a walk in such a way that he will cross each of these bridges once but not more than once. I was told that while some denied the possibility of doing this and others were in doubt, there were none who maintained that it was actually possible. On the basis of the above I formulated the following very general problem for myself: Given any configuration of the river and the branches into which it may divide, as well as any number of bridges, to determine whether or not it is possible to cross each bridge exactly once.

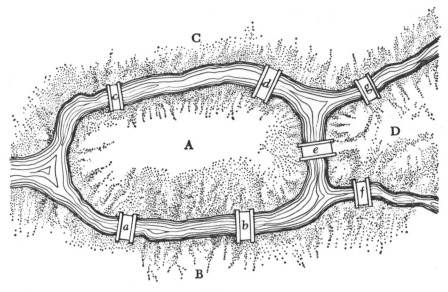

Fig. 1

3. The particular problem of the seven bridges of Königsberg could be solved by carefully tabulating all possible paths, thereby ascertaining by inspection which of them, if any, met the requirement. This method of solution, however, is too tedious and too difficult because of the large number of possible combinations, and in other problems where many more bridges are involved it could not be used at all. When the analysis is undertaken in the manner just described it yields a great many details that are irrelevant to the problem; undoubtedly this is the reason the method is so onerous. Hence I discarded it and searched for another more restricted in its scope; namely, a method which would show only whether a journey satisfying the prescribed condition could in the first instance be discovered; such an approach, I believed, would be much simpler.

4. My entire method rests on the appropriate and convenient way in which I denote the crossing of bridges, in that I use capital letters, A, B, C, D, to designate the various land areas that are separated from one another by the river. Thus when a person goes from area A to area B

across bridge a or b, I denote this crossing by the letters AB, the first of which designates the area whence he came, the second the area where he arrives after crossing the bridge. If the traveller then crosses from B over bridge f into D, this crossing is denoted by the letters BD; the two crossings AB and BD performed in succession I denote simply by the three letters ABD, since the middle letter B designates the area into which the first crossing leads as well as the area out of which the second crossing leads.

5. Similarly, if the traveller proceeds from D across bridge g into C, I designate these three successive crossings by the four letters ABDC. These four letters signify that the traveller who was originally in A crossed over into B, then to D, and finally to C; and since these areas are separated from one another by the river the traveller must necessarily have crossed three bridges. The crossing of four bridges will be represented by five letters, and if the traveller crosses an arbitrary number of bridges his journey will be described by a number of letters that is one greater than the number of bridges. For example, eight letters are needed to denote the crossing of seven bridges.

6. With this method I pay no attention to which bridges are used; that is to say, if the crossing from one area to another can be made by way of several bridges it makes no difference which one is used, so long as it leads to the desired area. Thus if a route could be laid out over the seven Königsberg bridges so that each bridge were crossed once and only once, we would be able to describe this route by using eight letters, and in this series of letters the combination AB (or BA) would have to occur twice, since there are two bridges a and b, connecting the regions A and B; similarly the combination AC would occur twice, while the combinations AD, BD, and CD would each occur once.

7. Our question is now reduced to whether from the four letters A, B, C, and D a series of eight letters can be formed in which all the combinations just mentioned occur the required number of times. Before making the effort, however, of trying to find such an arrangement we do well to consider whether its existence is even theoretically possible or not. For if it could be shown that such an arrangement is in fact impossible, then the effort expended on finding it would be wasted. Therefore I have sought for a rule that would determine without difficulty as regards this and all similar questions whether the required arrangement of letters is feasible.

8. For the purpose of finding such a rule I take a single region A into which an arbitrary number of bridges, a, b, c, d, etc., leads (Fig. 2).

Of these bridges I first consider only a. If the traveller crosses this bridge he must either have been in A before crossing or have reached A after crossing, so that according to the above method of denotation the letter A will appear exactly once. If there are three bridges, a, b, c, leading

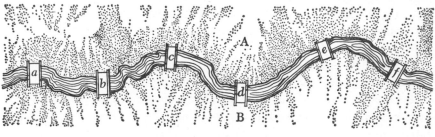

Fig. 2

to A and the traveller crosses all three, then the letter A will occur twice in the expression for his route, whether it begins at A or not. And if there are five bridges leading to A the expression for a route that crosses them all will contain the letter A three times. If the number of bridges is odd, increase it by one, and take half the sum; the quotient represents the number of times the letter A appears.

9. Let us now return to the Königsberg problem (Fig. 1). Since there are five bridges, a, b, c, d, e, leading to (and from) island A, the letter A must occur three times in the expression describing the route. The letter B must occur twice, since three bridges lead to B; similarly D and C must each occur twice. That is to say, the series of eight letters that represents the crossing of the seven bridges must contain A three times and B, C, and D each twice; but this is quite impossible with a series of eight letters. Thus it is apparent that a crossing of the seven bridges of Königsberg in the manner required cannot be effected.

10. Using this method we are always able, whenever the number of bridges leading to a particular region is odd, to determine whether it is possible, in a journey, to cross each bridge exactly once. Such a route exists if the number of bridges plus one is equal to the sum of the numbers that indicate how often each individual letter must occur. On the other hand, if this sum is greater than the number of bridges plus one, as it is in our example, then the desired route cannot be constructed. The rule that I gave (section 8) for determining from the number of bridges that lead to A how often the letter A will occur in the route description is independent of whether these bridges all come from a single region B, as in Fig. 2, or from several regions, because I am considering only the

region A, and attempting to determine how often the letter A must occur.

11. When the number of bridges leading to A is even, we must take into account whether the route begins in A or not. For example, if there are two bridges that lead to A and the route starts from A, then the letter A will occur twice, once to indicate the departure from A by one of the bridges and a second time to indicate the return to A by the other bridge. However, if the traveller starts his journey in another region, the letter A will occur only once, since by my method of description the single occurrence of A indicates an entrance into as well as a departure from A.

12. Suppose, as in our case, there are four bridges leading into the region A, and the route is to begin at A. The letter A will then occur three times in the expression for the whole route, while if the journey had started in another region, A would occur only twice. With six bridges leading to A the letter A will occur four times if A is the starting point, otherwise only three times. In general, if the number of bridges is even, the number of occurrences of the letter A, when the starting region is not A, will be half the number of the bridges; one more than half, when the route starts from A.

13. Every route must, of course, start in some one region, thus from the number of bridges that lead to each region I determine the number of times that the corresponding letter will occur in the expression for the entire route as follows: When the number of the bridges is odd I increase it by one and divide by two; when the number is even I simply divide it by two. Then if the sum of the resulting numbers is equal to the actual number of bridges plus one, the journey can be accomplished, though it must start in a region approached by an odd number of bridges. But if the sum is one less than the number of bridges plus one, the journey is feasible if its starting point is a region approached by an even number of bridges, for in that case the sum is again increased by one.

14. My procedure for determining whether in any given system of rivers and bridges it is possible to cross each bridge exactly once is as follows: 1. First I designate the individual regions separated from one another by the water as A, B, C, etc. 2. I take the total number of bridges, increase it by one, and write the resulting number uppermost. 3. Under this number I write the letters A, B, C, etc., and opposite each of these I note the number of bridges that lead to that particular region. 4. I place an asterisk next the letters that have even numbers opposite them. 5. Opposite each even number I write the half of that number and opposite each odd number I write half of the sum formed by that number plus one. 6. I add up the last column of numbers. If the sum is one less

than, or equal to, the number written at the top, I conclude that the required journey can be made. But it must be noted that when the sum is one less than the number at the top, the route must start from a region marked with an asterisk. And in the other case, when these two numbers are equal, it must start from a region that does not have an asterisk.

For the Königsberg problem I would set up the tabulation as follows:

Number of bridges 7, giving 8 (= 7 + 1) bridges

| A, | 5 | 3 |
|----|---|---|
| B, | 3 | 2 |
| C, | 3 | 2 |
| D, | 3 | 2 |

The last column now adds up to more than 8, and hence the required journey cannot be made.

15. Let us take an example of two islands, with four rivers forming the surrounding water, as shown in Fig. 3. Fifteen bridges, marked a, b, c, d,

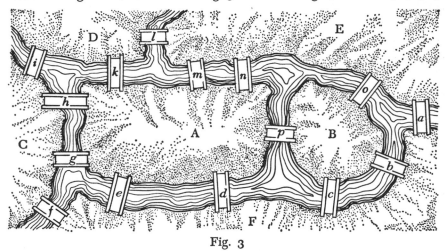

Fig. 3

etc., cross the water around the islands and the adjoining rivers; the question is whether a journey can be arranged that will pass over all the bridges, but not over any of them more than once. 1. I begin by marking all the regions that are separated from one another by the water with the letters A, B, C, D, E, F—there are six of them. 2. I take the number of bridges—15—add one and write this number—16—uppermost. 3. I write the letters A, B, C, etc., in a column and opposite each letter I write the number of bridges connecting with that region, *e.g.*, 8 bridges for A, 4 for B, etc. 4. The letters that have even numbers opposite them

I mark with an asterisk. 5. In a third column I write the half of each corresponding even number, or, if the number is odd, I add one to it,
and put down half the sum. 6. Finally I add the numbers in the third
column and get 16 as the sum. This is the same as the number 16 that

|       |   | 16 |
|-------|---|----|
| A*,   | 8 | 4  |
| B*,   | 4 | 2  |
| C*,   | 4 | 2  |
| D,    | 3 | 2  |
| E,    | 5 | 3  |
| F*,   | 6 | 3  |
|       |   | 16 |

appears above, and hence it follows that the journey can be effected if it
begins in regions D or E, whose symbols have no asterisk. The following
expression represents such a route:

$$EaFbBcFdAeFfCgAhCiDkAmEnApBoElD.$$

Here I have also indicated, by small letters between the capitals, which
bridges are crossed.

16. By this method we can easily determine, even in cases of considerable complexity, whether a single crossing of each of the bridges in sequence is actually possible. But I should now like to give another and
much simpler method, which follows quite easily from the preceding,
after a few preliminary remarks. In the first place, I note that the sum of
all the numbers of bridges to each region, that are written down in the
second column opposite the letters A, B, C, etc., is necessarily double the
actual number of bridges. The reason is that in the tabulation of the
bridges leading to the various regions each bridge is counted twice, once
for each of the two regions that it connects.

17. From this observation it follows that the sum of the numbers in
the second column must be an even number, since half of it represents
the actual number of bridges. Hence it is impossible for exactly one of
these numbers (indicating how many bridges connect with each region)
to be odd, or, for that matter, three or five, etc. In other words, if *any*
of the numbers opposite the letters A, B, C, etc., are odd, an even number
of them must be odd. In the Königsberg problem, for instance, all four of
the numbers opposite the letters A, B, C, D were odd, as explained in
section 14, while in the example just given (section 15) only two of the
numbers were odd, namely those opposite D and E.

18. Since the sum of the numbers opposite A, B, C, etc., is double the number of bridges, it is clear that if this sum is increased by two and then divided by 2 the result will be the number written at the top. When all the numbers in the second column are even, and the half of each is written down in the third column, the total of this column will be one less than the number at the top. In that case it will always be possible to cross all the bridges. For in whatever region the journey begins, there will be an even number of bridges leading to it, which is the requirement. In the Königsberg problem we could, for instance, arrange matters so that each bridge is crossed twice, which is equivalent to dividing each bridge into two, whence the number of bridges leading to each region would be even.

19. Further, when only two of the numbers opposite the letters are odd, and the others even, the required route is possible provided it begins in a region approached by an odd number of bridges. We take half of each even number, and likewise half of each odd number after adding one, as our procedure requires; the sum of these halves will then be one greater than the number of bridges, and hence equal to the number written at the top.

Similarly, where four, six, or eight, etc., of the numbers in the second column are odd it is evident that the sum of the numbers in the third column will be one, two, three, etc., greater than the top number, as the case may be, and hence the desired journey is impossible.

20. Thus for any configuration that may arise the easiest way of determining whether a single crossing of all the bridges is possible is to apply the following rules:

If there are more than two regions which are approached by an odd number of bridges, no route satisfying the required conditions can be found.

If, however, there are only two regions with an odd number of approach bridges, the required journey can be completed provided it originates in one of the regions.

If, finally, there is no region with an odd number of approach bridges, the required journey can be effected, no matter where it begins. These rules solve completely the problem initially proposed.

21. After we have determined that a route actually exists we are left with the question how to find it. To this end the following rule will serve: Wherever possible we mentally eliminate any two bridges that connect the same two regions; this usually reduces the number of bridges considerably. Then—and this should not be difficult—we proceed to trace the

required route across the remaining bridges. The pattern of this route, once we have found it, will not be substantially affected by the restoration of the bridges which were first eliminated from consideration—as a little thought will show; therefore I do not think I need say more about finding the routes themselves.

# Norman Robert Campbell

## 1880–1949

Norman Robert Campbell was a British physicist and philosopher of science. Born in 1880, he was educated at Eton and at Trinity College, Cambridge. While his researches in physics were highly regarded by his fellow-specialists, he is best known to the general public for his skill in popularizing science. For many years he gave freely of his time to adult education groups. Always clear and original, he had the ability to provoke thoughtful consideration of basic ideas. When he died in 1949 he had published nine books and some eighty-nine research papers.

The selections below are taken from Campbell's book, *What is Science?*, published in 1921. It is part of the effort that has been made in this century to define our mathematical concepts. Further investigations into the idea of number will be found in this volume, in selections from Tobias Dantzig, Bertrand Russell, and the joint work of Edward Kasner and James R. Newman.

For the scientist who undertakes to explain his field to the layman, it is not enough to know the subject thoroughly—he must also be able to imagine what it is like *not* to know the subject. This is especially difficult when what is being examined is the origin of an idea so familiar that its absence is almost unthinkable. In *Measurement*, Campbell surmounts this difficulty by erasing the idea. He provides a clean slate in the form of a pre-numeral measuring system. Then our present-day use of numerals for the process of measuring is shown as a fairly recent invention of the human mind.

The distinction that Campbell makes between "numeral" and "number" is very important. The first is a symbol for the second, which is a property. Numerals can be added, subtracted, and manipulated in other ways without regard to what properties these numerals represent. As the numerals themselves fall into patterns, it is often valuable to ask whether or not a new pattern is a picture of something that exists in the material world. It is the discovery of these new pictures that makes measurement of such importance to science.

The use of numerals in measurement leads, in the second article, to an examination of numerical laws and the further uses of mathematics in science. And here we see the mathematician as artist. His sense of form, neatness, and beauty tells him when an arrangement of symbols looks good. Feeling that such an attractive array of scrawls should have some counterpart in the physical world, he often finds that they do, and a new scientific law is discovered. Henri Poincaré has written on this aesthetic sense which all great mathematicians have, but has confessed that he could not explain it.

In his repeated wonder that the world conforms to such a great extent to our ideas, Campbell sees logic as something that is inborn in the human mind. Ideas arrived at by intellectual activity may be logically true, but they must be tested by experiment before they can be accepted as descriptions of the way the world actually works.

Campbell is not writing for the mathematician here. He is conscientiously nontechnical. He does more than describe some applications of mathematics to science: he leads you into thinking *about* thinking.

# Measurement

Every one knows that measurement is a very important part of many sciences; they know too, that many sciences are "mathematical" and can only be apprehended completely by those versed in mathematics. But very few people could explain exactly how measurement enters into science, why it enters into some and not in others, why it is so important, what mathematics is and why it is so intimately connected with measurement and with the sciences in which measurement is involved. . . . I propose to attempt some answer to these questions. Any answer to these questions that can be attempted here will not, of course, enable anyone to start immediately the study of one of the mathematical sciences in the hope of understanding it completely. But if he can be convinced that even in the most abstruse parts of those sciences there is something that he can comprehend and appreciate without the smallest knowledge of mathematics, something may be done towards extending the range of the sciences that are open to the layman.

*What Is Measurement?* Measurement is one of the notions which modern science has taken over from common sense. Measurement does not appear as part of common sense until a comparatively high stage of civilization is reached; and even the common-sense conception has changed and developed enormously in historic times. When I say that measurement belongs to common sense, I only mean that it is something with which every civilized person to-day is entirely familiar. It may be defined, in general, as the assignment of numbers to represent properties. If we say that the time is 3 o'clock, that the price of coal is 56 shillings a ton, and that we have just bought 2 tons of it—in all such cases we are using numbers to convey important information about the "properties" of the day, of coal in general, of the coal in our cellar, or so on; and our statement depends somehow upon measurement.

The first point I want to notice is that it is only some properties and not all that can be thus represented by numbers. If I am buying a sack of potatoes I may ask what it weighs and what it costs; to those questions I shall expect a number in answer; it weighs 56 lbs. and costs 5 shillings. But I may also ask of what variety the potatoes are, and whether they are good cookers; to those questions I shall not expect a number in answer. The dealer may possibly call the variety "No. 11" in somebody's catalogue; but even if he does, I shall feel that such use of a number is not real measurement, and is not of the same kind as the use in connection with weight or cost. What is the difference? Why are some properties measurable and others not? Those are the questions I want to discuss. And I will outline the answer immediately in order that the reader may see at what the subsequent discussion is aiming. The difference is this. Suppose I have two sacks of potatoes which are identical in weight, cost, variety, and cooking qualities; and that I pour the two sacks into one so that there is now only one sack of potatoes. This sack will differ from the two original sacks in weight and cost (the measurable properties), but will not differ from them in variety and cooking qualities (the properties that are not measurable). The measurable properties of a body are those which are changed by the combination of similar bodies; the non-measurable properties are those that are not changed. We shall see that this definition is rather too crude, but it will serve for the present.

*Numbers.* In order to see why this difference is so important we must inquire more closely into the meaning of "number." And at the outset we must note that confusion is apt to arise because that word is used to denote two perfectly different things. It sometimes means a mere name or word or symbol, and it sometimes means a property of an object. Thus, besides the properties which have been mentioned, the sack of potatoes has another definite property, namely the number of potatoes in it, and the number is as much a property of the object which we call a sack of potatoes as its weight or its cost. This property can be (and must be) "represented by a number" just as the weight can be; for instance, it might be represented by 200. But this "200" is not itself a property of the sack; it is a mere mark on the paper for which would be substituted, if I was speaking instead of writing, a spoken sound; it is a name or symbol for the property. When we say that measurement is the representation of properties by "numbers," we mean that it is the representation of properties, other than number, by the symbols which are always used to represent number. Moreover, there is a separate word for these symbols; they are called "numerals." We shall always use that word in future and confine "number" to the meaning of the property which is always represented by numerals.

These considerations are not mere quibbling over words; they bring out clearly an important point, namely, that the measurable properties of an object must resemble in some special way the property number, since they can be fitly represented by the same symbols; they must have some quality common with number. We must proceed to ask what this common quality is, and the best way to begin is to examine the property number rather more closely.

The number of a sack of potatoes, or, as it is more usually expressed, the number of potatoes contained in it, is ascertained by the process of counting. Counting is inseparably connected in our minds to-day with numerals, but the process can be, and at an earlier stage of civilization was, carried on without them. Without any use of numerals I can determine whether the number of one sack of potatoes is equal to that of another. For this purpose I take a potato from one sack, mark it in some way to distinguish it from the rest (*e.g.* by putting it into a box), and then perform a similar operation on a potato from the other sack. I then repeat this double operation continually until I have exhausted the potatoes from one sack. If the operation which exhausts the potatoes from one sack exhausts also the potatoes from the other, then I know that the sacks had the same number of potatoes; if not, then the sack which is not exhausted had a larger number of potatoes than the other.

*The Rules for Counting.* This process could be applied equally well if the objects counted against each other were not of the same nature. The potatoes in a sack can be counted, not only against another collection of potatoes, but also against the men in a regiment or against the days in the year. The "mark," which is used for distinguishing the objects in the process of counting, may have to be altered to suit the objects counted, but some other suitable mark could be found which would enable the process to be carried out. If, having never heard of counting before, we applied the process to all kinds of different objects, we should soon discover certain rules which would enable us to abbreviate and simplify the process considerably. These rules appear to us to-day so obvious as to be hardly worth stating, but as they are undoubtedly employed in modern methods of counting, we must notice them here. The first is that if two sets of objects, when counted against a third set, are found to have the same number as that third set, then, when counted against each other they will be found to have the same number. This rule enables us to determine whether two sets of objects have the same number without bringing them together; if I want to find out whether the number of potatoes in the sack I propose to buy is the same as that in a sack I have at home, I need not bring my sack to the shop; I can count the potatoes at the shop against some third collection, take this collection home, and count it against my potatoes. Accordingly the discovery of this first rule immediately suggests the use of portable collections which can be counted, first against one collection and then against another, in order to ascertain whether these two have the same number.

The value of this suggestion is increased greatly by the discovery of a second rule. It is that by starting with a single object and continually adding to it another single object, we can build up a series of collections of which one will have the same number as any other collection whatsoever. This rule helps us in two ways. First, since it states that it is possible to make a standard series of collections one of which will have the same number as any other collection, it suggests that it might be well to count collections, not against each other, but against a standard series of collections. If we could carry this standard series about with us, we could always ascertain whether any one collection had the same number as any other by observing whether the member of the standard series which had the same number as the first had also the same number as the second. Next, it shows us how to make such a standard series with the least possible cumbrousness. If we had to have a totally different collection for each member of the standard series, the whole series would be impossibly cumbrous; but our rule shows that the earlier members of the series (that is those with the smaller number) may be all parts of the later members. Suppose we have a collection of objects, each distinguishable from each other, and agree to take one of these objects as the first member of the series; this object together with some other as the next member; these objects with yet another as the next member; and so on. Then we shall obtain, according to our rule, a series, some member of which has the same number as any other collection we want to count, and yet the number of objects, in all the members of the standard series taken together, will not be greater than that of the largest collection we want to count.

And, of course, this is the process actually adopted. For the successive members of the standard series compounded in this way, primitive man chose, as portable, distinguishable objects, his fingers and toes. Civilized man invented numerals for the same purpose. Numerals are simply distinguishable objects out of which we build our standard series of collections by adding them in turn to previous members of the series. The first member of our standard series is 1, the next 1, 2, the next 1, 2, 3 and so on. We count other collections against these members of the standard

series and so ascertain whether or no two collections so counted have the
same number. By an ingenious convention we describe which member
of the series has the same number as a collection counted against it by
quoting simply the last numeral in that member; we describe the fact
that the collection of the days of the week has the same number as the
collection 1, 2, 3, 4, 5, 6, 7, by saying "that the number" of the days of
the week is 7. But when we say that what we really mean, and what is
really important, is that this collection has the same number as the collection of numerals (taken in the standard order) which ends in 7 and the
same number as any other collection which also has the same number as
the collection of numerals which ends in 7.[1]

The two rules that have been mentioned are necessary to explain what
we mean by "the number" of a collection and how we ascertain that number. There is a third rule which is of great importance in the use of numbers. We often want to know what is the number of a collection which is
formed by combining two other collections of which the numbers are
known, or, as it is usually called, adding the two collections. For instance
we may ask what is the number of the collection made by adding a collection of 2 objects to a collection of 3 objects. We all know the answer, 5.
It can be found by arguing thus: The first collection can be counted
against the numerals 1, 2; the second against the numerals 1, 2, 3. But
the numerals 1, 2, 3, 1, 2, a collection formed by adding the two first
collections, can be counted against 1, 2, 3, 4, 5. Therefore the number of
the combined collection is 5. However, a little examination will show that
in reaching this conclusion we have made use of another rule, namely
that if two collections A and *a*, have the same number, and two other
collections B and *b*, have the same number, then the collection formed
by adding A to B has the same number as that formed by adding *a* to *b;*
in other words, equals added to equals produce equal sums. This is a
third rule about numbers and counting; it is quite as important as the
other two rules; all three are so obvious to us to-day that we never think
about them, but they must have been definitely discovered at some time

---

1. Numerals have also an immense advantage over fingers and toes as objects of which
   the standard series may be formed, in that the series can be extended indefinitely
   by a simple rule which automatically gives names to any new numerals that may be
   required. Even if we have never hitherto had reason to carry the series beyond
   (say) 131679 in order to count all the collections we have met with, when we
   do meet at last with a larger collection, we know at once that the objects we must
   add to our standard series are 131680, 131681, and so on. This is a triumph of
   conventional nomenclature, much more satisfactory than the old convention that
   when we have exhausted our fingers we must begin on our toes, but it is not essentially different.

in the history of mankind, and without them all, our habitual use of numbers would be impossible.

*What Properties Are Measurable?* And now, after this discussion of number, we can return to the other measurable properties of objects which, like number, can be represented by numerals. We can now say more definitely what is the characteristic of these properties which makes them measurable. It is that there are rules true of these properties, closely analogous to the rules on which the use of number depends. If a property is to be measurable it must be such that (1) two objects which are the same in respect of that property as some third object are the same as each other; (2) by adding objects successively we must be able to make a standard series one member of which will be the same in respect of the property as any other object we want to measure; (3) equals added to equals produce equal sums. In order to make a property measurable we must find some method of judging equality and of adding objects, such that these rules are true.

Let me explain what is meant by using as an example the measurable property, weight.

Weight is measured by the balance. Two bodies are judged to have the same weight if, when they are placed in opposite pans, neither tends to sink; and two bodies are added in respect of weight when they are both placed on the same pan of the balance. With these definitions of equality and addition, it is found that the three rules are obeyed. (1) If the body A balances the body B, and B balances C, then A balances C. (2) By placing a body in one pan and continually adding it to others, collections can be built up which will balance any other body placed in the other pan. (3) If the body A balances the body B, and C balances D, then A and C in the same pan will balance B and D in the other pan. To make the matter yet clearer let us take another measurable property, length. Two straight rods are judged equal in length, if they can be placed so that both ends of one are contiguous to both ends of the other; they are added in respect of length, when they are placed with one end of one contiguous with one end of the other, while the two form a single straight rod. Here again we find the three rules fulfilled. Bodies which are equal in length to the same body are equal in length to each other. By adding successively rods to each other, a rod can be built up which is equal to any other rod. And equal rods added to equal rods produce equal rods. Length is therefore a measurable property.

It is because these rules are true that measurement of these properties is useful and possible; it is these rules that make the measurable properties so similar to numbers, that it is possible and useful to represent them by numerals the primary purpose of which is to represent numbers. It is because of them that it is possible to find one, and only one numeral, which will fitly represent each property; and it is because of them, that these numerals, when they are found, tell us something useful about the properties. One such use arises in the combination of bodies possessing the properties. We may want to know how the property varies when bodies possessing it are added in the way characteristic of measurement. When we have assigned numerals to represent the property we shall know that the body with the property 2 added to that with the property 3 will have the same property as that with the property 5, or as the combination of the bodies with properties 4 and 1. This is not the place to examine exactly how these conclusions are shown to be universally valid; but they are valid only because the three rules are true.

*The Laws of Measurement.* But what is the nature of these rules? They are laws established by definite experiment. The word "rule" has been used hitherto, because it is not quite certain whether they are truly laws in their application to number; but they certainly are laws in their application to other measurable properties, such as weight or length. The fact that the rules are true can be, and must be, determined by experiment in the same way as the fact that any other laws are true. Perhaps it may have appeared to the reader that the rules must be true; that it requires no experiment to determine that bodies which balance the same body will balance each other; and that it is inconceivable that this rule should not be true. But I think he will change his opinion if it is pointed out that the rule is actually true only in certain conditions; for instance, it is only true if the balance is a good one, and has arms of equal length and pans of equal weight. If the arms were unequal, the rule would not be found to be true unless it were carefully prescribed in which pan the bodies were placed during the judgment of equality. Again, the rules would not be true of the property length, unless the rods were straight and were rigid. In implying that the balance is good, and the rods straight and rigid, we have implied definite laws which must be true if the properties are to be measurable, namely that it is possible to make a perfect balance, and that there are rods which are straight and rigid. These are experimental laws; they could not be known apart from definite experiment and observation of the external world; they are not self-evident.

Accordingly the process of discovering that a property is measurable in the way that has been described, and setting up a process for measuring it, is one that rests entirely upon experimental inquiry. It is a part, and a most important part, of experimental science. Whenever a new branch of physics is opened up (for, as has been said, physics is the science that deals with such processes of measurement), the first step is always to find some process for measuring the new properties that are investigated; and it is not until this problem has been solved, that any great progress can be made along the branch. Its solution demands the discovery of new laws. We can actually trace the development of new measurable properties in this way in the history of science. Before the dawn of definite history, laws had been discovered which made measurable some of the properties employed by modern science. History practically begins with the Greeks, but before their time the properties, weight, length, volume, and area had been found to be measurable; the establishment of the necessary laws had probably occurred in the great period of Babylonian and Egyptian civilization. The Greeks, largely in the person of Archimedes, found how to measure force by establishing the laws of the lever, and other mechanical systems. Again from the earliest era, there have been rough methods of measuring periods of time,[2] but a true method, really obeying the three rules, was not discovered till the seventeenth century; it arose out of Galileo's laws of the pendulum. Modern science has added greatly to the list of measurable properties; the science of electricity is based on the discovery, by Cavendish and Coulomb, of the law necessary to measure an electric charge; on the laws, discovered by Oersted and Ampère, necessary to measure an electric current; and on the laws, discovered by Ohm and Kirchhoff, necessary to measure electrical resistance. And the discovery of similar laws has made possible the development of other branches of physics.

But, it may be asked, has there ever been a failure to discover the necessary laws? The answer is that there are certainly many properties which are not measurable in the sense that we have been discussing; there are more properties, definitely recognized by science, that are not so measurable than are so measurable. But, as will appear presently, the very nature of these properties makes it impossible that they should be measured in this way. For the only properties to which this kind of measurement seems conceivably applicable, are those which fulfil the condition stated provisionally on p. 205; they must be such that the combina-

2. By a period of time I mean the thing that is measured when we say that it took us 3 hours to do so-and-so. This is a different "time" from that which is measured when we say it is 3 o'clock. The difference is rather abstruse and cannot be discussed here; but it may be mentioned that the "measurement" involved in "3 o'clock" is more like that discussed later in the chapter.

tion of objects possessing the property increases that property. For this is the fundamental significance of the property number; it is something that is increased by addition; any property which does not agree with number in this matter cannot be very closely related to number and cannot possibly be measured by the scheme that has been described. But it will be seen that fulfilment of this condition only makes rule (2) true; it is at least conceivable that a property might obey rule (2) and not rules (1) and (3). Does that ever happen, or can we always find methods of addition and of judging equality such that, if rule (2) is true, the laws are such that rules (1) and (3) are also true? In the vast majority of cases we can find such methods and such laws; and it is a very remarkable fact that we can; it is only one more instance of the way in which nature kindly falls in with our ideas of what ought to be. But I think there is one case in which the necessary methods and laws have not yet been found and are not likely to be found. It is a very difficult matter concerning which even expert physicists might differ, and so no discussion of it can be entered on here. But it is mentioned in order to impress the reader with the fact that measurement does depend upon experimental laws; that it does depend upon the facts of the external world; and that it is not wholly within our power to determine whether we will or will not measure a certain property. That is the feature of measurement which it is really important to grasp for a proper understanding of science.

*Multiplication.* Before we pass to another kind of measurement reference must be made to a matter which space does not allow to be discussed completely. In stating the rules that were necessary in order that weight should be measurable (p. 209), it was said that a collection having the same weight as any given body could be made by adding other bodies to that first selected. Now this statement is not strictly true; it is only true if the body first selected has a smaller weight than any other body it is desired to weigh; and even if this condition is fulfilled, it is not true if the bodies added successively to the collection are of the same weight as that first selected. Thus if my first body weighs 1 lb., I cannot by adding to it make a collection which weighs less than 1 lb., and by adding bodies which each weigh 1 lb., I cannot make a collection which has the same weight as a body weighing (say) 2½ lb.

These facts, to which there is no true analogy in connection with number, force us to recognize "fractions." A considerable complication is thereby introduced, and the reader must accept my assurance that they can all be solved by simple developments of the process of measurement that has been sketched. But for a future purpose it is necessary to notice very briefly the processes of the multiplication and division of magnitudes on which the significance of fractions depends.

Suppose I have a collection of bodies, each of which has the same weight 3, the number of bodies in the collection being 4. I may ask what is the weight of the whole collection. The answer is given of course by multiplying 3 by 4, and we all know now that the result of that operation is 12. That fact, and all the other facts summed up in the multiplication table which we learn at school, can be proved from the rules on which weighing depend together with facts determined by counting numerals. But the point I want to make is that multiplication represents a definite experimental operation, namely the combination into a single collection, placed on one pan of the balance, of a set of bodies, all of the same weight, the number of those bodies being known. Division arises directly out of multiplication. In place of asking what will be the weight of a collection formed of a given number of bodies all of the same weight, we ask what must be the weight of each of a collection of bodies, having a given number, when the whole collection has a given weight. *E.g.*, what must each body weigh in order that the whole collection of 4 bodies weighs 12? The answer is obtained by dividing 12 by 4. That answer is obtained, partly from the multiplication table, partly by inventing new numerals which we call fractions; but once again division corresponds to a definite experimental operation and has its primary significance because it corresponds to that operation. This is this conclusion that we shall use in the sequel. But it is worth while noting that the fractions which we obtain by this method of addition overcome the difficulty from which this paragraph started. If we make all possible fractions of our original weight (*i.e.*, all possible bodies, such that some number of them formed into a single collection have the same weight as the original body), then, by adding together suitable collections of these fractions, we can make up a collection which will have the same weight as any body whatever that we desire to weigh. This result is an experimental fact which could not have been predicted without experimental inquiry. And the result is true, not only for the measurable property weight, but for all properties measurable by the process that is applicable to weight. Once more we see how much simpler and more conveniently things turn out than we have really any right to expect; measurement would have been a much more complex business if the law that has just been stated were not always true.

*Derived Measurement.* Measurement, it was said on p. 204, is the assignment of numbers (or, as we say now, numerals) to represent properties. We have now considered one way in which this assignment is made, and have brought to light the laws which must be true if this way is to be possible. And it is the fundamental way. We are now going to consider some other ways in which numerals are assigned to represent properties; but it is important to insist at the outset, and to remember throughout, that these other ways are wholly dependent upon the fundamental process, which we have just been discussing, and must be so dependent if the numerals are to represent "real properties" and to tell us something scientifically significant about the bodies to which they are attached. This statement is confirmed by history; all properties measured in the definitely pre-scientific era were measured (or at least measurable) by the fundamental process; that is true of weight, length, volume, area and periods of time. The dependent measurement, which we are now about to consider, is a product of definitely and consciously scientific investigation, although the actual discovery may, in a few cases, be lost in the mists of the past.

The property which we shall take as an example of this dependent or, as it will be termed, derived measurement, is *density*. Every one has some idea of what density means and realizes, vaguely at least, why we say that iron is denser than wood or mercury than water; and most people probably know how density is measured, and what is meant when it is said that the density of iron is 8 times that of wood, and the density of mercury 13½ times that of water. But they will feel also that there is something more scientific and less purely common-sense about the measurement of density than about the measurement of weight; as a matter of fact the discovery of the measurement of density certainly falls within the historic period and probably may be attributed to Archimedes (about 250 B.C.). And a little reflection will convince them that there is something essentially different in the two processes.

For what we mean when we say a body has a weight 2 is that a body of the same weight can be made by combining 2 bodies of the weight 1; that is the fundamental meaning of weight; it is what makes weight physically important and, as we have just seen, makes it measurable. But when we say that mercury has a density 13½ we do *not* mean that a body of the same density can be prepared by combining 13½ bodies of the density 1 (water). For, if we did mean that, the statement would not be true. However many pieces of water we take, all of the same density, we cannot produce a body with any different density. Combine water with water as we will, the resulting body has the density of water. And this, a little reflection will show, is part of the fundamental meaning of density; density is something that is characteristic of all pieces of water, large and small. The density of water, a "quality" of it, is something fundamentally independent of and in contrast with the weight of water, the "quantity" of it.

But the feature of density, from which it derives its importance, makes it totally impossible to measure density by the fundamental process discussed earlier in the chapter. How then do we measure it? Before we answer that question, it will be well to put another. As was insisted before, if measurement is really to mean anything, there must be some important resemblance between the property measured, on the one hand, and the numerals assigned to represent it, on the other. In fundamental measurement, this resemblance (or the most important part of it) arises from the fact that the property is susceptible to addition following the same rules as that of number, with which numerals are so closely associated. That resemblance fails here. What resemblance is left?

*Measurement and Order.* There is left a resemblance in respect of "order." The numerals are characterized, in virtue of their use to represent numbers, by a definite order; they are conventionally arranged in a series in which the sequence is determined: "2" follows "1" and is before "3"; "3" follows "2" and is before "4" and so on. This characteristic order of numerals is applied usefully for many purposes in modern life; we "number" the pages of a book or the houses of a street, not in order to know the number of pages in the book or of houses in the street—nobody but the printer or the rate-surveyor cares about that—but in order to be able to find any given page or house easily. If we want p. 201 and the book opens casually at p. 153 we know in which direction to turn the pages.[3] Order then is characteristic of numerals; it is also characteristic of the properties represented by numerals in the manner we are considering now. This is our feature which makes the "measurement" significant. Thus, in our example, bodies have a natural order of density which is independent of actual measurement. We might define the words "denser" or "less dense" as applied to liquids (and the definition could easily be extended to solids) by saying that the liquid A is denser than B, and B less dense than A, if a substance can be found which will float in A but not in B. And, if we made the attempt, we should find that by use of this definition we could place all liquids in a definite order, such that each

3. Numerals are also used to represent objects, such as soldiers or telephones, which have no natural order. They are used here because they provide an *inexhaustible* series of names, in virtue of the ingenious device by which new numerals can always be invented when the old ones have been used up.

member of the series was denser than the preceding and less dense than the following member. We might then assign to the first liquid the density 1, to the second 2, and so on; and we should then have assigned numerals in a way which would be physically significant and indicate definite physical facts. The fact that A was represented by 2 and B by 7 would mean that there was some solid body which would float in B, but not in A. We should have achieved something that might fairly be called measurement.

Here again it is important to notice that the possibility of such measurement depends upon definite laws; we could not have predicted beforehand that such an arrangement of liquids was possible unless we knew these laws. One law involved is this: If B is denser than A, and C denser than B, then C is denser than A. That sounds like a truism; but it is not. According to our definition it implies that the following statement is always true: If a body X floats in B and sinks in A, then if another body Y sinks in B it will also sink in A. That is a statement of facts; nothing but experiment could prove that it is true; it is a law. And if it were not true, we could not arrange liquids naturally in a definite order. For the test with X would prove that B was denser than A, while the test with Y (floating in A, but sinking in B) would prove that A was denser than B. Are we then to put A before or after B in the order of density? We should not know. The order would be indeterminate and, whether we assigned a higher or a lower numeral to A than to B, the assignment would represent no definite physical fact: it would be arbitrary.

In order to show that the difficulty might occur, and that it is an experimental law that it does not occur, an instance in which a similar difficulty has actually occurred may be quoted. An attempt has been made to define the "hardness" of a body by saying that A is harder than B if A will scratch B. Thus diamond will scratch glass, glass iron, iron lead, lead chalk, and chalk butter; so that the definition leads to the order of hardness: diamond, glass, iron, lead, chalk, butter. But if there is to be a definite order, it must be true in all cases that if A is harder than B and B than C, then A is harder than C; in other words, if A will scratch B and B C, then A will scratch C. But it is found experimentally that there are exceptions to this rule, when we try to include all bodies within it and not only such simple examples as have been quoted. Accordingly the definition does not lead to a definite order of hardness and does not permit the measurement of hardness.

There are other laws of the same kind that have to be true if the order is to be definite and the measurement significant; but they will not be given in detail. One of them the reader may discover for himself, if he will consider the property colour. Colour is not a property measurable in the way we are considering, and for this reason. If we take all reds (say) of a given shade, we can arrange them definitely in an order of lightness and darkness; but no colour other than red will fall in this order. On the other hand, we might possibly take all shades and arrange them in order of redness—pure red, orange, yellow, and so on; but in this order there would be no room for reds of different lightness. Colours cannot be arranged in a single order, and it is for this reason that colour is not measurable as is density.

*Numerical Laws.* But though arrangement in this manner in an order and the assignment of numerals in the order of the properties are to some extent measurement and represent something physically significant, there is still a large arbitrary element involved. If the properties A, B, C, D, are naturally arranged in that order, then in assigning numerals to represent the properties I must *not* assign to A 10, to B 3, to C 25, to D 18; for if I did so the order of the numerals would not be that of the properties. But I have an endless number of alternatives left; I might put A 1, B 2, C 3, D 4; or A 10, B 100, C 1,000, D 10,000; or A 3, B 9, C 27, D 81; and so on. In the true and fundamental measurement of the first part of the chapter there was no such latitude. When I had fixed the numeral to be assigned to one property, there was no choice at all of the numerals to be assigned to the others; they were all fixed. Can I remove this latitude here too and find a way of fixing definitely what numeral is to be assigned to represent each property?

In some cases, I can; and one of these cases is density. The procedure is this. I find that by combining the numerals representing other properties of the bodies, which can be measured definitely according to the fundamental process, I can obtain a numeral for each body, and that these numerals lie in the order of the property I want to measure. If I take these numerals as representing the property, then I still get numerals in the right order, but the numeral for each property is definitely fixed. An example will be clearer than this general statement. In the case of density, I find that if I measure the weight and the volume of a body (both measurable by the fundamental process and therefore definitely fixed), and I divide the weight by the volume, then the numerals thus obtained for different bodies lie in the order of their densities, as density was defined on pp. 215–216. Thus I find that 1 gallon of water weighs 10 lb., but 1 gallon of mercury weighs 135 lb.; the weight divided by the volume for water is 10, for mercury is 135; 135 is greater than 10; accordingly, if the method is correct, mercury should be denser than water and any body which sinks in mercury should sink in water. And that is actually found to be true. If therefore I take as the measure of the density of a substance, its weight divided by its volume, then I get a number which is definitely fixed,[4] and the order of which represents the order of density. I have arrived at a method of measurement which is as definitely fixed as the fundamental process and yet conveys adequately the physically significant facts about order.

The invention of this process of measurement for properties not suited for fundamental measurement is a very notable achievement of deliberate scientific investigation. The process was not invented by common sense; it was certainly invented in the historic period, but it was not until the middle of the eighteenth century that its use became widespread.[5] To-day it is one of the most powerful weapons of scientific investigation; and it is because so many of the properties of importance to other sciences are measured in this way that physics, the science to which this process belongs, is so largely the basis of other sciences. But it may appear exceedingly obvious to the reader, and he may wonder why the invention was delayed so long. He may say that the notion of density, in the sense that a given volume of the denser substance weighs more than the same volume of the less dense, is the fundamental notion; it is what we mean when we speak of one substance being denser (or in popular language "heavier") than another; and that all that has been discovered in this instance is that the denser body, in this sense, is also denser in the sense of pp. 215–216. This in itself would be a very noteworthy discovery, but the reader who raises such an objection has overlooked a yet more noteworthy discovery that is involved.

For we have observed that it is one of the most characteristic features of density that it is the same for all bodies, large and small, made of the same substance. It is this feature which makes it impossible to measure it by the fundamental process. The new process will be satisfactory only if it preserves this feature. If we are going to represent density by the weight divided by the volume, the density of all bodies made of the same sub-

---

4. Except in so far as I may change the units in which I measure weights and volume. I should get a different number if I measured the volume in pints and the weight in tons. But this latitude in the choice of units introduces a complication which it will be better to leave out of account here. There is no reason why we should not agree once and for all to use the same units; and if we did that the complication would not arise.
5. I think that until the eighteenth century only two properties were measured in this way which were not measurable by the fundamental process, namely density and constant acceleration.

stance will be the same, as it should be, only if for all of them the weight divided by the density is the same, that is to say, in rather more technical language, if the weight is proportional to the density. In adopting the new process for measuring density and assigning numerals to represent it in a significant manner, we are, in fact, assuming that, for portions of the same substance, whether they are large or small, the weight is proportional to the volume. If we take a larger portion of the same substance and thereby double the weight, we must find, if the process of measurement is to be a success, that we also double the volume; and this law must be true for all substances to which the conception of density is applicable at all.

Of course every one knows that this relation is actually true; it is so familiar that we are apt to forget that it is an experimental truth that was discovered relatively late in the history of civilization, which easily might not be true. Perhaps it is difficult to-day to conceive that when we take "more" of a substance (meaning thereby a greater volume) the weight should not increase, but it is quite easy to conceive that the weight should not increase proportionally to the volume; and yet it is upon strict proportionality that the measurement of density actually depends. If the weight had not been proportional to the volume, it might still have been possible to measure density, so long as there was some fixed numerical relation between weight and volume. It is this idea of a fixed numerical relation, or, as we shall call it henceforward, a numerical law, that is the basis of the "derived" process of measurement that we are considering; and the process is of such importance to science because it is so intimately connected with such numerical laws. The recognition of such laws is the foundation of modern physics.

*The Importance of Measurement.* For why is the process of measurement of such vital importance; why are we so concerned to assign numerals to represent properties. One reason doubtless is that such assignment enables us to distinguish easily and minutely between different but similar properties. It enables us to distinguish between the density of lead and iron far more simply and accurately than we could do by saying that lead is rather denser than iron, but not nearly so dense as gold—and so on. But for that purpose the "arbitrary" measurement of density, depending simply on the arrangements of the substances in their order (pp. 215-216), would serve equally well. The true answer to our question is seen by remembering . . . that the terms between which laws express relationships are themselves based on laws and represent collections of other terms related by laws. When we measure a property, either by the fundamental process or by the derived process, the numeral which we assign to represent it is assigned as the result of experimental laws; the assignment implies laws. And therefore, in accordance with our principle, we should expect to find that other laws could be discovered relating the numerals so assigned to each other or to something else; while if we assigned numerals arbitrarily without reference to laws and implying no laws, then we should not find other laws involving these numerals. This expectation is abundantly fulfilled, and nowhere is there a clearer example of the fact that the terms involved in laws themselves imply laws. When we can measure a property truly, as we can volume (by the fundamental process) or density (by the derived process) then we are always able to find laws in which these properties are involved; we find, *e.g.*, the law that volume is proportional to weight or that density determines, in a certain precise fashion, the sinking or floating of bodies. But when we cannot measure it truly, then we do not find a law. An example is provided by the property "hardness" (p. 216); the difficulties met with in arranging bodies in order of hardness have been overcome; but we still do not know of any way of measuring, by the derived process, the property hardness; we know of no numerical law which leads to a numeral which always follows the order of hardness. And so, as we expect, we do not know any accurate and general laws relating hardness to other properties. It is because true measurement is essential to the discovery of laws that it is of such vital importance to science.

One final remark should be made before we pass on. In this chapter there has been much insistence on the distinction between fundamental measurement (such as is applicable to weight) and derived measurement (such as is applicable to density). And the distinction is supremely important, because it is the first kind of measurement which alone makes the second possible. But the reader who, when he studies some science in detail, tries, as he should, to discover which of the two processes is involved in the measurement of the various properties characteristic of that science, may occasionally find difficulty in answering the question. It should be pointed out, therefore, that it is quite possible for a property to be measurable by both processes. For all properties measurable by the fundamental process must have a definite order; for the physical property, number, to which they are so similar, has an order—the order of "more" or "less." This order of number is reflected in the order of the numerals used to represent number. But if it is to be measurable by the derived process, it must also be such that it is also a "constant" in a numerical law—a term that is just going to be explained in the next chapter. There is nothing in the nature of fundamental measurement to show that a property to which it is applicable may not fulfil this condition also; and sometimes the condition is fulfilled, and then the property is measurable either by the fundamental or the derived process. However, it must be remembered that the properties involved in the numerical law must be such that they are fundamentally measurable; for otherwise the law could not be established. The neglect of this condition is apt to lead to confusion; but with this bare hint the matter must be left.

# Numerical Laws and the Use
# of Mathematics in Science

In the previous chapter we concluded that density was a measurable property because there is a fixed numerical relation, asserted by a "numerical law," between the weight of a substance and its volume. In this chapter we shall examine more closely the idea of a numerical law, and discover how it leads to such exceedingly important developments.

Let us first ask exactly what we do when we are trying to discover a numerical law, such as that between weight and volume. We take various portions of a substance, measure their weights and their volumes, and put down the result in two parallel columns in our notebook. Thus I may find these results:

### Table I

| Weight | Volume | | Weight | Volume |
|--------|--------|---|--------|--------|
| 1 | 7 | | 4 | 28 |
| 2 | 14 | | 10 | 70 |
| 3 | 21 | | 29 | 203 |

I now try to find some fixed relation between the corresponding numbers in the two columns; and I shall succeed in that attempt if I can find some rule whereby, starting with the number in one column, I can arrive at the corresponding number in the other. If I find such a rule—and if the rule holds good for all the further measurements that I may make—then I have discovered a numerical law.

In the example we have taken the rule is easy to find. I have only to divide the numbers in the second column by 7 in order to arrive at those in the first, or multiply those in the first by 7 in order to arrive at those in the second. That is a definite rule which I can always apply whatever the numbers are; it is a rule which might always be true, but need not always be true; whether or no it is true is a matter for experiment to decide. So much is obvious; but now I want to ask a further and important question.

How did we ever come to discover this rule; what suggested to us to try division or multiplication by 7: and what is the precise significance of division and multiplication in this connection?

*The Source of Numerical Relations.* The answer to the first part of this question is given by the discussion on p. 213. Division and multiplication are operations of importance in the counting of objects; in such counting the relation between 21, 7, 3 (the third of which results from the division of the first by the second) corresponds to a definite relation between the things counted; it implies that if I divide the 21 objects into 7 groups, each containing the same number of objects, then the number of objects in each of the 7 groups is 3. By examining such relations through the experimental process of counting we arrive at the multiplication (or division) table. This table, when it is completed, states a long series of relations between numerals, each of which corresponds to an experimental fact; the numerals represent physical properties (numbers) and in any given relation (*e.g.*, $7 \times 3 = 21$) each numeral represents a different property. But when we have got the multiplication table, a statement of relations between numerals, we can regard it, and do usually regard it, *simply* as a statement of relations between numerals; we can think about it without any regard to what those numerals represented when we were drawing up the table. And if any other numerals are presented to our notice, it is possible and legitimate to ask whether these numerals, whatever they may represent, are in fact related as are the numerals in the multiplication table. In particular, when we are seeking a numerical relation between the columns of Table I, we may inquire, and it is natural for us to inquire, whether by means of the multiplication we can find a rule which will enable us to arrive at the numeral in the second column starting from that in the first.

That explains why it is so natural to us to try division when we are seeking a relation between numbers. But it does not answer the second part of the question; for in the numerical law that we are considering, the relation between the things represented by the numerals is *not* that which we have just noticed between things counted. When we say that, by dividing the volume by 7, we can arrive at the weight, we do *not* mean that the weight *is* the volume of each of the things at which we arrive by dividing the substance into 7 portions, each having the same volume. For a weight can never *be* a volume, any more than a soldier can *be* a number; it can only be represented by the same numeral as a volume, as a soldier can be represented by a numeral which also represents a number.

The distinction is rather subtle, but if the reader is to understand what follows, he must grasp it. The relation which we have found between weight and volume is a pure numerical relation; it is suggested by the relation between actual things, namely collections which we count; but it is not that relation. The difference may be expressed again by means of the distinction between numbers and numerals. The relation between actual things counted is a relation between the numbers—which are physical properties—of those things; the relation between weight and volume is a relation between numerals, the numerals that are used to represent those properties. The physical relation in the second case is not between numbers at all, but between weight and volume which are properties quite different from numbers; it appears very similar to that between numbers only because we use numerals, originally invented to represent numbers, to represent other properties. The relation stated by a numerical law is a relation between numerals, and only between numerals, though the idea that there may be such a relation has been suggested to us by the study of the physical property, number.

If we understand this, we shall see what a very remarkable thing it is that there should be numerical laws at all, and shall see why the idea of such a law arose comparatively late in the history of science. For even when we know the relations between numbers, there is no reason to believe that there must be any relations of the same kind between the numerals which are used to represent, not only numbers, but also other properties. Until we actually tried, there was no reason to think that it must be possible to find at all numerical laws, stating numerical relations such as those of division and multiplication. The fact that there are such relations is a new fact, and ought to be surprising. As has been said so often, it does frequently turn out that suggestions made simply by our habits of mind are actually true; and it is because they are so often true that science is interesting. But every time they are true there is reason for wonder and astonishment.

And there is a further consequence yet more deserving of our attention at present. If we realize that the numerical relations in numerical laws, though suggested by relations between numbers, are not those relations, we shall be prepared to find also numerical relations which are not even suggested by relations between numbers, but only by relations between numerals. Let me take an example. Consider the pairs of numerals $(1, 1)$, $(2, 4)$, $(3, 9)$, $(4, 16)$ . . . Our present familiarity with numerals enables us to see at once what is the relation between each pair; it is that the second numeral of the pair is arrived at by multiplying the first numeral *by itself;* 1 is equal to $1 \times 1$, 4 to $2 \times 2$, 9 to $3 \times 3$; and so on. But, if the reader will consider the matter, he will see that the multiplication of a number (the physical property of an object) by itself does not correspond to any simple relation between the things counted; by the mere examination of counted objects, we should never be led to consider such an operation at all. It is suggested to us only because we have drawn up our multiplication table and have reached the idea of multiplying one *numeral* by another, irrespective of what is represented by that numeral. We know what is the result of multiplying 3 × 3, when the two 3's represent different numbers and the multiplication corresponds to a physical operation on things counted; it occurs to us that the multiplication of 3 by *itself*, when the two 3's represent the same thing, although it does not correspond to a physical relation, may yet correspond to the numerical relation in a numerical law. And we find once more that this suggestion turns out to be true; there are numerical laws in which this numerical relation is found. Thus if we measure (1) the time during which a body starting from rest has been falling (2) the distance through which it has fallen during that time, we should get in our notebook parallel columns like this:

### Table II

| Time | Distance | | Time | Distance |
|------|----------|---|------|----------|
| 1 | 1 | | 4 | 16 |
| 2 | 4 | | 5 | 25 |
| 3 | 9 | | 6 | 36 |

The numerals in the second column are arrived at by multiplying those in the first by themselves; in technical language, the second column is the "square" of the first.

Another example. In place of dividing one column by some fixed number in order to get the other, we may use the multiplication table to divide some fixed number (*e.g.*, 1) by that column. Then we should get the table

| 1 | 1.00 | | 3 | 0.33 |
|---|------|---|---|------|
| 2 | 0.50 | | 4 | 0.25 |
| | | | 5 | 0.20 |

and so on. Here, again, is a pure numerical operation which does not correspond to any simple physical relation upon numbers; there is no collection simply related to another collection in such a way that the number of the first is equal to that obtained by dividing 1 by the number of the second. (Indeed, as we have seen that fractions have no application to number, and since this rule must lead to fractions, there cannot be such a relation.) And yet once more we find that this numerical relation does occur in a numerical law. If the first column represented the pressure on a given amount of gas, the second would represent the volume of that gas.

So far, all the relations we have considered were derived directly from the multiplication table. But an extension of the process that we are tracing leads to relations which cannot be derived directly and thus carries us further from the original suggestions indicated by mere counting. Let us return to Table II, and consider what would happen if we found for the numerals in the second column values intermediate between those given. Suppose we measured the distance first and found 2, 3, 5, 6, 7, 8, 10, 11, 12, 13, 14, 15 . . . ; what does the rule lead us to expect for the corresponding entries in the first column, the values of the time. The answer will be given if in the multiplication table we can find numerals which, when multiplied by themselves, give 2, 3, 5 . . . But a search will reveal that there are no such numerals. We can find numerals which, when multiplied by themselves give very nearly 2, 3, 5 . . . ; for instance, 1.41, 1.73, 2.24 give 1.9881, 2.9929, 5.0166, and we could find numerals which would come even closer to those desired. And that is really all we want, for our measurements are never perfectly accurate, and if we can get numerals which agree very nearly with our rule, that is all that we can expect. But the search for such numerals would be a very long and tedious business; it would involve our drawing up an enormously complicated multiplication table, including not only whole numbers but also fractions with many decimal places. And so the question arises if we cannot find some simpler rule for obtaining quickly the number which multiplied by itself will come as close as we please to 2, 3, 4 . . . Well, we can; the rule is given in every textbook of arithmetic; it need not be given here. The point which interests us is that, just as the simple multiplication of two numerals suggested a new process, namely the multiplication of a numeral by itself, so this new process suggests in its turn many other and more complicated processes. To each of these new processes corresponds a new rule for relating numerals and for arriving at one starting from another; and to each new rule may correspond a numerical law. We thus get many fresh forms of numerical law suggested, and some of them will be found to represent actual experiments.

This process for extending arithmetical operations beyond the simple division and multiplication from which we start; the consequent invention of new rules for relating numerals and deriving one from another; and the study of the rules, when they are invented—all this is a purely intellectual process. It does not depend on experiment at all; experiment enters only when we inquire whether there is an actual experimental law stating one of the invented numerical relations between measured properties. The process is, in fact, part of mathematics, not of experimental science; and one of the reasons why mathematics is useful to science is that it suggests possible new forms for numerical laws. Of course the examples that have been given are extremely elementary, and the actual mathematics of to-day has diverged very widely from such simple considerations; but the invention of such rules leads, logically if not historically, to one of the great branches of modern mathematics, the theory of functions. (When two numbers are related as in our tables, they are technically said to be "functions" of each other.) It has been developed by mathematicians to satisfy their own intellectual needs, their sense of logical neatness and of form; but though great tracts of it have no bearing whatever upon experimental science, it still remains remarkable how often relations developed by the mathematician for his own purposes prove in the end to have direct and immediate application to the experimental facts of science.

*Numerical Laws and Derived Measurement.* In this discussion there has been overlooked temporarily the feature of numerical laws which, in the previous chapter, we decided gave rise to their importance, namely, that they made possible systems of derived measurement. In the first law, taken as an example (Table I), the rule by which the numerals in the second column were derived from those in the first involved a numeral 7, which was not a member of those columns, but an additional number applicable equally to all members of the columns. This constant numeral, characteristic of the rule asserted by the numerical law, represented a property of the system investigated and permitted a derived measurement of that system. But in Table II, there is no such constant numeral; the rule for obtaining the second from the first column is simply that the numerals in the first column are to be multiplied by themselves; no other numeral is involved. But this simplicity is really misleading; we should not, except by a mere "fluke," ever get such a table as Table II as a result of our measurements. The reason is this. Suppose that, in obtaining Table II, we have measured the time in seconds and the distance fallen in feet; and that we now propose to write down the result of exactly the same measurements, measuring the time in minutes and the distances in yards. Then the numerals in the first column, representing exactly the same observations, would all be divided by 60 and those in the second would all be divided by 3; the observation which was represented before by 60 in the first column would now be represented by 1; and the number in the second column represented before by 3 would now be represented by 1. If I now apply the rule to the two columns I shall find it will not work; the second is *not* the first multiplied by itself. But there will be a new rule, as the reader may see for himself; it will be that the second column is the same as the first, when the first is (1) multiplied by itself, and (2) the result multiplied by 1,200. And if we measured the time and the distance in some other units (say hours and miles), we should again have to amend our rule, but it would only differ from the former rule in the substitution for 1,200 of some other numeral. If we choose our units in yet a third way, we should get a third rule, and this time the constant numeral might be 1. We should have exactly Table II; but we should get that table exactly only because we had chosen our units of time and distance in a particular way.

These considerations are quite general. Whatever the numerical law, the rule involved in it will be changed by changing the unit in which we measure the properties represented by the two columns; but the change will only consist in the substitution of one constant numeral for another. If we chance to choose the units in some particular way, that constant numeral may turn out to be 1 and so will disappear from sight. But it will always be there. There must be associated with every numerical law, involving a rule for arriving at the numerals in one column from those in the other, some constant numeral which is applicable to all members of the column alike. And this constant may always, as in the case of density, be the measure of some property to which derived measurement is applicable. Every numerical law therefore—this is the conclusion to be enforced—may give rise to a system of derived measurement; and as a matter of fact all important numerical laws do actually so give rise.

*Calculation.* But though the establishment of system of derived measurement is one use of numerical laws, they have also another use, which is even more important. They permit *calculation.* This is an extremely important conception which deserves our close attention.

Calculation is the process of combining two or more numerical laws in such a way as to produce a third numerical law. The simplest form of it may be illustrated by the following example. We know the following two laws which, in rather different forms, have been quoted before: (1) the weight of a given volume of any substance is proportional to its density; (2) the density of a gas is proportional to the pressure upon it. From these two laws we can deduce the third law: the weight of a given volume of any gas is proportional to the pressure upon it. That conclusion seems to follow directly without any need for further experiments. Accordingly we appear to have arrived at a fresh numerical law without adducing any fresh experimental evidence. But is that possible? All our previous inquiry leads us to believe that laws, whether numerical or other, can only be proved by experimental inquiry and that the proof of a new law without new experimental evidence is impossible. How are we to reconcile the two conclusions? When we have answered that question we shall understand what is the importance of calculation for science.

Let us first note that it is possible, without violating the conclusions already reached, to deduce *something* from a numerical law by a process of mere thought without new experiment. For instance, from the law that the density of iron is 7, I can deduce that a portion of it which has a volume 1 will have a weight 7. But this deduction is merely stating in new terms what was asserted by the original law; when I said that the density of iron was 7, I meant (among other things) that a volume 1 had a weight 7; if I had not meant that I should never have asserted the law. The "deduction" is nothing but a translation of the law (or of part of it) into different language, and is of no greater scientific importance than a translation from (say) English into French. One kind of translation, like the other, may have useful results, but it is not the kind of useful result that is obtained from calculation. Pure deduction never achieves anything but this kind of translation; it never leads to anything new. But the calculation taken as an example does lead to something new. Neither when I asserted the first law, nor when I asserted the second did I mean what is asserted by the third; I might have asserted the first without knowing the second and the second without knowing the first (for I might have known what the density of a gas was under different conditions without knowing precisely how it is measured); and I might have asserted either of them, without knowing the third. The third law is not merely an expression in different words of something known before; it is a new addition to knowledge.

But we have added to knowledge only because we have introduced an assertion which was not contained in the two original statements. The deduction depends on the fact that if one thing (A) is proportional to another thing (B) and if B is proportional to a third thing (C), then A is proportional to C. This proposition was not contained in the original statements. But, the reader may reply, it *was* so contained, because it is involved in the very meaning of "proportional"; when we say that A is proportional to B, we mean to imply the fact which has just been stated. Now that is perfectly true if we are thinking of the mathematical meaning of "proportional," but it is not true if we are thinking of the physical meaning. The proposition which we have really used in making our deduction is this: If weight is proportional (in the mathematical sense) to density, when weight is varied by taking different substances, then it is also proportional to density when weight is varied by compressing more of the same substance into the same volume. That is a statement which experiment alone can prove, and it is because we have in fact assumed that experimental statement that we have been able to "deduce" a new piece of experimental knowledge. It is involved in the original statements only if, when it is said that density is proportional to pressure, it is implied that it has been ascertained by experiment that the law of density is true, and that there is a constant density of a gas, however compressed, given by dividing the weight by the volume.

The conclusion I want to draw is this. When we appear to arrive at new scientific knowledge by mere deduction from previous knowledge, we are always assuming some experimental fact which is not clearly involved in the original statements. What we usually assume is that some law is true in circumstances rather more general than those we have considered hitherto. Of course the assumption may be quite legitimate, for the great value of laws is that they are applicable to circumstances more general than those of the experiments on which they are based; but we can never be perfectly sure that it is legitimate until we try. Calculation, then, when it appears to add anything to our knowledge, is always slightly precarious; like theory, it suggests strongly that some law may be true, rather than proves definitely that some law must be true.

So far we have spoken of calculation as if it were merely deduction; we have not referred to the fact that calculation always involves a special type of deduction, namely mathematical deduction. For there are, of course, forms of deduction which are not mathematical. All argument is based, or should be based, upon the logical processes which are called deduction; and most of us are prepared to argue, however slight our mathematical attainments. I do not propose to discuss here generally what are the distinctive characteristics of mathematical argument; for an exposition of that matter the reader should turn to works in which mathematicians expound their own study.[1] I want only to consider why it is that

---

1. See, for example, the essays in this volume by Alfred North Whitehead, Henri Poincaré, A. R. Forsyth, and Lancelot Hogben.

this kind of deduction has such a special significance for science. And, stated briefly, the reason is this. The assumption, mentioned in the last paragraph, which is introduced in the process of deduction, is usually suggested by the form of the deduction and by the ideas naturally associated with it. (Thus, in the example we took, the assumption is suggested by the proposition quoted about proportionality which is the idea especially associated by the form of the deduction). The assumptions thus suggested by mathematical deduction are almost invariably found to be actually true. It is this fact which gives to mathematical deduction its special significance for science.

*The Newtonian Assumption.* Again an example is necessary and we will take one which brings us close to the actual use of mathematics in science. Let us return to Table II which gives the relation between the time for which a body has fallen and the distance through which it has fallen. The falling body, like all moving bodies, has a "velocity." By the velocity of a body we mean the distance that it moves in a given time, and we measure the velocity by dividing that distance by that time (as we measure density by dividing the weight by the volume). But this way of measuring velocity gives a definite result only when the velocity is constant, that is to say, when the distance travelled is proportional to the time and the distance travelled in any given time is always the same (compare what was said about density on pp. 217–218). This condition is not fulfilled in our example; the distance fallen in the first second is 1, in the next 3, in the third 5, in the next 7—and so on. We usually express that fact by saying that the velocity increases as the body falls; but we ought really to ask ourselves whether there is such a thing as velocity in this case and whether, therefore, the statement can mean anything. For what is the velocity of the body at the end of the 3rd second—*i.e.* at the time called 3. We might say that it is to be found by taking the distance travelled in the second before 3, which is 5, or in the second after 3, which is 7, or in the second of which the instant "3" is the middle (from 2½ to 3½), which turns out to be 6. Or again we might say it is to be found by taking *half* the distance travelled in the two seconds of which "3" is the middle (from 2 to 4) which is again 6. We get different values for the velocity according to which of these alternatives we adopt. There are doubtless good reasons in this example for choosing the alternative 6, for two ways (and really many more than two ways, all of them plausible) lead to the same result. But if we took a more complicated relation between time and distance than that of Table II, we should find that these two ways gave different results, and that neither of them were obviously more plausible than any alternative. Do then we mean anything by velocity in such cases and, if so, what do we mean?

It is here that mathematics can help us. By simply thinking about the matter Newton, the greatest of mathematicians, devised a rule by which he suggested that velocity might be measured in all such cases.[2] It is a rule applicable to every kind of relation between time and distance that actually occurs; and it gives the "plausible" result whenever that relation is so simple that one rule is more plausible than another. Moreover it is a very pretty and ingenious rule; it is based on ideas which are themselves attractive and in every way it appeals to the aesthetic sense of the mathematician. It enables us, when we know the relation between time and distance, to measure uniquely and certainly the velocity at every instant, in however complicated a way the velocity may be changing. It is therefore strongly suggested that we take as the velocity the value obtained according to this rule.

But can there be any question whether we are right or wrong to take that value; can experiment show that we ought to take one value rather than another? Yes, it can; and in this way. When the velocity is constant and we can measure it without ambiguity, then we can establish laws between that velocity and certain properties of the moving body. Thus, if we allow a moving steel ball to impinge on a lead block, it will make a dent in it determined by its velocity; and when we have established by observations of this kind a relation between the velocity and the size of the dent, we can obviously use the size of the dent to measure the velocity. Suppose now our falling body is a steel ball, and we allow it to impinge on a lead block after falling through different distances; we shall find that its velocity, estimated by the size of the dent, agrees exactly with the velocity estimated by Newton's rule, and not with that estimated by any other rule (so long, of course, as the other rule does not give the same result as Newton's). That, I hope the reader will agree, is a very definite proof that Newton's rule is right.

On this account only Newton's rule would be very important, but it has a wider and much more important application. So far we have expressed the rule as giving the velocity at any instant when the relation between time and distance is known; but the problem might be reversed. We might know the velocity at any instant and want to find out how far the body has moved in any given time. If the velocity were the same at all instants, the

2. I purposely refrain from giving the rule, not because it is really hard to explain, but because I want to make clear that what is important is to have *some* rule, not any particular rule.

problem would be easy; the distance would be the velocity multiplied by the time. But if it is not the same, the right answer is by no means easy to obtain; in fact the only way of obtaining it is by the use of Newton's rule. The form of that rule makes it easy to reverse it and, instead of obtaining the velocity from the distance, to obtain the distance from the velocity; but until that rule was given, the problem could not have been solved; it would have baffled the wisest philosophers of Greece. Now this particular problem is not of any very great importance, for it would be easier to measure by experiment the distance moved than to measure the velocity and calculate the distance. But there are closely analogous cases—one of which we shall notice immediately—in which the position will be reversed. Let us therefore ask what is the assumption which, in accordance with the conclusion reached on p. 230, must be introduced, if the solution of the problem is to give new experimental knowledge.

We have seen that the problem could be solved easily if the velocity were constant; what we are asking, is how it is to be solved if the velocity does not remain constant. If we examined the rule by which the solution is obtained, we should find that it involves the assumption that the effect upon the distance travelled of a certain velocity at a given instant of time is the same as it would be if the body had at that instant the same *constant* velocity. We know how far the body would travel at that instant if the velocity were constant, and the assumption tells us that it will travel at that instant the same distance although the velocity is not constant. To obtain the whole distance travelled in any given time, we have to add up the distances travelled at the instants of which that time is made up; the reversed Newtonian rule gives a simple and direct method for adding up these distances, and thus solves the problem. It should be noted that the assumption is one that cannot possibly be proved by experiment; we are assuming that something would happen if things were not what they actually are; and experiment can only tell us about things as they are. Accordingly calculation of this kind must, in all strictness, always be confirmed by experiment before it is certain. But as a matter of fact, the assumption is one of which we are almost more certain than we are of any experiment. It is characteristic, not only of the particular example that we have been considering, but of the whole structure of modern mathematical physics which has arisen out of the work of Newton. We should never think it really necessary to-day to confirm by experiment the results of calculation based on that assumption; indeed if experiment and calculation did not agree, we should always maintain that the former and not the latter was wrong. But the assumption is there, and it is primarily suggested by the aesthetic sense of the mathematician, not dictated by the facts of the external world. Its certainty is yet one more striking instance of the conformity of the external world with our desires.

And now let us glance at an example in which such calculation becomes of real importance. Let us take a pendulum, consisting of a heavy bob at the end of a pivoted rod, draw it aside and then let it swing. We ask how it will swing, what positions the bob will occupy at various times after it is started. Our calculation proceeds from two known laws. (1) We know how the force on the pendulum varies with its position. That we can find out by actual experiments. We hang a weight by a string over a pulley, attach the other end of the string to the bob, and notice how far the bob is pulled aside by various weights hanging at the end of the string. We thus get a numerical law between the force and the angle which the rod of the pendulum makes with the vertical. (2) We know how a body will move under a constant force. It will move in accordance with Table II, the distance travelled being proportional to the "square" of the time during which the force acts. Now we introduce the Newtonian assumption. We know the force in each position; we know how it would move in that position if the force on it were constant; actually it is not constant, but we assume that the motion will be the same as it would be if, in that position, the force were constant. With that assumption, the general Newtonian rule (of which the application to velocity is only a special instance) enables us to sum up the effects of the motions in the different positions, and thus to arrive at the desired relation between the time and the positions successively occupied by the pendulum. The whole of the calculation which plays so large a part in modern science is nothing but an elaboration of that simple example.

## MATHEMATICAL THEORIES

We have now examined two of the applications of mathematics to science. Both of them depend on the fact that relations which appeal to the sense of the mathematician by their neatness and simplicity are found to be important in the external world of experiment. The relations between numerals which he suggests are found to occur in numerical laws, and the assumptions which are suggested by his arguments are found to be true. We have finally to notice a yet more striking example of the same fact, and one which is much more difficult to explain to the layman.

This last application is in formulating theories. . . . A theory, to be valuable, must have two features. It must be such that laws can be predicted from it and such that it explains these laws by introducing some analogy based on laws more familiar than those to be explained. In recent developments of physics, theories have been developed which conform to the first of these conditions but not to the second. In place of the analogy with familiar laws, there appears the new principle of mathematical simplicity. These theories explain the laws, as do the older theories, by replacing less acceptable by more acceptable ideas; but the greater acceptability of the ideas introduced by the theories is not derived from an analogy with familiar laws, but simply from the strong appeal they make to the mathematician's sense of form.

I do not feel confident that I can explain the matter further to those who have not some knowledge of both physics and mathematics, but I must try. The laws on the analogy with which theories of the older type are based were often (in physics, usually) numerical laws, such laws for example as that of the falling body. Now numerical laws, since they involve mathematical relations, are usually expressed, not in words, but in the symbols in which, as every one knows, mathematicians express their ideas and their arguments. I have been careful to avoid these symbols; until this page there is hardly an "x" or a "y" in the book. And I have done so because experience shows that they frighten people; they make them think that something very difficult is involved. But really, of course, symbols make things easier; it is conceivable that some superhuman intellect might be able to study mathematics, and even to advance it, expressing all his thoughts in words. Actually, the wonderful symbolism mathematics has invented makes such efforts unnecessary; [symbols] make the processes of reasoning quite easy to follow. They are actually inseparable from mathematics; they make exceedingly difficult arguments easy to follow by means of simple rules for juggling with these symbols—interchanging their order, replacing one by another, and so on. The consequence is that the expert mathematician has a sense about symbols, as symbols; he looks at a page covered with what, to anyone else, are unintelligible scrawls of ink, and he immediately realizes whether the argument expressed by them is such as is likely to satisfy his sense of form; whether the argument will be "neat" and the results "pretty." (I can't tell you what those terms mean, any more than I can tell you what I mean when I say that a picture is beautiful.)

Now sometimes, but not always, simple folk can understand what he means; let me try an example. Suppose you found a page with the following marks on it—never mind if they mean anything:

$$i = \frac{d\gamma}{dy} - \frac{d\beta}{dz} \qquad \frac{dX}{dt} = \frac{d\gamma}{dy} - \frac{d\beta}{dz}$$

$$j = \frac{d\alpha}{dz} - \frac{d\gamma}{dx} \qquad \frac{dY}{dt} = \frac{d\alpha}{dz} - \frac{d\gamma}{dx}$$

$$k = \frac{d\beta}{dx} - \frac{d\alpha}{dy} \qquad \frac{dZ}{dt} = \frac{d\beta}{dx} - \frac{d\alpha}{dy}$$

$$\frac{d\alpha}{dt} = \frac{dY}{dz} - \frac{dZ}{dy} \qquad \frac{d\alpha}{dt} = \frac{dY}{dz} - \frac{dZ}{dy}$$

$$\frac{d\beta}{dt} = \frac{dZ}{dx} - \frac{dX}{dz} \qquad \frac{d\beta}{dt} = \frac{dZ}{dx} - \frac{dX}{dz}$$

$$\frac{d\gamma}{dt} = \frac{dX}{dy} - \frac{dY}{dx} \qquad \frac{d\gamma}{dt} = \frac{dX}{dy} - \frac{dY}{dx}$$

I think you would see that the set of symbols on the right side are "prettier" in some sense than those on the left; they are more symmetrical. Well, the great physicist James Clerk Maxwell, about 1870, thought so too; and by substituting the symbols on the right side for those on the left, he founded modern physics, and, among other practical results, made wireless telegraphy possible.

It sounds incredible; and I must try to explain a little more. The symbols on the left side represent two well-known electrical laws: Ampère's Law and Faraday's Law; or rather a theory suggested by an analogy with those laws. The symbols i, j, k represent in those laws an electric current. For these symbols Maxwell substituted $\frac{dX}{dt}\ \frac{dY}{dt}\ \frac{dZ}{dt}$; that substitution was roughly equivalent to saying that an electric current was related to the things represented by X, Y, Z, t (never mind what they are) in a way nobody had ever thought of before; it was equivalent to saying that so long as X, Y, Z, t were related in a certain way, there might be an electric current in circumstances in which nobody had believed that an electric current could flow. As a matter of fact, such a current would be one flowing in an absolutely empty space without any material conductor along which it might flow, and such a current was previously thought to be impossible. But Maxwell's feeling for symbolism suggested to him that there might be such a current, and when he worked out the consequences of supposing that there were such currents (not currents perceptible in the ordinary way, but theoretical currents, as molecules are theoretical hard particles), he arrived at the unexpected result that an alteration in an electric current in one place would be reproduced at another far distant from it by waves travelling from one to the other through absolutely empty space between. Hertz actually produced and detected such waves; and Marconi made them a commercial article.

That is the best attempt I can make at explaining the matter. It is one more illustration of the marvellous power of pure thought, aiming only at the satisfaction of intellectual desires, to control the external world. Since Maxwell's time, there have been many equally wonderful theories, the form of which is suggested by nothing but the mathematician's sense for symbols. The latest are those of Sommerfeld, based [on] the ideas of Niels Bohr, and of Einstein. Every one has heard of the latter, but the former (which concerns the constitution of the atom) is quite as marvellous. But of these I could not give, even if space allowed, even such an explanation as I have attempted for Maxwell's. And the reason is this: A theory by itself means nothing experimental; . . . it is only when something is deduced from it that it is brought within the range of our material senses. Now in Maxwell's theory, the symbols, in the alteration of which the characteristic feature of the theory depends, are retained through the deduction and appear in the law which is compared with experiment. Accordingly it is possible to give some idea of what these symbols mean in terms of things experimentally observed. But in Sommerfeld's or Einstein's theory the symbols, which are necessarily involved in the assumption which differentiates their theories from others, disappear during the deduction; they leave a mark on the other symbols which remain and alter the relation between them; but the symbols on the relations of which the whole theory hangs do not appear at all in any law deduced from the theory. It is quite impossible to give any idea of what they mean in terms of experiment.[3] Probably some of my readers will have read the very interesting and ingenious attempts to "explain Einstein" which have been published, and will feel that they really have a grasp of the matter. Personally I doubt it; the only way to understand what Einstein did is to look at the symbols in which his theory must ultimately be expressed and to realize that it was reasons of symbolic form, and such reasons alone,

---

3. The same is true really of the exposition of the Newtonian assumption attempted on p. 233. It is strictly impossible to state exactly what is the assumption discussed there without using symbols. The acute reader will have guessed already that on that page I felt myself skating on very thin ice.

which led him to arrange the symbols in the way he did and in no other.

But now I have waded into such deep water that it is time to retrace my steps and return to the safe shore of the affairs of practical life.

---

*The foregoing two selections are Chapters VI & VII from Campbell's* WHAT IS SCIENCE?

# William Kingdon Clifford

## 1845–1879

William Kingdon Clifford was born at Exeter, England, in 1845. He studied at King's College, London, and then at Trinity College, Cambridge, where he was a brilliant student. He was elected a fellow of Trinity but gave up the position, in 1871, to become professor of mathematics at University College, London. While still a student he began to produce original mathematical papers, and he later made important contributions to mathematics. He was primarily a geometer, treating especially the problems of the new non-Euclidean geometries, but his thought ranged over all mathematical questions.

He was also much concerned to understand, and to make others understand, the basic ideas which underlie all science, and he gave many popular lectures in which he discussed these matters in a lucid, witty, and eloquent style. Though many eminent nineteenth-century scientists gave popular lectures—among them Faraday, Helmholtz, T. H. Huxley, and Tyndall, all of whom are represented in these volumes—it is possible that Clifford took the task more seriously than any of them. At any rate, his popular lectures, though they do not avoid all difficulties, are as entertaining and also enlightening as those of any of his contemporaries.

Clifford published several books before he died of pulmonary tuberculosis in Madeira on March 3, 1879, when he was only 35 years old. In the last year or two before his death he was engaged in writing a book to be called *The First Principles of the Mathematical Sciences Explained to the Non-Mathematical*. He did not have time to finish the work. It was published six years after his death, edited by Karl Pearson, under the title *The Common Sense of the Exact Sciences.* Clifford chose the new title a few days before he died.

Clifford's mathematical interests lay chiefly in geometry, which underwent disturbing and exciting changes in the nineteenth century. For more than two thousand years the system perfected by Euclid had been accepted as a true description of geometric relations in space. But this position was undermined by the investigations of several outstanding mathematicians. Among them were Clifford, Lobachevski, and Riemann.

*The Postulates of the Science of Space* deals with what Euclid left unsaid. When Euclid listed his basic premises, he made some assumptions about space that he did not state. He was probably unaware that he was making them. Our intuition seems to tell us that all parts of space are exactly alike, and that space is continuous. But is it "true"? It is reasonable to suppose that, like most of us, even the mighty Euclid never thought of asking that question. As a matter of fact, it is in the very nature of a postulate that we do not ask if it is true. It is merely some statement that we agree to accept without proof. The postulates may be any that we please, provided only that they do not lead to flat contradictions.

In contrast to Bertrand Russell, Clifford does not question the logic of Euclid's geometry. But, he suggests, other geometries deduced from postulates differing from those framed by Euclid— especially his parallel postulates—are not only logically sound, but might turn out to be better descriptions of space. Lobachevski knocked the "eternal truth" out of geometry. Clifford compares him to Copernicus, who revolutionized astronomy.

The development of several geometries, each consistent within itself, but each contradictory to all others, offered the makings of a first-class battle. The battle was fought, and it ended. No one lost— or won. In a state of coexistence, each has found important applications in science. One famous example is Einstein's non-Euclidean universe, based on Riemann's geometry.

---

*Notes from the artist: ". . . recalling that Clifford was described as 'above all and before all a geometer,' an early Cubist technique, after the manner of Picasso and Braque, was used in this portrait of the bearded mathematician."*

Does any geometry present a picture of the way things really are? That, says Clifford, can only be tested by observation. And our tools for observing are limited. "The geometer of today knows nothing about the nature of actually existing space at an infinite distance; he knows nothing about the properties of this present space in a past or future eternity."

Clifford's writings in science, mathematics, and philosophy are both profound and clear. In *The Postulates of the Science of Space* his gift for making difficult ideas understandable is applied to that most delicate task—examining what we have always taken for granted.

# The Postulates
## of the Science of Space

In my first lecture I said that, out of the pictures which are all that we can really see, we imagine a world of solid things; and that this world is constructed so as to fulfil a certain code of rules, some called axioms, and some called definitions, and some called postulates, and some assumed in the course of demonstration, but all laid down in one form or another in Euclid's *Elements of Geometry*. It is this code of rules that we have to consider to-day. I do not, however, propose to take this book that I have mentioned, and to examine one after another the rules as Euclid has laid them down or unconsciously assumed them; notwithstanding that many things might be said in favour of such a course. This book has been for nearly twenty-two centuries the encouragement and guide of that scientific thought which is one thing with the progress of man from a worse to a better state. The encouragement; for it contained a body of knowledge that was really known and could be relied on, and that moreover was growing in extent and application. For even at the time this book was written—shortly after the foundation of the Alexandrian Museum—Mathematic was no longer the merely ideal science of the Platonic school, but had started on her career of conquest over the whole world of Phenomena. The guide; for the aim of every scientific student of every subject was to bring his knowledge of that subject into a form as perfect as that which geometry had attained. Far up on the great mountain of Truth, which all the sciences hope to scale, the foremost of that sacred sisterhood was seen, beckoning to the rest to follow her. And hence she was called, in the dialect of the Pythagoreans, "the purifier of the reasonable soul." Being thus in itself at once the inspiration and the aspiration of scientific thought, this book of Euclid's has had a history as chequered as that of human progress itself. It embodied and systematized the truest results of the search after truth that was made by Greek,

243

Egyptian, and Hindu. It presided for nearly eight centuries over that promise of light and right that was made by the civilized Aryan races on the Mediterranean shores; that promise, whose abeyance for nearly as long an interval is so full of warning and of sadness for ourselves. It went into exile along with the intellectual activity and the goodness of Europe. It was taught, and commented upon, and illustrated, and supplemented, by Arab and Nestorian, in the Universities of Bagdad and of Cordova. From these it was brought back into barbaric Europe by terrified students who dared tell hardly any other thing of what they had learned among the Saracens. Translated from Arabic into Latin, it passed into the schools of Europe, spun out with additional cases for every possible variation of the figure, and bristling with words which had sounded to Greek ears like the babbling of birds in a hedge. At length the Greek text appeared and was translated; and, like other Greek authors, Euclid became an authority. There had not yet arisen in Europe "that fruitful faculty," as Mr. Winwood Reade calls it, "with which kindred spirits contemplate each other's works; which not only takes, but gives; which produces from whatever it receives; which embraces to wrestle, and wrestles to embrace." Yet it was coming; and though that criticism of first principles which Aristotle and Ptolemy and Galen underwent waited longer in Euclid's case than in theirs, it came for him at last. What Vesalius was to Galen, what Copernicus was to Ptolemy, that was Lobachevski to Euclid. There is, indeed, a somewhat instructive parallel between the last two cases. Copernicus and Lobachevski were both of Slavic origin. Each of them has brought about a revolution in scientific ideas so great that it can only be compared with that wrought by the other. And the reason of the transcendent importance of these two changes is that they are changes in the conception of the Cosmos. Before the time of Copernicus, men knew all about the Universe. They could tell you in the schools, pat off by heart, all that it was, and what it had been, and what it would be. There was the flat earth, with the blue vault of heaven resting on it like the dome of a cathedral, and the bright cold stars stuck into it; while the sun and planets moved in crystal spheres between. Or, among the better informed, the earth was a globe in the centre of the universe, heaven a sphere concentric with it; intermediate machinery as before. At any rate, if there was anything beyond heaven, it was a void space that needed no further description. The history of all this could be traced back to a certain definite time, when it began; behind that was a changeless eternity that needed no further history. Its future could be predicted in general terms as far forward as a certain epoch, about the precise determination of which there were, indeed, differences among the learned. But after that would come again a changeless eternity, which was fully accounted for and described. But in any case the Universe was a known thing. Now the enormous effect of the Copernican system, and of the astronomical discoveries that have followed it, is that, in place of this knowledge of a little, which was called knowledge of the Universe, of Eternity and Immensity, we have now got knowledge of a great deal more; but we only call it the knowledge of Here and Now. We can tell a great deal about the solar system; but, after all, it is our house, and not the city. We can tell something about the star-system to which our sun belongs; but, after all, it is our star-system, and not the Universe. We are talking about Here with the consciousness of a There beyond it, which we may know some time, but do not at all know now. And though the nebular hypothesis tells us a great deal about the history of the solar system, and traces it back for a period compared with which the old measure of the duration of the Universe from beginning to end is not a second to a century, yet we do not call this the history of eternity. We may put it all together and call it Now, with the consciousness of a Then before it, in which things were happening that may have left records; but we have not yet read them. This, then, was the change effected by Copernicus in the idea of the Universe. But there was left another to be made. For the laws of space and motion, that we are presently going to examine, implied an infinite space and an infinite duration, about whose properties as space and time everything was accurately known. The very constitution of those parts of it which are at an infinite distance from us, "geometry upon the plane at infinity," is just as well known, if the Euclidean assumptions are true, as the geometry of any portion of this room. In this infinite and thoroughly well-known space the Universe is situated during at least some portion of an infinite and thoroughly well-known time. So that here we have real knowledge of something at least that concerns the Cosmos; something that is true throughout the Immensities and the Eternities. That something Lobachevski and his successors have taken away. The geometer of to-day knows nothing about the nature of actually existing space at an infinite distance; he knows nothing about the properties of this present space in a past or a future eternity. He knows, indeed, that the laws assumed by Euclid are true with an accuracy that no direct experiment can approach, not only in this place where we are, but in places at a distance from us that no astronomer has conceived; but he knows this as of Here and Now; beyond his range is a There and Then of which he knows nothing at present, but may ultimately come to know more. So, you see, there is a real parallel between the work of Copernicus and his successors on the one hand, and the work of Lobachevski and his successors on the other. In both of these the knowledge of Immensity and Eternity is replaced by knowledge of Here and Now. And in virtue of these two revolutions the idea of the Universe, the Macrocosm, the All, as subject of human knowledge, and therefore of human interest, has fallen to pieces.

It will now, I think, be clear to you why it will not do to take for our present consideration the postulates of geometry as Euclid has laid them down. While they were all certainly true, there might be substituted for them some other group of equivalent propositions; and the choice of the particular set of statements that should be used as the groundwork of the science was to a certain extent arbitrary, being only guided by convenience of exposition. But from the moment that the actual truth of these assumptions becomes doubtful, they fall of themselves into a necessary order and classification; for we then begin to see which of them may be true independently of the others. And for the purpose of criticizing the evidence for them, it is essential that this natural order should be taken; for I think you will see presently that any other order would bring hopeless confusion into the discussion.

Space is divided into parts in many ways. If we consider any material thing, space is at once divided into the part where that thing is and the part where it is not. The water in this glass, for example, makes a distinction between the space where it is and the space where it is not. Now, in order to get from one of these to the other you must cross the *surface* of the water; this surface is the boundary of the space where the water is which separates it from the space where it is not. Every *thing*, considered as occupying a portion of space, has a surface which separates the space where it is from the space where it is not. But, again, a surface may be divided into parts in various ways. Part of the surface of this water is against the air, and part is against the glass. If you travel over the surface from one of these parts to the other, you have to cross the *line* which divides them; it is this circular edge where water, air, and glass meet. Every part of a surface is separated from the other parts by a line which bounds it. But now suppose, further, that this glass had been so constructed that the part towards you was blue and the part towards me was white, as it is now. Then this line, dividing two parts of the surface of the water, would itself be divided into two parts; there would be a part where it was against the blue glass, and a part where it was against the white glass. If you travel in thought along that line, so as to get from one of these two parts to the other, you have to cross a *point* which separates them, and is the boundary between them. Every part of a line is separated from the other parts by points which bound it. So we may say alto-gether—

The boundary of a solid ( *i.e.*, of a part of space) is a surface.

The boundary of a part of a surface is a line.

The boundaries of a part of a line are points.

And we are only settling the meanings in which words are to be used. But here we may make an observation which is true of all space that we are acquainted with: it is that the process ends here. There are no parts of a point which are separated from one another by the next link in the series. This is also indicated by the reverse process.

For I shall now suppose this point—the last thing that we got to—to move round the tumbler so as to trace out the line, or edge, where air, water, and glass meet. In this way I get a series of points, one after an-other; a series of such a nature that, starting from any one of them, only two changes are possible that will keep it within the series: it must go forwards or it must go backwards, and each of these is perfectly definite. The line may then be regarded as an aggregate of points. Now let us imagine, further, a change to take place in this line, which is nearly a circle. Let us suppose it to contract towards the centre of the circle, until it becomes indefinitely small, and disappears. In so doing it will trace out the upper surface of the water, the part of the surface where it is in contact with the air. In this way we shall get a series of circles one after another—a series of such a nature that, starting from any one of them, only two changes are possible that will keep it within the series: it must expand or it must contract. This series, therefore, of circles, is just similar to the series of points that make one circle; and just as the line is regarded as an aggregate of points, so we may regard this surface as an aggregate of lines. But this surface is also in another sense an aggregate of points, in being an aggregate of aggregates of points. But, starting from a point in the surface, more than two changes are possible that will keep it within the surface, for it may move in any direction. The surface, then, is an aggregate of points of a different kind from the line. We speak of the line as a point-aggregate of one dimension, because, starting from one point, there are only two possible directions of change; so that the line can be traced out in one motion. In the same way, a surface is a line-aggregate of one dimension, because it can be traced out by one mo-tion of the line; but it is a point-aggregate of two dimensions, because, in order to build it up of points, we have first to aggregate points into a line, and then lines into a surface. It requires two motions of a point to trace it out.

Lastly, let us suppose this upper surface of the water to move downwards, remaining always horizontal till it becomes the under surface. In so doing it will trace out the part of space occupied by the water. We shall thus get a series of surfaces one after another, precisely analogous to the series of points which make a line, and the series of lines which make a surface. The piece of solid space is an aggregate of surfaces, and an aggregate of the same kind as the line is of points; it is a surface-aggregate of one dimension. But at the same time it is a line-aggregate of two dimensions, and a point-aggregate of three dimensions. For if you consider a particular line which has gone to make this solid, a circle partly contracted and part of the way down, there are more than two opposite changes which it can undergo. For it can ascend or descend, or expand or contract, or do both together in any proportion. It has just as great a variety of changes as a point in a surface. And the piece of space is called a point-aggregate of three dimensions, because it takes three distinct motions to get it from a point. We must first aggregate points into a line, then lines into a surface, then surfaces into a solid.

At this step it is clear, again, that the process must stop in all the space we know of. For it is not possible to move that piece of space in such a way as to change every point in it. When we moved our line or our surface, the new line or surface contained no point whatever that was in the old one; we started with one aggregate of points, and by moving it we got an entirely new aggregate, all the points of which were new. But this cannot be done with the solid; so that the process is at an end. We arrive, then, at the result that *space is of three dimensions.*

Is this, then, one of the postulates of the science of space? No; it is not. The science of space, as we have it, deals with relations of distance existing in a certain space of three dimensions, but it does not at all require us to assume that no relations of distance are possible in aggregates of more than three dimensions. The fact that there are only three dimensions does regulate the number of books that we write, and the parts of the subject that we study: but it is not itself a postulate of the science. We investigate a certain space of three dimensions, on the hypothesis that it has certain elementary properties; and it is the assumptions of these elementary properties that are the real postulates of the science of space. To these I now proceed.

The first of them is concerned with *points,* and with the relation of space to them. We spoke of a line as an aggregate of points. Now there are two kinds of aggregates, which are called respectively continuous and discrete. If you consider this line, the boundary of part of the surface of the water, you will find yourself believing that between any two points of it you can put more points of division, and between any two of these more again, and so on; and you do not believe there can be any end to the process. We may express that by saying you believe that between any two points of the line there is an infinite number of other points. But now here is an aggregate of marbles, which, regarded as an aggregate, has many characters of resemblance with the aggregate of points. It is a series of marbles, one after another; and if we take into account the relations of nextness or contiguity which they possess, then there are only two changes possible from one of them as we travel along the series: we must go to the next in front, or to the next behind. But yet it is not true that between any two of them here is an infinite number of other marbles; between these two, for example, there are only three. There, then, is a distinction at once between the two kinds of aggregates. But there is another, which was pointed out by Aristotle in his *Physics* and made the basis of a definition of continuity. I have here a row of two different kinds of marbles, some white and some black. This aggregate is divided into two parts, as we formerly supposed the line to be. In the case of the line the boundary between the two parts is a point which is the element of which the line is an aggregate. In this case before us, a marble is the element; but here we cannot say that the boundary between the two parts is a marble. The boundary of the white parts is a white marble, and the boundary of the black parts is a black marble; these two adjacent parts have different boundaries. Similarly, if instead of arranging my marbles in a series, I spread them out on a surface, I may have this aggregate divided into two portions—a white portion and a black portion; but the boundary of the white portion is a row of white marbles, and the boundary of the black portion is a row of black marbles. And lastly, if I made a heap of white marbles, and put black marbles on the top of them, I should have a discrete aggregate of three dimensions divided into two parts: the boundary of the white part would be a layer of white marbles, and the boundary of the black part would be a layer of black marbles. In all these cases of discrete aggregates, when they are divided into two parts, the two adjacent parts have different boundaries. But if you come to consider an aggregate that you believe to be continuous, you will see that you think of two adjacent parts as having the *same* boundary. What is the boundary between water and air here? Is it water? No; for there would still have to be a boundary to divide that water from the air. For the same reason it cannot be air. I do not want you at present to think of the actual physical facts by the aid of any molecular theories; I want you only to think of what appears to be, in order to understand clearly a conception that we all have. Suppose the things actually in contact. If, however much we magnified them, they still appeared to be thoroughly homogeneous, the water filling up a certain space, the air an adjacent space; if this held good indefinitely through all degrees of conceivable magnifying, then we could not say that the surface of the water was a layer of water and the surface of air a layer of air; we should have to say that the same surface was the surface of both of them, and was itself neither one nor the other—that this surface occupied *no* space at all. Accordingly, Aristotle defined the continuous as that of which two adjacent parts have the same boundary; and the discontinuous or discrete as that of which two adjacent parts have direct boundaries.

Now the first postulate of the science of space is that space is a continuous aggregate of points, and not a discrete aggregate. And this postulate—which I shall call the postulate of continuity—is really involved in those three of the six postulates of Euclid for which Robert Simson has retained the name of postulate. You will see, on a little reflection, that a discrete aggregate of points could not be so arranged that any two of them should be relatively situated to one another in exactly the same manner, so that any two points might be joined by a straight line which should always bear the same definite relation to them. And the same difficulty occurs in regard to the other two postulates. But perhaps the most conclusive way of showing that this postulate is really assumed by Euclid is to adduce the proposition he proves, that every finite straight line may be bisected. Now this could not be the case if it consisted of an odd number of separate points. As the first of the postulates of the science of space, then, we must reckon this postulate of Continuity; according to which two adjacent portions of space, or of a surface, or of a line, have the *same* boundary, viz., a surface, a line, or a point; and between every two points on a line there is an infinite number of intermediate points.

The next postulate is that of Elementary Flatness. You know that if you get hold of a small piece of a very large circle, it seems to you nearly straight. So, if you were to take any curved line, and magnify it very much, confining your attention to a small piece of it, that piece would seem straighter to you than the curve did before it was magnified. At least, you can easily conceive a curve possessing this property, that the more you magnify it, the straighter it gets. Such a curve would possess the property of elementary flatness. In the same way, if you perceive a portion of the surface of a very large sphere, such as the earth, it appears to you to be flat. If, then, you take a sphere of say a foot diameter, and magnify it more and more, you will find that the more you magnify it the flatter it gets. And you may easily suppose that this process would go on indefinitely; that the curvature would become less and less the more the surface was magnified. Any curved surface which is such that the more you magnify it the flatter it gets, is said to possess the property of elementary flatness. But if every succeeding power of our imaginary microscope disclosed new wrinkles and inequalities without end, then we should say that the surface did not possess the property of elementary flatness.

But how am I to explain how solid space can have this property of elementary flatness? Shall I leave it as a mere analogy, and say that it is the same kind of property as this of the curve and surface, only in three dimensions instead of one or two? I think I can get a little nearer to it than that; at all events I will try.

If we start to go out from a point on a surface, there is a certain choice of directions in which we may go. These directions make certain angles with one another. We may suppose a certain direction to start with, and then gradually alter that by turning it round the point: we find thus a single series of directions in which we may start from the point. According to our first postulate, it is a continuous series of directions. Now when I speak of a direction from the point, I mean a direction of starting; I say nothing about the subsequent path. Two different paths may have the same direction at starting; in this case they will touch at the point; and there is an obvious difference between two paths which touch and two paths which meet and form an angle. Here, then, is an aggregate of directions, and they can be changed into one another. Moreover, the changes by which they pass into one another have magnitude, they constitute distance-relations; and the amount of change necessary to turn one of them into another is called the angle between them. It is involved in this postulate that we are considering, that angles can be compared in respect of magnitude. But this is not all. If we go on changing a direction of start, it will, after a certain amount of turning, come round into itself again, and be the same direction. On every surface which has the property of elementary flatness, the amount of turning necessary to take a direction all round into its first position is the same for all points of the surface. I will now show you a surface which at one point of it has not this property. I take this circle of paper from which a sector has been cut out, and bend it round so as to join the edges; in this way I form a surface which is called a *cone*. Now on all points of this surface but one, the law of elementary flatness holds good. At the vertex of the cone, however, notwithstanding that there is an aggregate of directions in which you may start, such that by continuously changing one of them you may get it round into its original position, yet the whole amount of change necessary to effect this is not the same at the vertex as it is at any other point of the surface. And this you can see at once when I unroll it; for only part of the directions in the plane have been included in the cone. At this point of the cone, then, it does not possess the property of elementary flatness; and no amount of magnifying would ever make a cone seem flat at its vertex.

To apply this to solid space, we must notice that here also there is a choice of directions in which you may go out from any point; but it is a much greater choice than a surface gives you. Whereas in a surface the aggregate of directions is only of one dimension, in solid space it is of two dimensions. But here also there are distance-relations, and the aggregate of directions may be divided into parts which have quantity. For example, the directions which start from the vertex of this cone are divided into those which go inside the cone, and those which go outside the cone. The part of the aggregate which is inside the cone is called a solid angle. Now in those spaces of three dimensions which have the property of elementary flatness, the whole amount of solid angle round one point is equal to the whole amount round another point. Although the space need not be exactly similar to itself in all parts, yet the aggregate of directions round one point is exactly similar to the aggregate of directions round another point, if the space has the property of elementary flatness.

How does Euclid assume this postulate of Elementary Flatness? In his fourth postulate he has expressed it so simply and clearly that you will wonder how anybody could make all this fuss. He says, "All right angles are equal."

Why could I not have adopted this at once, and saved a great deal of trouble? Because it assumes the knowledge of a surface possessing the property of elementary flatness in all its points. Unless such a surface is first made out to exist, and the definition of a right angle is restricted to lines drawn upon it—for there is no necessity for the word *straight* in that definition—the postulate in Euclid's form is obviously not true. I can make two lines cross at the vertex of a cone so that the four adjacent angles shall be equal, and yet not one of them equal to a right angle.

I pass on to the third postulate of the science of space—the postulate of Superposition. According to this postulate a body can be moved about in space without altering its size or shape. This seems obvious enough, but it is worth while to examine a little closely into the meaning of it. We must define what we mean by size and by shape. When we say that a body can be moved about without altering its size, we mean that it can be so moved as to keep unaltered the length of all the lines in it. This postulate therefore involves that lines can be compared in respect of magnitude, or that they have a length independent of position; precisely as the former one involved the comparison of angular magnitudes. And when we say that a body can be moved about without altering its shape, we mean that it can be so moved as to keep unaltered all the angles in it. It is not necessary to make mention of the motion of a body, although that is the easiest way of expressing and of conceiving this postulate; but we may, if we like, express it entirely in terms which belong to space, and that we should do in this way. Suppose a figure to have been constructed in some portion of space; say that a triangle has been drawn whose sides are the shortest distances between its angular points. Then if in any other portion of space two points are taken whose shortest distance is equal to a side of the triangle, and at one of them an angle is made equal to one of the angles adjacent to that side, and a line of shortest distance drawn equal to the corresponding side of the original triangle, the distance from the extremity of this to the other of the two points will be equal to the third side of the original triangle, and the two will be equal in all respects; or generally, if a figure has been constructed anywhere, another figure, with all its lines and all its angles equal to the corresponding lines and angles of the first, can be constructed anywhere else. Now this is exactly what is meant by the principle of superposition employed by Euclid to prove the proposition that I have just mentioned. And we may state it again in this short form—all parts of space are exactly alike.

But this postulate carries with it a most important consequence. It enables us to make a pair of most fundamental definitions—those of the plane and of the straight line. In order to explain how these come out of it when it is granted, and how they cannot be made when it is not granted, I must here say something more about the nature of the postulate itself, which might otherwise have been left until we come to criticize it.

We have stated the postulate as referring to solid space. But a similar property may exist in surfaces. Here, for instance, is part of the surface of a sphere. If I draw any figure I like upon this, I can suppose it to be moved about in any way upon the sphere, without alteration of its size or shape. If a figure has been drawn on any part of the surface of a sphere, a figure equal to it in all respects may be drawn on any other part of the surface. Now I say that this property belongs to the surface itself, is a part of its own internal economy, and does not depend in any way upon its relation to space of three dimensions. For I can pull it about and bend it in all manner of ways, so as altogether to alter its relation to solid space; and yet, if I do not stretch it or tear it, I make no difference whatever in

the length of any lines upon it, or in the size of any angles upon it.[1] I
do not in any way alter the figures drawn upon it, or the possibility of
drawing figures upon it, *so far as their relations with the surface itself are
concerned.* This property of the surface, then, could be ascertained by
people who lived entirely in it, and were absolutely ignorant of a third
dimension. As a point-aggregate of two dimensions, it has in itself
properties determining the distance-relations of the points upon it, which
are absolutely independent of the existence of any points which are not
upon it.

Now here is a surface which has not that property. You observe that it
is not of the same shape all over, and that some parts of it are more curved
than other parts. If you drew a figure upon this surface, and then tried to
move it about, you would find that it was impossible to do so without
altering the size and shape of the figure. Some parts of it would have to
expand, some to contract, the lengths of the lines could not all be kept the
same, the angles would not hit off together. And this property of the
surface—that its parts are different from one another—is a property of the
surface itself, a part of its internal economy, absolutely independent of
any relations it may have with space outside of it. For, as with the other
one, I can pull it about in all sorts of ways, and, so long as I do not
stretch it or tear it, I make no alteration in the length of lines drawn upon
it or in the size of the angles.

Here, then, is an intrinsic difference between these two surfaces, as
surfaces. They are both point-aggregates of two dimensions; but the
points in them have certain relations of distance (distance measured always *on* the surface), and these relations of distance are not the same
in one case as they are in the other.

The supposed people living in the surface and having no idea of a
third dimension might, without suspecting that third dimension at all,
make a very accurate determination of the nature of their *locus in quo*. If
the people who lived on the surface of the sphere were to measure the
angles of a triangle, they would find them to exceed two right angles by a
quantity proportional to the area of the triangle. This excess of the angles
above two right angles, being divided by the area of the triangle, would
be found to give exactly the same quotient at all parts of the sphere. That

---

1. This figure was made of linen, starched upon a spherical surface, and taken off
when dry. That mentioned in the next paragraph was similarly stretched upon the
irregular surface of the head of a bust. For durability these models should be made
of two thicknesses of linen starched together in such a way that the fibres of one
bisect the angles between the fibres of the other, and the edge should be bound by
a thin slip of paper. They will then retain their curvature unaltered for a long time.

quotient is called the curvature of the surface; and we say that a sphere is a surface of uniform curvature. But if the people living on this irregular surface were to do the same thing, they would not find quite the same result. The sum of the angles would, indeed, differ from two right angles, but sometimes in excess, and sometimes in defect, according to the part of the surface where they were. And though for small triangles in any one neighbourhood the excess or defect would be nearly proportional to the area of the triangle, yet the quotient obtained by dividing this excess or defect by the area of the triangle would vary from one part of the surface to another. In other words, the curvature of this surface varies from point to point; it is sometimes positive, sometimes negative, sometimes nothing at all.

But now comes the important difference. When I speak of a triangle, what do I suppose the sides of that triangle to be?

If I take two points near enough together upon a surface, and stretch a string between them, that string will take up a certain definite position upon the surface, marking the line of shortest distance from one point to the other. Such a line is called a geodesic line. It is a line determined by the intrinsic properties of the surface, and not by its relations with external space. The line would still be the shortest line, however the surface were pulled about without stretching or tearing. A geodesic line may be *produced*, when a piece of it is given; for we may take one of the points, and, keeping the string stretched, make it go round in a sort of circle until the other end has turned through two right angles. The new position will then be a prolongation of the same geodesic line.

In speaking of a triangle, then, I meant a triangle whose sides are geodesic lines. But in the case of a spherical surface—or, more generally, of a surface of constant curvature—these geodesic lines have another and most important property. They are *straight*, so far as the surface is concerned. On this surface a figure may be moved about without altering its size or shape. It is possible, therefore, to draw a line which shall be of the same shape all along and on both sides. That is to say, if you take a piece of the surface on one side of such a line, you may slide it all along the line and it will fit; and you may turn it round and apply it to the other side, and it will fit there also. This is Leibnitz's definition of a straight line, and, you see, it has no meaning except in the case of a surface of constant curvature, a surface all parts of which are alike.

Now let us consider the corresponding things in solid space. In this also we may have geodesic lines; namely, lines formed by stretching a string between two points. But we may also have geodesic surfaces; and they are produced in this manner. Suppose we have a point on a surface, and this surface possesses the property of elementary flatness. Then among all the directions of starting from the point, there are some which start *in the surface,* and do not make an angle with it. Let all these be prolonged into geodesics; then we may imagine one of these geodesics to travel round and coincide with all the others in turn. In so doing it will trace out a surface which is called a geodesic surface. Now in the particular case where a space of three dimensions has the property of superposition, or is all over alike, these geodesic surfaces are *planes.* That is to say, since the space is all over alike, these surfaces are also of the same shape all over and on both sides; which is Leibnitz's definition of a plane. If you take a piece of space on one side of such a plane, partly bounded by the plane, you may slide it all over the plane, and it will fit; and you may turn it round and apply it to the other side, and it will fit there also. Now it is clear that this definition will have no meaning unless the third postulate be granted. So we may say that when the postulate of Superposition is true, then there are planes and straight lines; and they are defined as being of the same shape throughout and on both sides.

It is found that the whole geometry of a space of three dimensions is known when we know the curvature of three geodesic surfaces at every point. The third postulate requires that the curvature of all geodesic surfaces should be everywhere equal to the same quantity.

I pass to the fourth postulate, which I call the postulate of Similarity. According to this postulate, any figure may be magnified or diminished in any degree without altering its shape. If any figure has been constructed in one part of space, it may be reconstructed to any scale whatever in any other part of space, so that no one of the angles shall be altered though all the lengths of lines will of course be altered. This seems to be a sufficiently obvious induction from experience; for we have all frequently seen different sizes of the same shape; and it has the advantage of embodying the fifth and sixth of Euclid's postulates in a single principle, which bears a great resemblance in form to that of Superposition, and may be used in the same manner. It is easy to show that it involves the two postulates of Euclid: "Two straight lines cannot enclose a space," and "Lines in one plane which never meet make equal angles with every other line."

This fourth postulate is equivalent to the assumption that the constant curvature of the geodesic surfaces is zero; or the third and fourth may be put together, and we shall then say that the three curvatures of space are all of them zero at every point.

The supposition made by Lobachevski was that the three first postulates were true, but not the fourth. Of the two Euclidean postulates included in this, he admitted one, viz., that two straight lines cannot enclose a space, or that two lines which once diverge go on diverging for ever. But he left out the postulate about parallels, which may be stated in this form. If through a point outside of a straight line there be drawn another, indefinitely produced both ways; and if we turn this second one round so as to make the point of intersection travel along the first line, then at the very instant that this point of intersection disappears at one end it will reappear at the other, and there is only one position in which the lines do not intersect. Lobachevski supposed, instead, that there was a finite angle through which the second line must be turned after the point of intersection had disappeared at one end, before it reappeared at the other. For all positions of the second line within this angle there is then no intersection. In the two limiting positions, when the lines have just done meeting at one end, and when they are just going to meet at the other, they are called parallel; so that two lines can be drawn through a fixed point parallel to a given straight line. The angle between these two depends in a certain way upon the distance of the point from the line. The sum of the angles of a triangle is less than two right angles by a quantity proportional to the area of the triangle. The whole of this geometry is worked out in the style of Euclid, and the most interesting conclusions are arrived at; particularly in the theory of solid space, in which a surface turns up which is not plane relatively to that space, but which, for purposes of drawing figures upon it, is identical with the Euclidean plane.

It was Riemann, however, who first accomplished the task of analysing all the assumptions of geometry, and showing which of them were independent. This very disentangling and separation of them is sufficient to deprive them for the geometer of their exactness and necessity; for the process by which it is effected consists in showing the possibility of conceiving these suppositions one by one to be untrue; whereby it is clearly made out how much is supposed. But it may be worth while to state formally the case for and against them.

When it is maintained that we know these postulates to be universally true, in virtue of certain deliverances of our consciousness, it is implied that these deliverances could not exist, except upon the supposition that the postulates are true. If it can be shown, then, from experience that our consciousness would tell us exactly the same things if the postulates are not true, the ground of their validity will be taken away. But this is a very easy thing to show.

That same faculty which tells you that space is continuous tells you that this water is continuous, and that the motion perceived in a wheel of life is continuous. Now we happen to know that if we could magnify this water as much again as the best microscopes can magnify it, we should perceive its granular structure. And what happens in a wheel of life is discovered by stopping the machine. Even apart, then, from our knowledge of the way nerves act in carrying messages, it appears that we have no means of knowing anything more about an aggregate than that it is too fine grained for us to perceive its discontinuity, if it has any.

Nor can we, in general, receive a conception as positive knowledge which is itself founded merely upon inaction. For the conception of a continuous thing is of that which looks just the same however much you magnify it. We may conceive the magnifying to go on to a certain extent without change, and then, as it were, leave it going on, without taking the trouble to doubt about the changes that may ensue.

In regard to the second postulate, we have merely to point to the example of polished surfaces. The smoothest surface that can be made is the one most completely covered with the minutest ruts and furrows. Yet geometrical constructions can be made with extreme accuracy upon such a surface, on the supposition that it is an exact plane. If, therefore, the sharp points, edges, and furrows of space are only small enough, there will be nothing to hinder our conviction of its elementary flatness. It has even been remarked by Riemann that we must not shrink from this supposition if it is found useful in explaining physical phenomena.

The first two postulates may therefore be doubted on the side of the very small. We may put the third and fourth together, and doubt them on the side of the very great. For if the property of elementary flatness exist on the average, the deviations from it being, as we have supposed, too small to be perceived, then, whatever were the true nature of space, we should have exactly the conceptions of it which we now have, if only the regions we can get at were small in comparison with the areas of curvature. If we suppose the curvature to vary in an irregular manner, the effect of it might be very considerable in a triangle formed by the nearest fixed stars; but if we suppose it approximately uniform to the limit of telescopic reach, it will be restricted to very much narrower limits. I cannot perhaps do better than conclude by describing to you as well as I can what is the nature of things on the supposition that the curvature of all space is nearly uniform and positive.

In this case the Universe, as known, becomes again a valid conception;

for the extent of space is a finite number of cubic miles.[2] And this comes about in a curious way. If you were to start in any direction whatever, and move in that direction in a perfect straight line according to the definition of Leibnitz; after travelling a most prodigious distance, to which the parallactic unit—200,000 times the diameter of the earth's orbit—would be only a few steps, you would arrive at—this place. Only, if you had started upwards, you would appear from below. Now, one of two things would be true. Either, when you had got half-way on your journey, you came to a place that is opposite to this, and which you must have gone through, whatever direction you started in; or else all paths you could have taken diverge entirely from each other till they meet again at this place. In the former case, every two straight lines in a plane meet in two points, in the latter they meet only in one. Upon this supposition of a positive curvature, the whole of geometry is far more complete and interesting; the principle of duality, instead of half breaking down over metric relations, applies to all propositions without exception. In fact, I do not mind confessing that I personally have often found relief from the dreary infinities of homaloidal space in the consoling hope that, after all, this other may be the true state of things.

---

2. The assumptions here made about the *Zusammenhang* [continuity] of space are the simplest ones, but even the finite extent does not follow necessarily from uniform positive curvature, as Riemann seems to have supposed.

# Henri Poincaré

## 1854–1912

Jules Henri Poincaré, the son of a physician, and a cousin of the President of France during World War I, was born at Nancy, France, in 1854. He studied at the École Polytechnique and at the School of Mines. After receiving a degree in mathematical sciences in 1879 from the University of Paris, he lectured for two years at Caen. He became *maître de conférence* in mathematical analysis at the University of Paris in 1881, and in 1886 he was promoted to professor of mathematical physics and the calculus of probabilities.

Henri Poincaré, the greatest mathematician of his time, conformed to the popular idea of a mathematical genius. Timid, frail, and precocious, he spent his childhood in a scholarly household that was frequented by philosophers and scientists. He early displayed a remarkable mathematical aptitude, but he drew geometrical diagrams so badly that he failed the drawing test in the entrance examinations for the École Polytechnique. In maturity, he was short, stooped, near-sighted, and absent-minded. Although he claimed that his memory was not good enough to make him a good chess player, it was fabulous in matters of great complexity.

His contribution to scientific writing is enormous. He wrote more than thirty books on mathematical physics and astronomy, nearly five hundred memoirs on mathematics, two books of popular essays,

---

*Notes from the artist: "The portrait of Poincaré is placed against a semiabstract background showing the execution of some of his equations and formulas. The quotation from* On Measuring Time *reflects Poincaré's thoughts about rhythm and duration."*

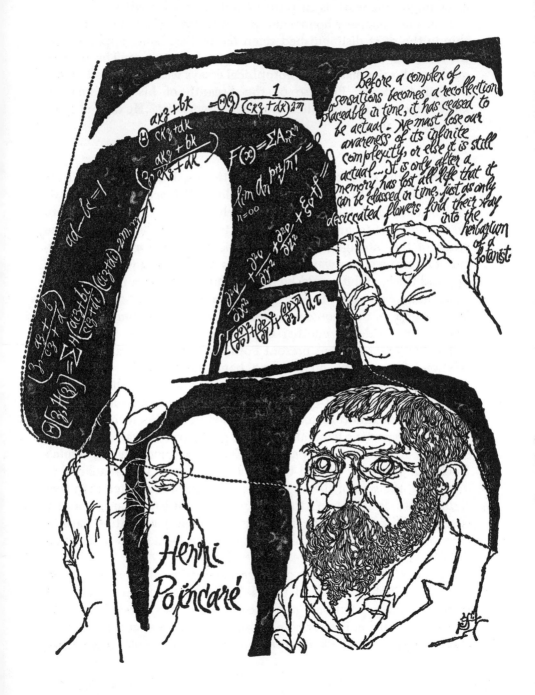

Before a complex of sensations becomes a recollection placeable in time, it has ceased to be actual. We must lose our awareness of its infinite complexity, or else it is still actual... It is only after a memory has lost all life that it can be classed in time, just as only desiccated flowers find their way into the herbarium of a botanist.

Henri Poincaré

and three books on the philosophy of science. His work falls into three main divisions: pure mathematics, astronomy, and physics. His most important work is in pure analytical mathematics.

Poincaré won many honors and prizes and was elected to membership in the most distinguished scientific bodies, being appointed to the Academy of Science at the early age of thirty-two. The literary quality of his popular and philosophical essays was recognized by the French Academy. Because of the breadth of his mathematical knowledge he has been called the "last universalist." He died at Paris on July 17, 1912.

Among the great creative mathematicians, Poincaré is noted for his philosophical breadth and lucid style. In *Science and Hypothesis* and *Science and Method,* from which the present selections are taken, the most technical and difficult topics are brought within the reach of the intelligent nonmathematical reader—or almost. Poincaré's intuitive power was immense. His insights, you will find, come fast and thick, and it would be ungrateful to complain if you do not understand every one. If your rich uncle writes you a check for an amount greater than you can handle at the moment, you simply put the balance aside for another day.

The first two selections present Poincaré's original ideas about the relation of geometry, on the one hand, and physical space and physics, on the other. It had been noted for centuries that Euclid's fifth axiom was not self-evident and could not be proved. This was regarded as an unfortunate flaw, but it led in the nineteenth century to a very important generalization of geometry. Bolyai, Lobachevski, and Riemann developed non-Euclidian geometry, of which Euclidian geometry proved to be a limiting case. In Lobachevski's geometry, the sum of the angles of a triangle was greater than two right angles, in Riemann's the sum was less. In Euclidian geometry the sum was equal to two right angles, which is a limiting case of "greater than" and "less than" two right angles—one possibility in an infinity of possibilities.

The starting point of this great generalization of geometry, however, was Euclid's axiom of parallels, which states, in effect, that through a given point only *one* line can be drawn parallel to a line on the same plane. Riemannian geometry said *none,* and Lobachevskian geometry said *an infinite number.* These three geometries, then, were very different. Many theorems which held for one would not hold for the others; yet there were common theorems, too. For example, "the base angles of an isosceles triangle are equal" and "two lines which are parallel to a third are parallel to each other" are common to both the Lobachevskian and the Euclidian geometries. On the other hand, "the area of a circle is $\pi r^2$" is valid only in one geometry—the Euclidian.

But how can these new geometries be true if the Euclidian geometry is? How can they be self-consistent? They are consistent if there is no contradiction among their theorems. But since all the infinity of possible theorems have not been deduced, how do we know that some contradiction will not turn up in the future? Poincaré points out that since a limiting case of both the Lobachevskian and the Riemannian geometries is equivalent to a branch of ordinary Euclidian geometry, neither can be regarded as inconsistent—unless Euclid is also inconsistent! The same conclusion is reached by the dictionary of terms given on pp. 268–269, whereby Lobachevskian theorems can be translated into Euclidian theorems.

The question which of the geometries is true still impends. Poincaré's answer was that "one geometry can not be more true than another; it can only be *more convenient.*" The most convenient is the Euclidian: it is simplest in itself, in the sense that plane trigonometry is simpler than spherical trigonometry, and it also accords best with the properties of the physical objects that we see, handle, and measure.

Little need be said of the second and third selections. They speak for themselves and almost read themselves. One thing that may occur to you in reading the chapter on mathematical discovery, though Poincaré does not spell it out, is that the creative mind is not one that simply has more new and important ideas. It is a mind that simply has *more ideas* and works faster in eliminating the uninteresting ones. Secondly, the new ideas would never be discovered if the mathematician were not always looking for "elegant" short cuts— shorter proofs and simplifications.

A good memory is necessary, of course, and also careful analysis which clarifies the problem. The originality of Poincaré's theory of discovery is the role which he assigns to the unconscious, and the interplay between conscious and "unconscious work." The solution to a problem may come suddenly, after the mathematician has given up hope and has turned to altogether unrelated activities.

You will see how Poincaré explains what seems to be a "sudden illumination" that comes to the mathematician when he has forgotten all about the problem and is thinking of other things. You might consider an additional explanation. Could it be that when the mathematician or we ourselves are trying to solve a problem, certain inhibitions develop which block the door to the correct answer, and that while engaging in other activities these inhibitions are relaxed? This would be what the psychologists call "disinhibition."

Poincaré was close to the spirit and all the developments of physical science of his time. He was too close to interpret "chance" as sheer absence of a cause. What evidence is there that things occur without a cause? And that what has a cause can always, in principle, be predicted? Nor could he be attracted by the view of some of the Enlightenment philosophers that all events—however trifling—have a cause, chance events being merely those whose causes we do not yet know.

The latter view is unsatisfactory. Chance is not the realm of ignorance. The motion of the molecules of a gas is random and fortuitous, yet we can predict what they are going to do *en masse* when the gas is heated. We can determine precisely the pressure which they will exert. Similarly, the actuarian cannot know *what* individuals will die next year, but he can predict *how many* will. It is not out of ignorance that insurance companies make money. Statistical laws are of course exceedingly important in science.

The question that has come before the stagelights since Poincaré wrote is whether the final form of scientific laws is to be statistical or causal. Poincaré apparently looked forward to the possibility of advancing beyond statistical laws to causal laws relating to the particles or individuals. But this was before the development of the quantum theory and recent theories of the structure of the atom. As a result of these developments, some of the greatest authorities believe that there is real indeterminacy in nature and that basic laws must remain statistical. What Poincaré would say if he were alive today is an interesting speculation.

# Space

## THE NON-EUCLIDEAN GEOMETRIES

Every conclusion supposes premises; these premises themselves either are self-evident and need no demonstration, or can be established only by relying upon other propositions, and since we cannot go back thus to infinity, every deductive science, and in particular geometry, must rest on a certain number of undemonstrable axioms. All treatises on geometry begin, therefore, by the enunciation of these axioms. But among these there is a distinction to be made: Some, for example, "Things which are equal to the same thing are equal to one another," are not propositions of geometry, but propositions of analysis. I regard them as analytic judgments a priori, and shall not concern myself with them.

But I must lay stress upon other axioms which are peculiar to geometry. Most treatises enunciate three of these explicitly: (1) Through two points can pass only one straight line. (2) The straight line is the shortest path from one point to another. (3) Through a given point there is not more than one parallel to a given straight line.

Although generally a proof of the second of these axioms is omitted, it would be possible to deduce it from the other two and from those, much more numerous, which are implicitly admitted without enunciating them, as I shall explain further on.

It was long sought in vain to demonstrate likewise the third axiom, known as Euclid's postulate. What vast effort has been wasted in this chimeric hope is truly unimaginable. Finally, in the first quarter of the nineteenth century, and almost at the same time, a Hungarian and a Russian, Bolyai and Lobachevski, established irrefutably that this demonstration is impossible; they have almost rid us of inventors of geometries "sans postulatum"; since then the Académie des Sciences receives only about one or two new demonstrations a year. The question was not exhausted; it soon made a great stride by the publication of Riemann's celebrated memoir entitled: *Ueber die Hypothesen welche der Geometrie zu Grunde liegen.* This paper has inspired most of the recent works of which I shall speak further on, and among which it is proper to cite those of Beltrami and of Helmholtz.

*The Bolyai-Lobachevski Geometry.* If it were possible to deduce Euclid's postulate from the other axioms, it is evident that in denying the postulate and admitting the other axioms, we should be led to contradictory consequences; it would therefore be impossible to base on such premises a coherent geometry.

Now this is precisely what Lobachevski did.

He assumes at the start that: *Through a given point can be drawn two parallels to a given straight line.*

And he retains besides all Euclid's other axioms. From these hypotheses he deduces a series of theorems among which it is impossible to find any contradiction, and he constructs a geometry whose faultless logic is inferior in nothing to that of the Euclidean geometry. The theorems are, of course, very different from those to which we are accustomed, and they cannot fail to be at first a little disconcerting. Thus the sum of the angles of a triangle is always less than two right angles, and the difference between this sum and two right angles is proportional to the surface of the triangle. It is impossible to construct a figure similar to a given figure but of different dimensions. If we divide a circumference into $n$ equal parts, and draw tangents at the points of division, these $n$ tangents will form a polygon if the radius of the circle is small enough; but if this radius is sufficiently great they will not meet.

It is useless to multiply these examples; Lobachevski's propositions have no relation to those of Euclid, but they are not less logically bound one to another.

*Riemann's Geometry.* Imagine a world uniquely peopled by beings of no thickness (height); and suppose these "infinitely flat" animals are all in the same plane and cannot get out. Admit besides that this world is sufficiently far from others to be free from their influence. While we are making hypotheses, it costs us no more to endow these beings with reason and believe them capable of creating a geometry. In that case, they will certainly attribute to space only two dimensions.

But suppose now that these imaginary animals, while remaining without thickness, have the form of a spherical, and not of a plane, figure, and are all on the same sphere without power to get off. What geometry will they construct? First it is clear they will attribute to space only two dimensions; what will play for them the role of the straight line will be the shortest path from one point to another on the sphere, that is to say, an arc of a great circle; in a word, their geometry will be the spherical geometry.

What they will call space will be this sphere on which they must stay, and on which happen all the phenomena they can know. Their space will therefore be *unbounded* since on a sphere one can always go forward without ever being stopped, and yet it will be *finite;* one can never find the end of it, but one can make a tour of it.

Well, Riemann's geometry is spherical geometry extended to three dimensions. To construct it, the German mathematician had to throw overboard, not only Euclid's postulate, but also the first axiom: *Only one straight line can pass through two points.*

On a sphere, through two given points we can draw *in general* only one great circle (which, as we have just seen, would play the role of the straight line for our imaginary beings); but there is an exception: if the two given points are diametrically opposite, an infinity of great circles can be drawn through them.

In the same way, in Riemann's geometry (at least in one of its forms), through two points will pass in general only a single straight line; but there are exceptional cases where through two points an infinity of straight lines can pass.

There is a sort of opposition between Riemann's geometry and that of Lobachevski.

Thus the sum of the angles of a triangle is: equal to two right angles in Euclid's geometry; less than two right angles in that of Lobachevski; greater than two right angles in that of Riemann.

The number of straight lines through a given point that can be drawn coplanar to a given straight line, but nowhere meeting it, is equal: to one in Euclid's geometry; to zero in that of Riemann; to infinity in that of Lobachevski.

Add that Riemann's space is finite, although unbounded, in the sense given above to these two words.

*The Surfaces of Constant Curvature.* One objection still remained possible. The theorems of Lobachevski and of Riemann present no contradiction; but however numerous the consequences these two geometers have drawn from their hypotheses, they must have stopped before exhausting them, since their number would be infinite; who can say then that if they had pushed their deductions farther they would not have eventually reached some contradiction?

This difficulty does not exist for Riemann's geometry, provided it is limited to two dimensions; in fact, as we have seen, two-dimensional Riemannian geometry does not differ from spherical geometry, which is only a branch of ordinary geometry, and consequently is beyond all discussion.

Beltrami, in correlating likewise Lobachevski's two-dimensional geometry with a branch of ordinary geometry, has equally refuted the objection so far as it is concerned. Here is how he accomplished it. Consider any figure on a surface. Imagine this figure traced on a flexible and inextensible canvas applied over this surface in such a way that when the canvas is displaced and deformed the various lines of this figure can change their form without changing their length. In general, this flexible and inextensible figure cannot be displaced without leaving the surface; but there are certain particular surfaces for which such a movement would be possible; these are the surfaces of constant curvature.

If we resume the comparison made above and imagine beings without thickness living on one of these surfaces, they will regard as possible the motion of a figure all of whose lines remain constant in length. On the contrary, such a movement would appear absurd to animals without thickness living on a surface of variable curvature.

These surfaces of constant curvature are of two sorts: Some are of *positive curvature*, and can be deformed so as to be applied over a sphere. The geometry of these surfaces reduces itself therefore to the spherical geometry, which is that of Riemann.

The others are of *negative curvature*. Beltrami has shown that the geometry of these surfaces is none other than that of Lobachevski. The two-dimensional geometries of Riemann and Lobachevski are thus correlated to the Euclidean geometry.

*Interpretation of Non-Euclidean Geometries.* So vanishes the objection so far as two-dimensional geometries are concerned.

It would be easy to extend Beltrami's reasoning to three-dimensional geometries. The minds that space of four dimensions does not repel will see no difficulty in it, but they are few. I prefer therefore to proceed otherwise.

Consider a certain plane, which I shall call the fundamental plane, and construct a sort of dictionary, by making correspond each to each a double series of terms written in two columns, just as correspond in the ordinary dictionaries the words of two languages whose significance is the same:

*Space:* Portion of space situated above the fundamental plane.
*Plane:* Sphere cutting the fundamental plane orthogonally.
*Straight line:* Circle cutting the fundamental plane orthogonally.
*Sphere:* Sphere.

*Circle:* Circle.

*Angle:* Angle.

*Distance between two points:* Logarithm of the cross ratio of these two points and the intersections of the fundamental plane with a circle passing through these two points and cutting it orthogonally. Etc., etc.

Now take Lobachevski's theorems and translate them with the aid of this dictionary as we translate a German text with the aid of a German-English dictionary. *We shall thus obtain theorems of the ordinary geometry.* For example, that theorem of Lobachevski: "the sum of the angles of a triangle is less than two right angles" is translated thus: "If a curvilinear triangle has for sides circle-arcs which prolonged would cut orthogonally the fundamental plane, the sum of the angles of this curvilinear triangle will be less than two right angles." Thus, however far the consequences of Lobachevski's hypotheses are pushed, they will never lead to a contradiction. In fact, if two of Lobachevski's theorems were contradictory, it would be the same with the translations of these two theorems, made by the aid of our dictionary, but these translations are theorems of ordinary geometry and no one doubts that the ordinary geometry is free from contradiction. Whence comes this certainty and is it justified? That is a question I cannot treat here because it would require to be enlarged upon, but which is very interesting and I think not insoluble.

Nothing remains then of the objection above formulated. This is not all. Lobachevski's geometry, susceptible of a concrete interpretation, ceases to be a vain logical exercise and is capable of applications; I have not the time to speak here of these applications, nor of the aid that Klein and I have gotten from them for the integration of linear differential equations.

This interpretation moreover is not unique, and several dictionaries analogous to the preceding could be constructed, which would enable us by a simple "translation" to transform Lobachevski's theorems into theorems of ordinary geometry.

*The Implicit Axioms.* Are the axioms explicitly enunciated in our treatises the sole foundations of geometry? We may be assured of the contrary by noticing that after they are successively abandoned there are still left over some propositions common to the theories of Euclid, Lobachevski and Riemann. These propositions must rest on premises the geometers admit without enunciation. It is interesting to try to disentangle them from the classic demonstrations.

[John] Stuart Mill has claimed that every definition contains an axiom, because in defining one affirms implicitly the existence of the object defined. This is going much too far; it is rare that in mathematics a definition is given without its being followed by the demonstration of the existence of the object defined, and when this is dispensed with it is generally because the reader can easily supply it. It must not be forgotten that the word existence has not the same sense when it refers to a mathematical entity and when it is a question of a material object. A mathematical entity exists, provided its definition implies no contradiction, either in itself, or with the propositions already admitted.

But if Stuart Mill's observation cannot be applied to all definitions, it is none the less just for some of them. The plane is sometimes defined as follows: The plane is a surface such that the straight line which joins any two of its points is wholly on this surface. This definition manifestly hides a new axiom; it is true we might change it, and that would be preferable, but then we should have to enunciate the axiom explicitly.

Other definitions would suggest reflections not less important. Such, for example, is that of the equality of two figures; two figures are equal when they can be superposed; to superpose them one must be displaced until it coincides with the other; but how shall it be displaced? If we should ask this, no doubt we should be told that it must be done without altering the shape and as a rigid solid. The vicious circle would then be evident.

In fact this definition defines nothing; it would have no meaning for a being living in a world where there were only fluids. If it seems clear to us, that is because we are used to the properties of natural solids which do not differ much from those of the ideal solids, all of whose dimensions are invariable.

Yet, imperfect as it may be, this definition implies an axiom.

The possibility of the motion of a rigid figure is not a self-evident truth, or at least it is so only in the fashion of Euclid's postulate and not as an analytic judgment a priori would be. Moreover, in studying the definitions and the demonstrations of geometry, we see that one is obliged to admit without proof not only the possibility of this motion, but some of its properties besides.

This is at once seen from the definition of the straight line. Many defective definitions have been given, but the true one is that which is implied in all the demonstrations where the straight line enters: "It may happen that the motion of a rigid figure is such that all the points of a line belonging to this figure remain motionless while all the points situated outside of this line move. Such a line will be called a straight line." We have designedly, in this enunciation, separated the definition from the axiom it implies.

Many demonstrations, such as those of the cases of the equality of triangles, of the possibility of dropping a perpendicular from a point to a straight line, presume propositions which are not enunciated, for they require the admission that it is possible to transport a figure in a certain way in space.

*The Fourth Geometry.* Among these implicit axioms, there is one which seems to me to merit some attention, because when it is abandoned a fourth geometry can be constructed as coherent as those of Euclid, Lobachevski and Riemann.

To prove that a perpendicular may always be erected at a point $A$ to a straight line $AB$, we consider a straight line $AC$ movable around the point $A$ and initially coincident with the fixed straight line $AB$; and we make it turn about the point $A$ until it comes into the prolongation of $AB$.

Thus two propositions are presupposed: First, that such a rotation is possible, and next that it may be continued until the two straight lines come into the prolongation one of the other. If the first point is admitted and the second rejected, we are led to a series of theorems even stranger than those of Lobachevski and Riemann, but equally exempt from contradiction. I shall cite only one of these theorems and that not the most singular: *A real straight line may be perpendicular to itself.*

*Lie's Theorem.* The number of axioms implicitly introduced in the classic demonstrations is greater than necessary, and it would be interesting to reduce it to a minimum. It may first be asked whether this reduction is possible, whether the number of necessary axioms and that of imaginable geometries are not infinite.

A theorem of Sophus Lie dominates this whole discussion. It may be thus enunciated: Suppose the following premises are admitted: (1) Space has $n$ dimensions. (2) The motion of a rigid figure is possible. (3) It requires $p$ conditions to determine the position of this figure in space.

*The number of geometries compatible with these premises will be limited.* I may even add that if $n$ is given, a superior limit can be assigned to $p$. If, therefore, the possibility of motion is admitted, there can be invented only a finite (and even a rather small) number of three-dimensional geometries.

*Riemann's Geometries.* Yet this result seems contradicted by Riemann, for this savant constructs an infinity of different geometries, and that to which his name is ordinarily given is only a particular case. All depends, he says, on how the length of a curve is defined. Now, there is an infinity of ways of defining this length, and each of them may be the starting point of a new geometry.

That is perfectly true, but most of these definitions are incompatible with the motion of a rigid figure, which in the theorem of Lie is supposed possible. These geometries of Riemann, in many ways so interesting, could never therefore be other than purely analytic and would not lend themselves to demonstrations analogous to those of Euclid.

*On the Nature of Axioms.* Most mathematicians regard Lobachevski's geometry only as a mere logical curiosity; some of them, however, have gone farther. Since several geometries are possible, is it certain ours is the true one? Experience no doubt teaches us that the sum of the angles of a triangle is equal to two right angles; but this is because the triangles we deal with are too little; the difference, according to Lobachevski, is proportional to the surface of the triangle; will it not perhaps become sensible when we shall operate on larger triangles or when our measurements shall become more precise? The Euclidean geometry would thus be only a provisional geometry.

To discuss this opinion, we should first ask ourselves what is the nature of the geometric axioms.

Are they synthetic a priori judgments, as Kant said? They would then impose themselves upon us with such force that we could not conceive the contrary proposition, nor build upon it a theoretic edifice. There would be no non-Euclidean geometry.

To be convinced of it take a veritable synthetic a priori judgment, the following, for instance, of which we have seen the preponderant role in the first chapter: *If a theorem is true for the number* 1, *and if it has been proved that it is true of* n + 1 *provided it is true of* n, *it will be true of all the positive whole numbers.*

Then try to escape from that and, denying this proposition, try to found a false arithmetic analogous to non-Euclidean geometry—it cannot be done; one would even be tempted at first blush to regard these judgments as analytic. Moreover, resuming our fiction of animals without thickness, we can hardly admit that these beings, if their minds are like ours, would adopt the Euclidean geometry which would be contradicted by all their experience. Should we therefore conclude that the axioms of geometry are experimental verities? But we do not experiment on ideal straight lines or circles; it can only be done on material objects. On what then could be based experiments which should serve as foundation for geometry? The answer is easy.

We have seen above that we constantly reason as if the geometric figures behaved like solids. What geometry would borrow from experience would therefore be the properties of these bodies. The properties of light and its rectilinear propagation have also given rise to some of the propositions of geometry, and in particular these of projective geometry, so that from this point of view one would be tempted to say that metric geometry is the study of solids, and projective, that of light. But a difficulty remains, and it is insurmountable. If geometry were an experimental science, it would not be an exact science, it would be subject to a continual revision. Nay, it would from this very day be convicted of error, since we know that there is no rigorously rigid solid.

*The axioms of geometry therefore are neither synthetic a priori judgments nor experimental facts.* They are *conventions;* our choice among all possible conventions is *guided* by experimental facts; but it remains *free* and is limited only by the necessity of avoiding all contradiction. Thus it is that the postulates can remain *rigorously* true even though the experimental laws which have determined their adoption are only approximate. In other words, *the axioms of geometry* (I do not speak of those of arithmetic) *are merely disguised definitions.*

Then what are we to think of that question: Is the Euclidean geometry true? It has no meaning. As well ask whether the metric system is true and the old measures false; whether Cartesian co-ordinates are true and polar co-ordinates false. One geometry cannot be more true than another; it can only be *more convenient.*

Now, Euclidean geometry is, and will remain, the most convenient: (1) because it is the simplest; and it is so not only in consequence of our mental habits, or of I know not what direct intuition that we may have of Euclidean space; it is the simplest in itself, just as a polynomial of the first degree is simpler than one of the second; the formulas of spherical trigonometry are more complicated than those of plane trigonometry, and they would still appear so to an analyst ignorant of their geometric signification; (2) because it accords sufficiently well with the properties of natural solids, those bodies which our hands and our eyes compare and with which we make our instruments of measure.

## SPACE AND GEOMETRY

Let us begin by a little paradox. Beings with minds like ours, and having the same senses as we, but without previous education, would receive from a suitably chosen external world impressions such that they would be led to construct a geometry other than that of Euclid and to localize the phenomena of that external world in a non-Euclidean space, or even in a space of four dimensions.

As for us, whose education has been accomplished by our actual world, if we were suddenly transported into this new world, we should have no difficulty in referring its phenomena to our Euclidean space. Conversely, if these beings were transported into our environment, they would be led to relate our phenomena to non-Euclidean space. Nay more; with a little effort we likewise could do it. A person who should devote his existence to it might perhaps attain to a realization of the fourth dimension.

*Geometric Space and Perceptual Space.* It is often said the images of external objects are localized in space, even that they cannot be formed except on this condition. It is also said that this space, which serves thus as a ready prepared *frame* for our sensations and our representations, is identical with that of the geometers, of which it possesses all the properties.

To all the good minds who think thus, the preceding statement must have appeared quite extraordinary. But let us see whether they are not subject to an illusion that a more profound analysis would dissipate. What, first of all, are the properties of space, properly so called? I mean of that space which is the object of geometry and which I shall call *geometric space*. The following are some of the most essential: (1) It is continuous. (2) It is infinite. (3) It has three dimensions. (4) It is homogeneous, that is to say, all its points are identical one with another. (5) It is isotropic, that is to say, all the straight lines which pass through the same point are identical one with another.

Compare it now to the frame of our representations and our sensations, which I may call *perceptual space*.

*Visual Space.* Consider first a purely visual impression, due to an image formed on the bottom of the retina. A cursory analysis shows us this image as continuous, but as possessing only two dimensions; this already distinguishes from geometric space what we may call *pure visual space*. Besides, this image is enclosed in a limited frame.

Finally, there is another difference not less important: *this pure visual space is not homogeneous*. All the points of the retina, aside from the images which may there be formed, do not play the same role. The yellow spot can in no way be regarded as identical with a point on the border of the retina. In fact, not only does the same object produce there much more vivid impressions, but in every *limited* frame the point occupying the center of the frame will never appear as equivalent to a point near one of the borders. No doubt a more profound analysis would show us that this continuity of visual space and its two dimensions are only an illusion; it would separate it therefore still more from geometric space, but we shall not dwell on this remark.

Sight, however, enables us to judge of distances and consequently to perceive a third dimension. But everyone knows that this perception of the third dimension reduces itself to the sensation of the effort at accommodation it is necessary to make, and to that of the convergence which must be given to the two eyes, to perceive an object distinctly. These are muscular sensations altogether different from the visual sensations which have given us the notion of the first two dimensions. The third dimension therefore will not appear to us as playing the same role as the other two. What may be called *complete visual space* is therefore not an isotropic space. It has, it is true, precisely three dimensions, which means that the elements of our visual sensations (those at least which combine to form the notion of extension) will be completely defined when three of them are known; to use the language of mathematics, they will be functions of three independent variables.

But examine the matter a little more closely. The third dimension is revealed to us in two different ways: by the effort of accommodation and by the convergence of the eyes. No doubt these two indications are always concordant, there is a constant relation between them, or, in mathematical terms, the two variables which measure these two muscular sensations do not appear to us as independent; or again, to avoid an appeal to mathematical notions already rather refined, we may go back to the language of the preceding chapter and enunciate the same fact as follows: If two sensations of convergence, A and B, are indistinguishable, the two sensations of accommodation, A' and B', which respectively accompany them, will be equally indistinguishable.

But here we have, so to speak, an experimental fact; a priori nothing prevents our supposing the contrary, and if the contrary takes place, if these two muscular sensations vary independently of one another, we shall have to take account of one more independent variable, and "complete visual space" will appear to us as a physical continuum of four dimensions. We have here even, I will add, a fact of *external* experience. Nothing prevents our supposing that a being with a mind like ours, having the same sense organs that we have, may be placed in a world where light would only reach him after having traversed reflecting media of complicated form. The two indications which serve us in judging distances would cease to be connected by a constant relation. A being who should achieve in such a world the education of his senses would no doubt attribute four dimensions to complete visual space.

*Tactile Space and Motor Space.* "Tactile space" is still more complicated than visual space and farther removed from geometric space. It is superfluous to repeat for touch the discussion I have given for sight.

But apart from the data of sight and touch, there are other sensations which contribute as much and more than they to the genesis of the notion of space. These are known to everyone; they accompany all our movements, and are usually called muscular sensations. The corresponding frame constitutes what may be called *motor space*. Each muscle gives rise to a special sensation capable of augmenting or of diminishing, so that the totality of our muscular sensations will depend upon as many variables as we have muscles. From this point of view, *motor space would have as many dimensions as we have muscles.*

I know it will be said that if the muscular sensations contribute to form the notion of space, it is because we have the sense of the *direction* of each movement and that it makes an integrant part of the sensation. If this were so, if a muscular sensation could not arise except accompanied by this geometric sense of direction, geometric space would indeed be a form imposed upon our sensibility. But I perceive nothing at all of this when I analyze my sensations.

What I do see is that the sensations which correspond to movements in the same direction are connected in my mind by a mere *association of ideas.* It is to this association that what we call "the sense of direction" is reducible. This feeling therefore cannot be found in a single sensation. This association is extremely complex, for the contraction of the same muscle may correspond, according to the position of the limbs, to movements of very different direction. Besides, it is evidently acquired; it is, like all associations of ideas, the result of a *habit;* this habit itself results from very numerous *experiences;* without any doubt, if the education of our senses had been accomplished in a different environment, where we should have been subjected to different impressions, contrary habits would have arisen and our muscular sensations would have been associated according to other laws.

*Characteristics of Perceptual Space.* Thus perceptual space, under its triple form, visual, tactile and motor, is essentially different from geometric space. It is neither homogeneous, nor isotropic; one cannot even say that it has three dimensions.

It is often said that we "project" into geometric space the objects of our external perception; that we "localize" them. Has this a meaning, and if so, what? Does it mean that we *represent* to ourselves external objects in geometric space?

Our representations are only the reproduction of our sensations; they can therefore be ranged only in the same frame as these, that is to say, in perceptual space. It is as impossible for us to represent to ourselves external bodies in geometric space as it is for a painter to paint on a plane canvas objects with their three dimensions.

Perceptual space is only an image of geometric space, an image altered in shape by a sort of perspective, and we can represent to ourselves objects only by bringing them under the laws of this perspective. Therefore we do not *represent* to ourselves external bodies in geometric space, but we *reason* on these bodies as if they were situated in geometric space.

When it is said then that we "localize" such and such an object at such and such a point of space, what does it mean? *It simply means that we represent to ourselves the movements it would be necessary to make to reach that object;* and one may not say that to represent to oneself these movements, it is necessary to project the movements themselves in space and that the notion of space must, consequently, pre-exist.

When I say that we represent to ourselves these movements, I mean only that we represent to ourselves the muscular sensations which accompany them and which have no geometric character whatever, which consequently do not at all imply the pre-existence of the notion of space.

*Change of State and Change of Position.* But, it will be said, if the idea of geometric space is not imposed upon our mind, and if, on the other hand, none of our sensations can furnish it, how could it have come into existence? This is what we have now to examine, and it will take some time, but I can summarize in a few words the attempt at explanation that I am about to develop.

*None of our sensations, isolated, could have conducted us to the idea of space; we are led to it only in studying the laws, according to which these sensations succeed each other.* We see first that our impressions are subject to change; but among the changes we ascertain we are soon led to make a distinction. At one time we say that the objects which cause these impressions have changed state, at another time that they have changed position, that they have only been displaced. Whether an object changes its state or merely its position, this is always translated for us in the same manner: *by a modification in an aggregate of impressions.*

How then could we have been led to distinguish between the two? It is easy to account for. If there has only been a change of position, we can restore the primitive aggregate of impressions by making movements which replace us opposite the mobile object in the same *relative* situation. We thus *correct* the modification that happened and we re-establish the initial state by an inverse modification. If it is a question of sight, for example, and if an object changes its place before our eye, we can "follow it with the eye" and maintain its image on the same point of the retina by appropriate movements of the eyeball. These movements we are conscious of because they are voluntary and because they are accompanied by muscular sensations, but that does not mean that we represent them to ourselves in geometric space. So what characterizes change of position, what distinguishes it from change of state, is that it can always be corrected in this way.

It may therefore happen that we pass from the totality of impressions *A* to the totality *B* in two different ways: (1) involuntarily and without experiencing muscular sensations; this happens when it is the object which changes place; (2) voluntarily and with muscular sensations; this happens when the object is motionless, but we move so that the object has relative motion with reference to us. If this be so, the passage from the totality *A* to the totality *B* is only a change of position.

It follows from this that sight and touch could not have given us the notion of space without the aid of the "muscular sense." Not only could this notion not be derived from a single sensation or even *from a series of sensations*, but what is more, an *immobile* being could never have acquired it, since, not being able to *correct* by his movements the effects of the changes of position of exterior objects, he would have had no reason whatever to distinguish them from changes of state. Just as little could he have acquired it if his motions had not been voluntary or were unaccompanied by any sensations.

*Conditions of Compensation.* How is a like compensation possible, of such sort that two changes, otherwise independent of each other, reciprocally correct each other?

A mind already familiar with geometry would reason as follows: Evidently, if there is to be compensation, the various parts of the external object, on the one hand, and the various sense organs, on the other hand, must be in the same *relative* position after the double change. And, for that to be the case, the various parts of the external object must likewise have retained in reference to each other the same relative position, and the same must be true of the various parts of our body in regard to each other. In other words, the external object, in the first change, must be displaced as is a rigid solid, and so must it be with the whole of our body in the second change which corrects the first. Under these conditions, compensation may take place.

But we who as yet know nothing of geometry, since for us the notion of space is not yet formed, we cannot reason thus, we cannot foresee a priori whether compensation is possible. But experience teaches us that it sometimes happens, and it is from this experimental fact that we start to distinguish changes of state from changes of position.

*Solid Bodies and Geometry.* Among surrounding objects there are some which frequently undergo displacements susceptible of being thus corrected by a correlative movement of our own body; these are the *solid bodies.* The other objects, whose form is variable, only exceptionally undergo like displacements (change of position without change of form). When a body changes its place *and its shape,* we can no longer, by appropriate movements, bring back our sense organs into the same *relative* situation with regard to this body; consequently we can no longer reestablish the primitive totality of impressions.

It is only later, and as a consequence of new experiences, that we learn how to decompose the bodies of variable form into smaller elements, such that each is displaced almost in accordance with the same laws as solid bodies. Thus we distinguish "deformations" from other changes of state; in these deformations, each element undergoes a mere change of position, which can be corrected, but the modification undergone by the aggregate is more profound and is no longer susceptible of correction by a correlative movement. Such a notion is already very complex and must have been relatively late in appearing; moreover it could not have arisen if the observation of solid bodies had not already taught us to distinguish changes of position. *Therefore, if there were no solid bodies in nature, there would be no geometry.*

Another remark also deserves a moment's attention. Suppose a solid body to occupy successively the positions $\alpha$ and $\beta$; in its first position, it will produce on us the totality of impressions $A$, and in its second position the totality of impressions $B$. Let there be now a second solid body, having qualities entirely different from the first, for example, a different color. Suppose it to pass from the position $\alpha$, where it gives us the totality of impressions $A'$, to the position $\beta$, where it gives the totality of impressions $B'$. In general, the totality $A$ will have nothing in common with the totality $A'$, nor the totality $B$ with the totality $B'$. The transition from the totality $A$ to the totality $B$ and that from the totality $A'$ to the totality $B'$ are therefore two changes which *in themselves* have in general nothing in common.

And yet we regard these two changes both as displacements and, furthermore, we consider them as the *same* displacement. How can that be? It is simply because they can both be corrected by the *same* correlative movement of our body. "Correlative movement" therefore constitutes the *sole connection* between two phenomena which otherwise we never should have dreamed of likening.

On the other hand, our body, thanks to the number of its articulations and muscles, may make a multitude of different movements; but all are not capable of "correcting" a modification of external objects; only those will be capable of it in which our whole body, or at least all those of our sense organs which come into play, are displaced as a whole, that is, without their relative positions varying, or in the fashion of a solid body.

To summarize:

(1) We are led at first to distinguish two categories of phenomena: some, involuntary, unaccompanied by muscular sensations, are attributed by us to external objects; these are external changes; others, opposite in character and attributed by us to the movements of our own body, are internal changes. (2) We notice that certain changes of each of these categories may be corrected by a correlative change of the other category. (3) We distinguish among external changes those which have thus a correlative in the other category; these we call displacements; and just so among the internal changes, we distinguish those which have a correlative in the first category.

Thus are defined, thanks to this reciprocity, a particular class of phenomena which we call displacements. *The laws of these phenomena constitute the object of geometry.*

*Law of Homogeneity.* The first of these laws is the law of homogeneity.

Suppose that, by an external change $\alpha$, we pass from the totality of impressions $A$ to the totality $B$, then that this change $\alpha$ is corrected by a correlative voluntary movement $\beta$, so that we are brought back to the totality $A$. Suppose now that another external change $\alpha'$ makes us pass anew from the totality $A$ to the totality $B$. Experience teaches us that this change $\alpha'$ is, like $\alpha$, susceptible of being corrected by a correlative voluntary movement $\beta'$ and that this movement $\beta'$ corresponds to the same muscular sensations as the movement $\beta$ which corrected $\alpha$. This fact is usually enunciated by saying that *space is homogeneous and isotropic.*

It may also be said that a movement which has once been produced may be repeated a second and a third time, and so on, without its properties varying. In the first chapter, where we discussed the nature of mathematical reasoning, we saw the importance which must be attributed to the possibility of repeating indefinitely the same operation. It is from this repetition that mathematical reasoning gets its power; it is, therefore, thanks to the law of homogeneity that it has a hold on the geometric facts. For completeness, to the law of homogeneity should be added a multitude of other analogous laws, into the details of which I do not wish to enter, but which mathematicians sum up in a word by saying that displacements form "a group."

*The Non-Euclidean World.* If geometric space were a frame imposed on *each* of our representations, considered individually, it would be impossible to represent to ourselves an image stripped of this frame, and we could change nothing of our geometry. But this is not the case; geometry is only the résumé of the laws according to which these images succeed each other. Nothing then prevents us from imagining a series of representations, similar in all points to our ordinary representations, but succeeding one another according to laws different from those to which we are accustomed. We can conceive then that beings who received their education in an environment where these laws were thus upset might have a geometry very different from ours.

Suppose, for example, a world enclosed in a great sphere and subject to the following laws: The temperature is not uniform; it is greatest at the center, and diminishes in proportion to the distance from the center, to sink to absolute zero when the sphere is reached in which this world is enclosed. To specify still more precisely the law in accordance with which this temperature varies: Let $R$ be the radius of the limiting sphere; let $r$ be the distance of the point considered from the center of this sphere. The absolute temperature shall be proportional to $R^2 - r^2$. I shall further suppose that, in this world, all bodies have the same coefficient of dilatation, so that the length of any rule is proportional to its absolute temperature. Finally, I shall suppose that a body transported from one point to another of different temperature is put immediately into thermal equilibrium with its new environment. Nothing in these hypotheses is contradictory or unimaginable.

A movable object will then become smaller and smaller in proportion as it approaches the limit-sphere. Note first that, though this world is limited from the point of view of our ordinary geometry, it will appear infinite to its inhabitants. In fact, when these try to approach the limit-sphere, they cool off and become smaller and smaller. Therefore the steps they take are also smaller and smaller, so that they can never reach the limiting sphere.

If, for us, geometry is only the study of the laws according to which rigid solids move, for these imaginary beings it will be the study of the laws of motion of solids *distorted by the differences of temperature* just spoken of. No doubt, in our world, natural solids likewise undergo variations of form and volume due to warming or cooling. But we neglect these variations in laying the foundations of geometry, because, besides their being very slight, they are irregular and consequently seem to us accidental. In our hypothetical world, this would no longer be the case, and these variations would follow regular and very simple laws. Moreover, the various solid pieces of which the bodies of its inhabitants would be composed would undergo the same variations of form and volume.

I will make still another hypothesis; I will suppose light traverses media diversely refractive and such that the index of refraction is inversely proportional to $R^2 - r^2$. It is easy to see that, under these conditions, the rays of light would not be rectilinear, but circular.

To justify what precedes, it remains for me to show that certain changes in the position of external objects can be *corrected* by correlative movements of the sentient beings inhabiting this imaginary world, and that in such a way as to restore the primitive aggregate of impressions experienced by these sentient beings.

Suppose in fact that an object is displaced, undergoing deformation, not as a rigid solid, but as a solid subjected to unequal dilatations in exact conformity to the law of temperature above supposed. Permit me for brevity to call such a movement a *non-Euclidean displacement*. If a sentient being happens to be in the neighborhood, his impressions will be modified by the displacement of the object, but he can re-establish them by moving in a suitable manner. It suffices if finally the aggregate of the object and the sentient being, considered as forming a single body, has undergone one of those particular displacements I have just called non-Euclidean. This is possible if it be supposed that the limbs of these beings dilate according to the same law as the other bodies of the world they inhabit.

Although from the point of view of our ordinary geometry there is a deformation of the bodies in this displacement and their various parts are no longer in the same relative position, nevertheless we shall see that the impressions of the sentient being have once more become the same. In fact, though the mutual distances of the various parts may have varied, yet the parts originally in contact are again in contact. Therefore the tactile impressions have not changed. On the other hand, taking into account the hypothesis made above in regard to the refraction and the curvature of the rays of light, the visual impressions will also have remained the same.

These imaginary beings will therefore like ourselves be led to classify the phenomena they witness and to distinguish among them the "changes of position" susceptible of correction by a correlative voluntary movement. If they construct a geometry, it will not be, as ours is, the study of the movements of our rigid solids; it will be the study of the changes of position which they will thus have distinguished and which are none other than the "non-Euclidean displacements"; *it will be non-Euclidean geometry.* Thus beings like ourselves, educated in such a world, would not have the same geometry as ours.

*The World of Four Dimensions.* We can represent to ourselves a four-dimensional world just as well as a non-Euclidean.

The sense of sight, even with a single eye, together with the muscular sensations relative to the movements of the eyeball, would suffice to teach us space of three dimensions. The images of external objects are painted on the retina, which is a two-dimensional canvas; they are *perspectives.* But, as eye and objects are movable, we see in succession various perspectives of the same body, taken from different points of view. At the same time, we find that the transition from one perspective to another is often accompanied by muscular sensations. If the transition from the perspective A to the perspective B, and that from the perspective A' to the perspective B' are accompanied by the same muscular sensations, we liken them one to the other as operations of the same nature.

Studying then the laws according to which these operations combine, we recognize that they form a group, which has the same structure as that of the movements of rigid solids. Now, we have seen that it is from the properties of this group we have derived the notion of geometric space and that of three dimensions. We understand thus how the idea of a space of three dimensions could take birth from the pageant of these perspectives, though each of them is of only two dimensions, since *they follow one another according to certain laws.*

Well, just as the perspective of a three-dimensional figure can be made on a plane, we can make that of a four-dimensional figure on a picture of three (or of two) dimensions. To a geometer this is only child's play. We can even take of the same figure several perspectives from several different points of view. We can easily represent to ourselves these perspectives, since they are of only three dimensions.

Imagine that the various perspectives of the same object succeed one another, and that the transition from one to the other is accompanied by muscular sensations. We shall of course consider two of these transitions as two operations of the same nature when they are associated with the same muscular sensations. Nothing then prevents us from imagining that these operations combine according to any law we choose, for example, so as to form a group with the same structure as that of the movements of a rigid solid of four dimensions. Here there is nothing unpicturable, and yet these sensations are precisely those which would be felt by a being possessed of a two-dimensional retina who could move in space of four dimensions. In this sense we may say the fourth dimension is imaginable.

*Conclusions.* We see that experience plays an indispensable role in the genesis of geometry; but it would be an error thence to conclude that geometry is, even in part, an experimental science. If it were experimental, it would be only approximative and provisional. And what rough approximation!

Geometry would be only the study of the movements of solids; but in reality it is not occupied with natural solids, it has for object certain ideal solids, absolutely rigid, which are only a simplified and very remote image of natural solids. The notion of these ideal solids is drawn from all parts of our mind, and experience is only an occasion which induces us to bring it forth from them.

The object of geometry is the study of a particular "group"; but the general group concept pre-exists, at least potentially, in our minds. It is imposed on us, not as form of our sense, but as form of our understanding. Only, from among all the possible groups, that must be chosen which will be, so to speak, the *standard* to which we shall refer natural phenomena. Experience guides us in this choice without forcing it upon us; it tells us not which is the truest geometry, but which is the most *convenient*.

Notice that I have been able to describe the fantastic worlds above imagined *without ceasing to employ the language of ordinary geometry*. And, in fact, we should not have to change it if transported thither. Beings educated there would doubtless find it more convenient to create a geometry different from ours, and better adapted to their impressions. As for us, in face of the *same* impressions, it is certain that we should find it more convenient not to change our habits.

### EXPERIENCE AND GEOMETRY

1. Already in the preceding pages I have several times tried to show that the principles of geometry are not experimental facts and that in particular Euclid's postulate cannot be proven experimentally. However decisive appear to me the reasons already given, I believe I should emphasize this point because here a false idea is profoundly rooted in many minds.

2. If we construct a material circle, measure its radius and circum-

ference, and see if the ratio of these two lengths is equal to $\pi$, what shall we have done? We shall have made an experiment on the properties of the matter with which we constructed this *round thing*, and of that of which the measure used was made.

3. *Geometry and Astronomy.* The question has also been put in another way. If Lobachevski's geometry is true, the parallax of a very distant star will be finite; if Riemann's is true, it will be negative. These are results which seem within the reach of experiment, and there have been hopes that astronomical observations might enable us to decide between the three geometries.

But in astronomy "straight line" means simply "path of a ray of light." If therefore negative parallaxes were found, or if it were demonstrated that all parallaxes are superior to a certain limit, two courses would be open to us: we might either renounce Euclidean geometry, or else modify the laws of optics and suppose that light does not travel rigorously in a straight line. It is needless to add that all the world would regard the latter solution as the more advantageous. The Euclidean geometry has, therefore, nothing to fear from fresh experiments.

4. Is the position tenable that certain phenomena, possible in Euclidean space, would be impossible in non-Euclidean space, so that experience, in establishing these phenomena, would directly contradict the non-Euclidean hypothesis? For my part I think no such question can be put. To my mind it is precisely equivalent to the following, whose absurdity is patent to all eyes: are there lengths expressible in meters and centimeters, but which cannot be measured in fathoms, feet and inches, so that experience, in ascertaining the existence of these lengths, would directly contradict the hypothesis that there are fathoms divided into six feet?

Examine the question more closely. I suppose that the straight line possesses in Euclidean space any two properties which I shall call A and B; that in non-Euclidean space it still possesses the property A, but no longer has the property B; finally I suppose that in both Euclidean and non-Euclidean space the straight line is the only line having the property A. If this were so, experience would be capable of deciding between the hypothesis of Euclid and that of Lobachevski. It would be ascertained that a definite concrete object, accessible to experiment, for example, a pencil of rays of light, possesses the property A; we should conclude that it is rectilinear, and then investigate whether or not it has the property B.

But *this is not so;* no property exists which, like this property A, can be an absolute criterion enabling us to recognize the straight line and to distinguish it from every other line. Shall we say, for instance: "The following is such a property: the straight line is a line such that a figure of which this line forms a part can be moved without the mutual distances of its points varying and so that all points of this line remain fixed"?

This, in fact, is a property which, in Euclidean or non-Euclidean space, belongs to the straight line and belongs only to it. But how shall we ascertain experimentally whether it belongs to this or that concrete object? It will be necessary to measure distances, and how shall one know that any concrete magnitude which I have measured with my material instrument really represents the abstract distance? We have only pushed back the difficulty. In reality the property just enunciated is not a property of the straight line alone, it is a property of the straight line and distance. For it to serve as absolute criterion, we should have to be able to establish not only that it does not also belong to a line other than the straight line and to distance, but in addition that it does not belong to a line other than the straight line and to a magnitude other than distance. Now this is not true. It is therefore impossible to imagine a concrete experiment which can be interpreted in the Euclidean system and not in the Lobachevskian system, so that I may conclude: No experience will ever be in contradiction to Euclid's postulate; nor, on the other hand, will any experience ever contradict the postulate of Lobachevski.

5. But it is not enough that the Euclidean (or non-Euclidean) geometry can never be directly contradicted by experience. Might it not happen that it can accord with experience only by violating the principle of sufficient reason or that of the relativity of space?

I will explain myself: Consider any material system; we shall have to regard, on the one hand, "the state" of the various bodies of this system (for instance, their temperature, their electric potential, etc.), and, on the other hand, their position in space; and among the data which enable us to define this position we shall, moreover, distinguish the mutual distances of these bodies, which define their relative positions, from the conditions which define the absolute position of the system and its absolute orientation in space.

The laws of the phenomena which will happen in this system will depend on the state of these bodies and their mutual distances; but, because of the relativity and passivity of space, they will not depend on the absolute position and orientation of the system. In other words, the state of the bodies and their mutual distances at any instant will depend solely on the state of these same bodies and on their mutual distances at the initial instant, but will not at all depend on the absolute initial position of the system or on its absolute initial orientation. This is what for brevity I shall call *the law of relativity*.

Hitherto I have spoken as a Euclidean geometer. As I have said, an experience, whatever it be, admits of an interpretation on the Euclidean hypothesis; but it admits of one equally on the non-Euclidean hypothesis. Well, we have made a series of experiments; we have interpreted them on the Euclidean hypothesis, and we have recognized that these experiments thus interpreted do not violate this "law of relativity."

We now interpret them on the non-Euclidean hypothesis: this is always possible; only the non-Euclidean distances of our different bodies in this new interpretation will not generally be the same as the Euclidean distances in the primitive interpretation.

Will our experiments, interpreted in this new manner, still be in accord with our "law of relativity"? And if there were not this accord, should we not have also the right to say experience had proven the falsity of the non-Euclidean geometry? It is easy to see that this is an idle fear; in fact, to apply the law of relativity in all rigor, it must be applied to the entire universe. For if only a part of this universe were considered, and if the absolute position of this part happened to vary, the distances to the other bodies of the universe would likewise vary, their influence on the part of the universe considered would consequently augment or diminish, which might modify the laws of the phenomena happening there.

But if our system is the entire universe, experience is powerless to give information about its absolute position and orientation in space. All that our instruments, however perfected they may be, can tell us will be the state of the various parts of the universe and their mutual distances.

So our law of relativity may be thus enunciated: The readings we shall be able to make on our instruments at any instant will depend only on the readings we could have made on these same instruments at the initial instant. Now such an enunciation is independent of every interpretation of experimental facts. If the law is true in the Euclidean interpretation, it will also be true in the non-Euclidean interpretation.

Allow me here a short digression. I have spoken above of the data which define the position of the various bodies of the system; I should likewise have spoken of those which define their velocities; I should then have had to distinguish the velocities with which the mutual distances of the different bodies vary; and, on the other hand, the velocities of translation and rotation of the system, that is to say, the velocities with which its absolute position and orientation vary.

To fully satisfy the mind, the law of relativity should be expressible thus: The state of bodies and their mutual distances at any instant, as well as the velocities with which these distances vary at this same instant, will depend only on the state of those bodies and their mutual distances at the initial instant, and the velocities with which these distances vary at this initial instant, but they will not depend either upon the absolute initial position of the system, or upon its absolute orientation, or upon the velocities with which this absolute position and orientation varied at the initial instant.

Unhappily the law thus enunciated is not in accord with experiments, at least as they are ordinarily interpreted. Suppose a man be transported to a planet whose heavens were always covered with a thick curtain of clouds, so that he could never see the other stars; on that planet he would live as if it were isolated in space. Yet this man could become aware that it turned, either by measuring its oblateness (done ordinarily by the aid of astronomic observations, but capable of being done by purely geodetic means), or by repeating the experiment of Foucault's pendulum. The absolute rotation of this planet could therefore be made evident.

That is a fact which shocks the philosopher, but which the physicist is compelled to accept. We know that from this fact Newton inferred the existence of absolute space; I myself am quite unable to adopt this view. . . . For the moment it is not my intention to enter upon this difficulty. Therefore I must resign myself, in the enunciation of the law of relativity, to including velocities of every kind among the data which define the state of the bodies. However that may be, this difficulty is the same for Euclid's geometry as for Lobachevski's; I therefore need not trouble myself with it, and have only mentioned it incidentally.

What is important is the conclusion: experiment cannot decide between Euclid and Lobachevski. To sum up, whichever way we look at it, it is impossible to discover in geometric empiricism a rational meaning.

6. Experiments only teach us the relations of bodies to one another; none of them bears or can bear on the relations of bodies with space, or on the mutual relations of different parts of space.

"Yes," you reply, "a single experiment is insufficient, because it gives me only a single equation with several unknowns; but when I shall have made enough experiments I shall have equations enough to calculate all my unknowns."

To know the height of the mainmast does not suffice for calculating the age of the captain. When you have measured every bit of wood in the ship you will have many equations, but you will know his age no better. All your measurements bearing only on your bits of wood can reveal to you nothing except concerning these bits of wood. Just so your experiments, however numerous they may be, bearing only on the relations of bodies to one another, will reveal to us nothing about the mutual relations of the various parts of space.

7. Will you say that if the experiments bear on the bodies, they bear at least upon the geometric properties of the bodies? But, first, what do you understand by geometric properties of the bodies? I assume that it is a question of the relations of the bodies with space; these properties are therefore inaccessible to experiments which bear only on the relations of the bodies to one another. This alone would suffice to show that there can be no question of these properties.

Still let us begin by coming to an understanding about the sense of the phrase: geometric properties of bodies. When I say a body is composed of several parts, I assume that I do not enunciate therein a geometric property, and this would remain true even if I agreed to give the improper name of points to the smallest parts I consider. When I say that such a part of such a body is in contact with such a part of such another body, I enunciate a proposition which concerns the mutual relations of these two bodies and not their relations with space. I suppose you will grant me these are not geometric properties; at least I am sure you will grant me these properties are independent of all knowledge of metric geometry.

This presupposed, I imagine that we have a solid body formed of eight slender iron rods, $OA$, $OB$, $OC$, $OD$, $OE$, $OF$, $OG$, $OH$, united at one of their extremities $O$. Let us besides have a second solid body, for example a bit of wood, to be marked with three little flecks of ink which I shall call $\alpha$, $\beta$, $\gamma$. I further suppose it ascertained that $\alpha\beta\gamma$ may be brought into contact with $AGO$ (I mean $\alpha$ with $A$, and at the same time $\beta$ with $G$ and $\gamma$ with $O$), then that we may bring successively into contact $\alpha\beta\gamma$ with $BGO$, $CGO$, $DGO$, $EGO$, $FGO$, then with $AHO$, $BHO$, $CHO$, $DHO$, $EHO$, $FHO$, then $\alpha\gamma$ successively with $AB$, $BC$, $CD$, $DE$, $EF$, $FA$.

These are determinations we may make without having in advance any notion about form or about the metric properties of space. They in nowise bear on the "geometric properties of bodies." And these determinations will not be possible if the bodies experimented upon move in accordance with a group having the same structure as the Lobachevskian group (I mean according to the same laws as solid bodies in Lobachevski's geometry). They suffice therefore to prove that these bodies move in accordance with the Euclidean group, or at least that they do not move according to the Lobachevskian group.

That they are compatible with the Euclidean group is easy to see. For they could be made if the body $\alpha\beta\gamma$ was a rigid solid of our ordinary geometry presenting the form of a right-angled triangle, and if the points *ABCDEFGH* were the summits of a polyhedron formed of two regular hexagonal pyramids of our ordinary geometry, having for common base *ABCDEF* and for apices the one *G* and the other *H*.

Suppose now that in place of the preceding determination it is observed that as above $\alpha\beta\gamma$ can be successively applied to *AGO, BGO, CGO, DGO, EGO, AHO, BHO, CHO, DHO, EHO, FHO*, then that $\alpha\beta$ (and no longer $\alpha\gamma$) can be successively applied to *AB, BC, CD, DE, EF* and *FA*.

These are determinations which could be made if non-Euclidean geometry were true, if the bodies $\alpha\beta\gamma$ and *OABCDEFGH* were rigid solids, and if the first were a right-angled triangle and the second a double regular hexagonal pyramid of suitable dimensions. Therefore these new determinations are not possible if the bodies move according to the Euclidean group; but they become so if it be supposed that the bodies move according to the Lobachevskian group. They would suffice, therefore (if one made them), to prove that the bodies in question do not move according to the Euclidean group.

Thus, without making any hypothesis about form, about the nature of space, about the relations of bodies to space, and without attributing to bodies any geometric property, I have made observations which have enabled me to show in one case that the bodies experimented upon move according to a group whose structure is Euclidean, in the other case that they move according to a group whose structure is Lobachevskian.

And one may not say that the first aggregate of determinations would constitute an experiment proving that space is Euclidean, and the second an experiment proving that space is non-Euclidean. In fact one could imagine (I say imagine) bodies moving so as to render possible the second series of determinations. And the proof is that the first mechanician met could construct such bodies if he cared to take the pains and make the outlay. You will not conclude from that, however, that space is non-Euclidean. Nay, since the ordinary solid bodies would continue to exist when the mechanician had constructed the strange bodies of which I have just spoken, it would be necessary to conclude that space is at the same time Euclidean and non-Euclidean.

Suppose, for example, that we have a great sphere of radius *R* and that the temperature decreases from the center to the surface of this sphere according to the law of which I have spoken in describing the non-Euclidean world. We might have bodies whose expansion would be negligible and which would act like ordinary rigid solids; and, on the other hand, bodies very dilatable and which would act like non-Euclidean solids. We might have two double pyramids $OABCDEFGH$ and $O'A'B'C'D'E'F'G'H'$ and two triangles $\alpha\beta\gamma$ and $\alpha'\beta'\gamma'$. The first double pyramid might be rectilinear and the second curvilinear; the triangle $\alpha\beta\gamma$ might be made of inexpansible matter and the other of a very dilatable matter. It would then be possible to make the first observations with the double pyramid $OAH$ and the triangle $\alpha\beta\gamma$, and the second with the double pyramid $O'A'H'$ and the triangle $\alpha'\beta'\gamma'$. And then experiment would seem to prove first that the Euclidean geometry is true and then that it is false. *Experiments therefore have a bearing, not on space, but on bodies.*

## SUPPLEMENT

8. To complete the matter, I ought to speak of a very delicate question, which would require long development; I shall confine myself to summarizing here what I have expounded in the *Revue de Métaphysique et de Morale* and in *The Monist*. When we say space has three dimensions, what do we mean?

We have seen the importance of those "internal changes" revealed to us by our muscular sensations. They may serve to characterize the various *attitudes* of our body. Take arbitrarily as origin one of these attitudes $A$. When we pass from this initial attitude to any other attitude $B$, we feel a series of muscular sensations, and this series $S$ will define $B$. Observe, however, that we shall often regard two series $S$ and $S'$ as defining the same attitude $B$ (since the initial and final attitudes $A$ and $B$ remaining the same, the intermediary attitudes and the corresponding sensations may differ). How then shall we recognize the equivalence of these two series? Because they may serve to compensate the same external change, or more generally because, when it is a question of compensating an external change, one of the series can be replaced by the other. Among these series, we have distinguished those which of themselves alone can compensate an external change, and which we have called "displacements." As we cannot discriminate between two displacements which are too close together, the totality of these displacements presents the characteristics of a physical continuum; experience teaches us that they are those of a physical continuum of six dimensions; but we do not yet know how many dimensions space itself has, we must first solve another question.

What is a point of space? Everybody thinks he knows, but that is an

illusion. What we see when we try to represent to ourselves a point of
space is a black speck on white paper, a speck of chalk on a blackboard,
always an object. The question should therefore be understood as follows:
What do I mean when I say the object $B$ is at the same point that the
object $A$ occupied just now? Or further, what criterion will enable me to
apprehend this?

I mean that, *although I have not budged* (which my muscular sense
tells me), my first finger which just now touched the object $A$ touches at
present the object $B$. I could have used other criteria; for instance another
finger or the sense of sight. But the first criterion is sufficient; I know that
if it answers yes, all the other criteria will give the same response. I know
it *by experience*, I cannot know it a priori. For the same reason I say
that touch cannot be exercised at a distance; this is another way of
enunciating the same experimental fact. And if, on the contrary, I say that
sight acts at a distance, it means that the criterion furnished by
sight may respond yes while the others reply no. And in fact, the object
although moved away may form its image at the same point of the retina.
Sight responds yes, the object has remained at the same point and touch
answers no, because my finger which just now touched the object at
present touches it no longer. If experience had shown us that one finger
may respond no when the other says yes, we should likewise say that
touch acts at a distance.

In short, for each attitude of my body, my first finger determines a
point, and this it is, and this alone, which defines a point of space. To each
attitude corresponds thus a point; but it often happens that the same point
corresponds to several different attitudes (in this case we say our finger
has not budged, but the rest of the body has moved). We distinguish,
therefore, among the changes of attitude those where the finger does not
budge. How are we led thereto? It is because often we notice that in these
changes the object which is in contact with the finger remains in contact
with it.

Range, therefore, in the same class all the attitudes obtainable from
each other by one of the changes we have thus distinguished. To all the
attitudes of the class will correspond the same point of space. Therefore to
each class will correspond a point and to each point a class. But one
may say that what experience arrives at is not the point, it is this class
of changes or, better, the corresponding class of muscular sensations. And
when we say space has three dimensions, we simply mean that the totality
of these classes appears to us with the characteristics of a physical continuum of three dimensions.

One might be tempted to conclude that it is experience which has taught us how many dimensions space has. But in reality here also our experiences have bearing, not on space, but on our body and its relations with the neighboring objects. Moreover they are excessively crude.

In our mind pre-existed the latent idea of a certain number of groups—those whose theory Lie has developed. Which group shall we choose, to make of it a sort of standard with which to compare natural phenomena? And, this group chosen, which of its sub-groups shall we take to characterize a point of space? Experience has guided us by showing us which choice best adapts itself to the properties of our body. But its role is limited to that.

### ANCESTRAL EXPERIENCE

It has often been said that if individual experience could not create geometry the same is not true of ancestral experience. But what does that mean? Is it meant that we could not experimentally demonstrate Euclid's postulate, but that our ancestors have been able to do it? Not in the least. It is meant that by natural selection our mind has *adapted* itself to the conditions of the external world, that it has adopted the geometry *most advantageous* to the species: or in other words *the most convenient*. This is entirely in conformity with our conclusions; geometry is not true, it is advantageous.

---

*The foregoing essay comprises Chapters III–V from Henri Poincaré's* SCIENCE AND HYPOTHESIS, *translated by George B. Halsted.*

# Mathematical Creation

The genesis of mathematical creation is a problem which should intensely interest the psychologist. It is the activity in which the human mind seems to take least from the outside world, in which it acts or seems to act only of itself and on itself, so that in studying the procedure of geometric thought we may hope to reach what is most essential in man's mind.

This has long been appreciated, and some time back the journal called *L'enseignement mathématique,* edited by Laisant and Fehr, began an investigation of the mental habits and methods of work of different mathematicians. I had finished the main outlines of this article when the results of that inquiry were published, so I have hardly been able to utilize them and shall confine myself to saying that the majority of witnesses confirm my conclusions; I do not say all, for when the appeal is to universal suffrage unanimity is not to be hoped.

A first fact should surprise us, or rather would surprise us if we were not so used to it. How does it happen there are people who do not understand mathematics? If mathematics invokes only the rules of logic, such as are accepted by all normal minds; if its evidence is based on principles common to all men, and that none could deny without being mad, how does it come about that so many persons are here refractory?

That not everyone can invent is nowise mysterious. That not everyone can retain a demonstration once learned may also pass. But that not everyone can understand mathematical reasoning when explained appears very surprising when we think of it. And yet those who can follow this reasoning only with difficulty are in the majority: that is undeniable, and will surely not be gainsaid by the experience of secondary-school teachers.

And further: how is error possible in mathematics? A sane mind should not be guilty of a logical fallacy, and yet there are very fine minds who do not trip in brief reasoning such as occurs in the ordinary doings of life, and who are incapable of following or repeating without error the mathematical demonstrations which are longer, but which after all are only an accumulation of brief reasonings wholly analogous to those they make so easily. Need we add that mathematicians themselves are not infallible?

The answer seems to me evident. Imagine a long series of syllogisms, and that the conclusions of the first serve as premises of the following: we shall be able to catch each of these syllogisms, and it is not in passing from premises to conclusion that we are in danger of deceiving ourselves. But between the moment in which we first meet a proposition as conclusion of one syllogism, and that in which we re-encounter it as premise of another syllogism occasionally some time will elapse, several links of the chain will have unrolled; so it may happen that we have forgotten it, or worse, that we have forgotten its meaning. So it may happen that we replace it by a slightly different proposition, or that, while retaining the same enunciation, we attribute to it a slightly different meaning, and thus it is that we are exposed to error.

Often the mathematician uses a rule. Naturally he begins by demonstrating this rule; and at the time when this proof is fresh in his memory he understands perfectly its meaning and its bearing, and he is in no danger of changing it. But subsequently he trusts his memory and afterward only applies it in a mechanical way; and then if his memory fails him, he may apply it all wrong. Thus it is, to take a simple example, that we sometimes make slips in calculation because we have forgotten our multiplication table.

According to this, the special aptitude for mathematics would be due only to a very sure memory or to a prodigious force of attention. It would be a power like that of the whist player who remembers the cards played; or, to go up a step, like that of the chess player who can visualize a great number of combinations and hold them in his memory. Every good mathematician ought to be a good chess player, and inversely; likewise he should be a good computer. Of course that sometimes happens; thus Gauss was at the same time a geometer of genius and a very precocious and accurate computer.

But there are exceptions, or rather I err: I cannot call them exceptions without the exceptions being more than the rule. Gauss it is, on the contrary, who was an exception. As for myself, I must confess, I am absolutely incapable even of adding without mistakes. In the same way I should be but a poor chess player; I would perceive that by a certain play I should expose myself to a certain danger; I would pass in review several other plays, rejecting them for other reasons, and then finally I should make the move first examined, having meantime forgotten the danger I had foreseen.

In a word, my memory is not bad, but it would be insufficient to make me a good chess player. Why then does it not fail me in a difficult piece of mathematical reasoning where most chess players would lose themselves? Evidently because it is guided by the general march of the reasoning. A mathematical demonstration is not a simple juxtaposition of syllogisms, it is syllogisms *placed in a certain order,* and the order in which these elements are placed is much more important than the elements themselves. If I have the feeling, the intuition, so to speak, of this order, so as to perceive at a glance the reasoning as a whole, I need no longer fear lest I forget one of the elements, for each of them will take its allotted place in the array, and that without any effort of memory on my part.

It seems to me then, in repeating a reasoning learned, that I could have invented it. This is often only an illusion; but even then, even if I am not so gifted as to create it by myself, I myself reinvent it in so far as I repeat it.

We know that this feeling, this intuition of mathematical order, that makes us divine hidden harmonies and relations, cannot be possessed by everyone. Some will not have either this delicate feeling so difficult to define, or a strength of memory and attention beyond the ordinary, and then they will be absolutely incapable of understanding higher mathematics. Such are the majority. Others will have this feeling only in a slight degree, but they will be gifted with an uncommon memory and a great power of attention. They will learn by heart the details one after another; they can understand mathematics and sometimes make applications, but they cannot create. Others, finally, will possess in a less or greater degree the special intuition referred to, and then not only can they understand mathematics even if their memory is nothing extraordinary, but they may become creators and try to invent with more or less success according as this intuition is more or less developed in them.

In fact, what is mathematical creation? It does not consist in making new combinations with mathematical entities already known. Anyone could do that, but the combinations so made would be infinite in number and most of them absolutely without interest. To create consists precisely in not making useless combinations and in making those which are useful and which are only a small minority. Invention is discernment, choice.

How to make this choice I have before explained; the mathematical facts worthy of being studied are those which, by their analogy with other facts, are capable of leading us to the knowledge of a mathematical law just as experimental facts lead us to the knowledge of a physical law. They are those which reveal to us unsuspected kinship between other facts, long known, but wrongly believed to be strangers to one another.

Among chosen combinations the most fertile will often be those formed of elements drawn from domains which are far apart. Not that I mean as sufficing for invention the bringing together of objects as disparate as possible; most combinations so formed would be entirely sterile. But certain among them, very rare, are the most fruitful of all.

To invent, I have said, is to choose; but the word is perhaps not wholly exact. It makes one think of a purchaser before whom are displayed a large number of samples, and who examines them, one after the other, to make a choice. Here the samples would be so numerous that a whole lifetime would not suffice to examine them. This is not the actual state of things. The sterile combinations do not even present themselves to the mind of the inventor. Never in the field of his consciousness do combinations appear that are not really useful, except some that he rejects but which have to some extent the characteristics of useful combinations. All goes on as if the inventor were an examiner for the second degree who would only have to question the candidates who had passed a previous examination.

But what I have hitherto said is what may be observed or inferred in reading the writings of the geometers, reading reflectively.

It is time to penetrate deeper and to see what goes on in the very soul of the mathematician. For this, I believe, I can do best by recalling memories of my own. But I shall limit myself to telling how I wrote my first memoir on Fuchsian functions. I beg the reader's pardon; I am about to use some technical expressions, but they need not frighten him, for he is not obliged to understand them. I shall say, for example, that I have found the demonstration of such a theorem under such circumstances. This theorem will have a barbarous name, unfamiliar to many, but that is unimportant; what is of interest for the psychologist is not the theorem but the circumstances.

For fifteen days I strove to prove that there could not be any functions like those I have since called Fuchsian functions. I was then very ignorant; every day I seated myself at my work-table, stayed an hour or two, tried a great number of combinations and reached no results. One evening, contrary to my custom, I drank black coffee and could not sleep. Ideas rose in crowds; I felt them collide until pairs interlocked, so to speak, making a stable combination. By the next morning I had established the existence of a class of Fuchsian functions, those which come from the hypergeometric series; I had only to write out the results, which took but a few hours.

Then I wanted to represent these functions by the quotient of two series; this idea was perfectly conscious and deliberate, the analogy with elliptic functions guided me. I asked myself what properties these series must have if they existed, and I succeeded without difficulty in forming the series I have called theta-Fuchsian.

Just at this time I left Caen, where I was then living, to go on a geological excursion under the auspices of the School of Mines. The changes of travel made me forget my mathematical work. Having reached Coutances, we entered an omnibus to go some place or other. At the moment when I put my foot on the step the idea came to me, without anything in my former thoughts seeming to have paved the way for it, that the transformations I had used to define the Fuchsian functions were identical with those of non-Euclidean geometry. I did not verify the idea; I should not have had time, as, upon taking my seat in the omnibus, I went on with a conversation already commenced, but I felt a perfect certainty. On my return to Caen, for conscience' sake I verified the result at my leisure.

Then I turned my attention to the study of some arithmetic questions apparently without much success and without a suspicion of any connection with my preceding researches. Disgusted with my failure, I went to spend a few days at the seaside, and thought of something else. One morning, walking on the bluff, the idea came to me, with just the same characteristics of brevity, suddenness and immediate certainty, that the arithmetic transformations of indeterminate ternary quadratic forms were identical with those of non-Euclidean geometry.

Returned to Caen, I meditated on this result and deduced the consequences. The example of quadratic forms showed me that there were Fuchsian groups other than those corresponding to the hypergeometric series; I saw that I could apply to them the theory of theta-Fuchsian series and that consequently there existed Fuchsian functions other than those from the hypergeometric series, the ones I then knew. Naturally I set myself to form all these functions. I made a systematic attack upon them and carried all the outworks one after another. There was one however that still held out, whose fall would involve that of the whole place. But all my efforts only served at first the better to show me the difficulty, which indeed was something. All this work was perfectly conscious.

Thereupon I left for Mont-Valérien, where I was to go through my military service; so I was very differently occupied. One day, going along the street, the solution of the difficulty which had stopped me suddenly appeared to me. I did not try to go deep into it immediately, and only after my service did I again take up the question. I had all the elements and had only to arrange them and put them together. So I wrote out my final memoir at a single stroke and without difficulty.

I shall limit myself to this single example; it is useless to multiply them. In regard to my other researches I would have to say analogous things, and the observations of other mathematicians given in *L'enseignement mathématique* would only confirm them.

Most striking at first is this appearance of sudden illumination, a manifest sign of long, unconscious prior work. The role of this unconscious work in mathematical invention appears to me incontestable, and traces of it would be found in other cases where it is less evident. Often when one works at a hard question, nothing good is accomplished at the first attack. Then one takes a rest, longer or shorter, and sits down anew to the work. During the first half-hour, as before, nothing is found, and then all of a sudden the decisive idea presents itself to the mind. It might be said that the conscious work has been more fruitful because it has been interrupted and the rest has given back to the mind its force and freshness. But it is more probable that this rest has been filled out with unconscious work and that the result of this work has afterwards revealed itself to the geometer just as in the cases I have cited; only the revelation, instead of coming during a walk or a journey, has happened during a period of conscious work, but independently of this work which plays at most a role of excitant, as if it were the goad stimulating the results already reached during rest, but remaining unconscious, to assume the conscious form.

There is another remark to be made about the conditions of this unconscious work: it is possible, and of a certainty it is only fruitful, if it is on the one hand preceded and on the other hand followed by a period of conscious work. These sudden inspirations (and the examples already cited sufficiently prove this) never happen except after some days of voluntary effort which has appeared absolutely fruitless and whence nothing good seems to have come, where the way taken seems totally astray. These efforts then have not been as sterile as one thinks; they have set agoing the unconscious machine and without them it would not have moved and would have produced nothing.

The need for the second period of conscious work, after the inspiration, is still easier to understand. It is necessary to put in shape the results of this inspiration, to deduce from them the immediate consequences, to arrange them, to word the demonstrations, but above all is verification necessary. I have spoken of the feeling of absolute certitude accompanying the inspiration; in the cases cited this feeling was no deceiver, nor is it usually. But do not think this a rule without exception; often this feeling deceives us without being any the less vivid, and we only find it out when we seek to put on foot the demonstration. I have especially noticed this fact in regard to ideas coming to me in the morning or evening in bed while in a semi-hypnagogic state.

Such are the realities; now for the thoughts they force upon us. The unconscious, or, as we say, the subliminal self plays an important role in mathematical creation; this follows from what we have said. But usually the subliminal self is considered as purely automatic. Now we have seen that mathematical work is not simply mechanical, that it could not be done by a machine, however perfect. It is not merely a question of applying rules, of making the most combinations possible according to certain fixed laws. The combinations so obtained would be exceedingly numerous, useless and cumbersome. The true work of the inventor consists in choosing among these combinations so as to eliminate the useless ones or rather to avoid the trouble of making them, and the rules which must guide this choice are extremely fine and delicate. It is almost impossible to state them precisely; they are felt rather than formulated. Under these conditions, how imagine a sieve capable of applying them mechanically?

A first hypothesis now presents itself: the subliminal self is in no way inferior to the conscious self; it is not purely automatic; it is capable of discernment; it has tact, delicacy; it knows how to choose, to divine. What do I say? It knows better how to divine than the conscious self, since it succeeds where that has failed. In a word, is not the subliminal self superior to the conscious self? You recognize the full importance of this question. Boutroux in a recent lecture has shown how it came up on a very different occasion, and what consequences would follow an affirmative answer. (See also, by the same author, *Science et Religion,* pp. 313 ff.)

Is this affirmative answer forced upon us by the facts I have just given? I confess that, for my part, I should hate to accept it. Re-examine the facts then and see if they are not compatible with another explanation.

It is certain that the combinations which present themselves to the mind in a sort of sudden illumination, after an unconscious working somewhat prolonged, are generally useful and fertile combinations, which seem the result of a first impression. Does it follow that the subliminal self, having divined by a delicate intuition that these combinations would be useful, has formed only these, or has it rather formed many others which were lacking in interest and have remained unconscious?

In this second way of looking at it, all the combinations would be formed in consequence of the automatism of the subliminal self, but only the interesting ones would break into the domain of consciousness. And this is still very mysterious. What is the cause that, among the thousand products of our unconscious activity, some are called to pass the threshold, while others remain below? Is it a simple chance which confers this privilege? Evidently not; among all the stimuli of our senses, for example, only the most intense fix our attention, unless it has been drawn to them by other causes. More generally the privileged unconscious phenomena, those susceptible of becoming conscious, are those which, directly or indirectly, affect most profoundly our emotional sensibility.

It may be surprising to see emotional sensibility invoked à *propos* of mathematical demonstrations which, it would seem, can interest only the intellect. This would be to forget the feeling of mathematical beauty, of the harmony of numbers and forms, of geometric elegance. This is a true esthetic feeling that all real mathematicians know, and surely it belongs to emotional sensibility.

Now, what are the mathematic entities to which we attribute this character of beauty and elegance, and which are capable of developing in us a sort of esthetic emotion? They are those whose elements are harmoniously disposed so that the mind without effort can embrace their totality while realizing the details. This harmony is at once a satisfaction of our esthetic needs and an aid to the mind, sustaining and guiding. And at the same time, in putting under our eyes a well-ordered whole, it makes us foresee a mathematical law. Now, as we have said above, the only mathematical facts worthy of fixing our attention and capable of being useful are those which can teach us a mathematical law. So that we reach the following conclusion: The useful combinations are precisely the most beautiful, I mean those best able to charm this special sensibility that all mathematicians know, but of which the profane are so ignorant as often to be tempted to smile at it.

What happens then? Among the great numbers of combinations blindly formed by the subliminal self, almost all are without interest and without utility; but just for that reason they are also without effect upon the esthetic sensibility. Consciousness will never know them; only certain ones are harmonious, and, consequently, at once useful and beautiful. They will be capable of touching this special sensibility of the geometer of which I have just spoken, and which, once aroused, will call our attention to them, and thus give them occasion to become conscious.

This is only a hypothesis, and yet here is an observation which may confirm it: when a sudden illumination seizes upon the mind of the mathematician, it usually happens that it does not deceive him, but it also sometimes happens, as I have said, that it does not stand the test of verification; well, we almost always notice that this false idea, had it been true, would have gratified our natural feeling for mathematical elegance.

Thus it is this special esthetic sensibility which plays the role of the delicate sieve of which I spoke, and that sufficiently explains why the one lacking it will never be a real creator.

Yet all the difficulties have not disappeared. The conscious self is narrowly limited, and as for the subliminal self we know not its limitations, and this is why we are not too reluctant in supposing that it has been able in a short time to make more different combinations than the whole life of a conscious being could encompass. Yet these limitations exist. Is it likely that it is able to form all the possible combinations, whose number would frighten the imagination? Nevertheless that would seem necessary, because if it produces only a small part of these combinations, and if it makes them at random, there would be small chance that the *good*, the one we should choose, would be found among them.

Perhaps we ought to seek the explanation in that preliminary period of conscious work which always precedes all fruitful unconscious labor. Permit me a rough comparison. Figure the future elements of our combinations as something like the hooked atoms of Epicurus. During the complete repose of the mind, these atoms are motionless, they are, so to speak, hooked to the wall; so this complete rest may be indefinitely prolonged without the atoms meeting, and consequently without any combination between them.

On the other hand, during a period of apparent rest and unconscious work, certain of them are detached from the wall and put in motion. They flash in every direction through the space ( I was about to say the room ) where they are enclosed, as would, for example, a swarm of gnats or, if you prefer a more learned comparison, like the molecules of gas in the kinematic theory of gases. Then their mutual impacts may produce new combinations.

What is the role of the preliminary conscious work? It is evidently to mobilize certain of these atoms, to unhook them from the wall and put them in swing. We think we have done no good, because we have moved these elements a thousand different ways in seeking to assemble them, and have found no satisfactory aggregate. But, after this shaking up imposed upon them by our will, these atoms do not return to their primitive rest. They freely continue their dance.

Now, our will did not choose them at random; it pursued a perfectly determined aim. The mobilized atoms are therefore not any atoms whatsoever; they are those from which we might reasonably expect the desired solution. Then the mobilized atoms undergo impacts which make them enter into combinations among themselves or with other atoms at rest which they struck against in their course. Again I beg pardon, my comparison is very rough, but I scarcely know how otherwise to make my thought understood.

However it may be, the only combinations that have a chance of forming are those where at least one of the elements is one of those atoms freely chosen by our will. Now, it is evidently among these that is found what I called the *good combination*. Perhaps this is a way of lessening the paradoxical in the original hypothesis.

Another observation. It never happens that the unconscious work gives us the result of a somewhat long calculation *all made*, where we have only to apply fixed rules. We might think the wholly automatic subliminal self particularly apt for this sort of work, which is in a way exclusively mechanical. It seems that thinking in the evening upon the factors of a multiplication we might hope to find the product ready made upon our awakening, or again that an algebraic calculation, for example a verification, would be made unconsciously. Nothing of the sort, as observation proves. All one may hope from these inspirations, fruits of unconscious work, is a point of departure for such calculations. As for the calculations themselves, they must be made in the second period of conscious work, that which follows the inspiration, that in which one verifies the results of this inspiration and deduces their consequences. The rules of these calculations are strict and complicated. They require discipline, attention, will, and therefore consciousness. In the subliminal self, on the contrary, reigns what I should call liberty, if we might give this name to the simple absence of discipline and to the disorder born of chance. Only, this disorder itself permits unexpected combinations.

I shall make a last remark: when above I made certain personal observations, I spoke of a night of excitement when I worked in spite of myself. Such cases are frequent, and it is not necessary that the abnormal cerebral activity be caused by a physical excitant as in that I mentioned. It seems, in such cases, that one is present at his own unconscious work, made partially perceptible to the over-excited consciousness, yet without having changed its nature. Then we vaguely comprehend what distinguishes the two mechanisms or, if you wish, the working methods of the two egos. And the psychologic observations I have been able thus to make seem to me to confirm in their general outlines the views I have given.

Surely they have need of it, for they are and remain in spite of all very hypothetical: the interest of the questions is so great that I do not repent of having submitted them to the reader.

# Chance

How dare we speak of the laws of chance? Is not chance the antithesis of all law?" So says Bertrand at the beginning of his *Calcul des probabilités*. Probability is opposed to certitude; so it is what we do not know and consequently it seems what we could not calculate. Here is at least apparently a contradiction, and about it much has already been written.

And first, what is chance? The ancients distinguished between phenomena seemingly obeying harmonious laws, established once for all, and those which they attributed to chance; these were the ones unpredictable because rebellious to all law. In each domain the precise laws did not decide everything, they only drew limits between which chance might act. In this conception the word chance had a precise and objective meaning; what was chance for one was also chance for another and even for the gods.

But this conception is not ours today. We have become absolute determinists, and even those who want to reserve the rights of human free will let determinism reign undividedly in the inorganic world at least. Every phenomenon, however minute, has a cause; and a mind infinitely powerful, infinitely well informed about the laws of nature, could have foreseen it from the beginning of the centuries. If such a mind existed, we could not play with it at any game of chance; we should always lose.

In fact for it the word chance would not have any meaning, or rather there would be no chance. It is because of our weakness and our ignorance that the word has a meaning for us. And, even without going beyond our feeble humanity, what is chance for the ignorant is not chance for the scientist. Chance is only the measure of our ignorance. Fortuitous phenomena are, by definition, those whose laws we do not know.

But is this definition altogether satisfactory? When the first Chaldean shepherds followed with their eyes the movements of the stars, they knew not as yet the laws of astronomy; would they have dreamed of saying that the stars move at random? If a modern physicist studies a new phenomenon, and if he discovers its law Tuesday, would he have said Monday that this phenomenon was fortuitous? Moreover, do we not often invoke what Bertrand calls the laws of chance, to predict a phenomenon? For example, in the kinetic theory of gases we obtain the known laws of Mariotte and of Gay-Lussac by means of the hypothesis that the velocities of the molecules of gas vary irregularly, that is to say at random. All physicists will agree that the observable laws would be much less simple if the velocities were ruled by any simple elementary law whatsoever, if the molecules were, as we say, *organized,* if they were subject to some discipline. It is due to chance, that is to say, to our ignorance, that we can draw our conclusions; and then if the word chance is simply synonymous with ignorance what does that mean? Must we therefore translate as follows?

"You ask me to predict for you the phenomena about to happen. If, unluckily, I knew the laws of these phenomena I could make the prediction only by inextricable calculations and would have to renounce attempting to answer you; but as I have the good fortune not to know them, I will answer you at once. And what is most surprising, my answer will be right."

So it must well be that chance is something other than the name we give our ignorance, that among phenomena whose causes are unknown to us we must distinguish fortuitous phenomena about which the calculus of probabilities will provisionally give information, from those which are not fortuitous and of which we can say nothing so long as we shall not have determined the laws governing them. For the fortuitous phenomena themselves, it is clear that the information given us by the calculus of probabilities will not cease to be true upon the day when these phenomena shall be better known.

The director of a life insurance company does not know when each of the insured will die, but he relies upon the calculus of probabilities and on the law of great numbers, and he is not deceived, since he distributes dividends to his stockholders. These dividends would not vanish if a very penetrating and very indiscreet physician should, after the policies were signed, reveal to the director the life chances of the insured. This doctor would dissipate the ignorance of the director, but he would have no influence on the dividends, which evidently are not an outcome of this ignorance.

To find a better definition of chance we must examine some of the facts which we agree to regard as fortuitous, and to which the calculus of probabilities seems to apply; we then shall investigate what are their common characteristics.

The first example we select is that of unstable equilibrium; if a cone rests upon its apex, we know well that it will fall, but we do not know toward what side; it seems to us chance alone will decide. If the cone were perfectly symmetric, if its axis were perfectly vertical, if it were acted upon by no force other than gravity, it would not fall at all. But the least defect in symmetry will make it lean slightly toward one side or the other, and if it leans, however little, it will fall altogether toward that side. Even if the symmetry were perfect, a very slight tremor, a breath of air could make it incline some seconds of arc; this will be enough to determine its fall and even the sense of its fall which will be that of the initial inclination.

A very slight cause, which escapes us, determines a considerable effect which we cannot help seeing, and then we say this effect is due to chance. If we could know exactly the laws of nature and the situation of the universe at the initial instant, we should be able to predict exactly the situation of this same universe at a subsequent instant. But even when the natural laws should have no further secret for us, we could know the initial situation only *approximately*. If that permits us to foresee the subsequent situation *with the same degree of approximation*, this is all we require, we say the phenomenon has been predicted, that it is ruled by laws. But this is not always the case; it may happen that slight differences in the initial conditions produce very great differences in the final phenomena; a slight error in the former would make an enormous error in the latter. Prediction becomes impossible and we have the fortuitous phenomenon.

Our second example will be very analogous to the first and we shall take it from meteorology. Why have the meteorologists such difficulty in predicting the weather with any certainty? Why do the rains, the tempests themselves seem to us to come by chance, so that many persons find it quite natural to pray for rain or shine, when they would think it ridiculous to pray for an eclipse? We see that great perturbations generally happen in regions where the atmosphere is in unstable equilibrium. The meteorologists are aware that this equilibrium is unstable, that a cyclone is arising somewhere; but where they cannot tell; one-tenth of a degree more or less at any point, and the cyclone bursts here and not there, and spreads its ravages over countries it would have spared. This we could have foreseen if we had known that tenth of a degree, but the observations were neither sufficiently close nor sufficiently precise, and for this reason all seems due to the agency of chance. Here again we find the same contrast between a very slight cause, unappreciable to the observer, and important effects, which are sometimes tremendous disasters.

Let us pass to another example, the distribution of the minor planets on the zodiac. Their initial longitudes may have been any longitudes whatever; but their mean motions were different and they have revolved for so long a time that we may say they are now distributed *at random* along the zodiac. Very slight initial differences between their distances from the sun, or, what comes to the same thing, between their mean motions, have ended by giving enormous differences between their present longitudes. An excess of the thousandth of a second in the daily mean motion will give in fact a second in three years, a degree in ten thousand years, an entire circumference in three or four million years, and what is that to the time which has passed since the minor planets detached themselves from the nebula of Laplace? Again therefore we see a slight cause and a great effect; or better, slight differences in the cause and great differences in the effect.

The game of roulette does not take us as far as might seem from the preceding example. Assume a needle to be turned on a pivot over a dial divided into a hundred sectors alternately red and black. If it stops on a red sector I win; if not, I lose. Evidently all depends upon the initial impulse I give the needle. The needle will make, suppose, ten or twenty turns, but it will stop sooner or not so soon, according as I shall have pushed it more or less strongly. It suffices that the impulse vary only by a thousandth or a two thousandth to make the needle stop over a black sector or over the following red one. These are differences the muscular sense cannot distinguish and which elude even the most delicate instruments. So it is impossible for me to foresee what the needle I have started will do, and this is why my heart throbs and I hope everything from luck. The difference in the cause is imperceptible, and the difference in the effect is for me of the highest importance, since it means my whole stake.

Permit me, in this connection, a thought somewhat foreign to my subject. Some years ago a philosopher said that the future is determined by the past, but not the past by the future; or, in other words, from knowledge of the present we could deduce the future, but not the past;

because, said he, a cause can have only one effect, while the same effect might be produced by several different causes. It is clear no scientist can subscribe to this conclusion. The laws of nature bind the antecedent to the consequent in such a way that the antecedent is as well determined by the consequent as the consequent by the antecedent. But whence came the error of this philosopher? We know that in virtue of Carnot's principle physical phenomena are irreversible and the world tends toward uniformity. When two bodies of different temperature come in contact, the warmer gives up heat to the colder; so we may foresee that the temperature will equalize. But once equal, if asked about the anterior state, what can we answer? We might say that one was warm and the other cold, but not be able to divine which formerly was the warmer.

And yet in reality the temperatures will never reach perfect equality. The difference of the temperatures only tends asymptotically toward zero. There comes a moment when our thermometers are powerless to make it known. But if we had thermometers a thousand times, a hundred thousand times as sensitive, we should recognize that there still is a slight difference, and that one of the bodies remains a little warmer than the other, and so we could say this it is which formerly was much the warmer.

So then there are, contrary to what we found in the former examples, great differences in cause and slight differences in effect. Flammarion once imagined an observer going away from the earth with a velocity greater than that of light; for him time would have changed sign. History would be turned about, and Waterloo would precede Austerlitz. Well, for this observer, effects and causes would be inverted; unstable equilibrium would no longer be the exception. Because of the universal irreversibility, all would seem to him to come out of a sort of chaos in unstable equilibrium. All nature would appear to him delivered over to chance.

Now for other examples where we shall see somewhat different characteristics. Take first the kinetic theory of gases. How should we picture a receptacle filled with gas? Innumerable molecules, moving at high speeds, flash through this receptacle in every direction. At every instant they strike against its walls or each other, and these collisions happen under the most diverse conditions. What above all impresses us here is not the littleness of the causes, but their complexity, and yet the former element is still found here and plays an important role. If a molecule deviated right or left from its trajectory, by a very small quantity, comparable to the radius of action of the gaseous molecules, it would avoid a collision or sustain it under different conditions, and that would vary the direction of its velocity after the impact, perhaps by ninety degrees or by a hundred and eighty degrees.

And this is not all; we have just seen that it is necessary to deflect the molecule before the clash by only an infinitesimal, to produce its deviation after the collision by a finite quantity. If then the molecule undergoes two successive shocks, it will suffice to deflect it before the first by an infinitesimal of the second order, for it to deviate after the first encounter by an infinitesimal of the first order, and after the second hit, by a finite quantity. And the molecule will not undergo merely two shocks; it will undergo a very great number per second. So that if the first shock has multiplied the deviation by a very large number $A$, after $n$ shocks it will be multiplied by $A^n$. It will therefore become very great not merely because $A$ is large, that is to say because little causes produce big effects, but because the exponent $n$ is large, that is to say because the shocks are very numerous and the causes very complex.

Take a second example. Why do the drops of rain in a shower seem to be distributed at random? This is again because of the complexity of the causes which determine their formatiom. Ions are distributed in the atmosphere. For a long while they have been subjected to air currents constantly changing, they have been caught in very small whirlwinds, so that their final distribution has no longer any relation to their initial distribution. Suddenly the temperature falls, vapor condenses, and each of these ions becomes the center of a drop of rain. To know what will be the distribution of these drops and how many will fall on each paving stone, it would not be sufficient to know the initial situation of the ions, it would be necessary to compute the effect of a thousand little capricious air currents.

And again it is the same if we put grains of powder in suspension in water. The vase is ploughed by currents whose law we know not, we only know it is very complicated. At the end of a certain time the grains will be distributed at random, that is to say uniformly, in the vase; and this is due precisely to the complexity of these currents. If they obeyed some simple law, if for example the vase revolved and the currents circulated around the axis of the vase, describing circles, it would no longer be the same, since each grain would retain its initial altitude and its initial distance from the axis.

We should reach the same result in considering the mixing of two liquids or of two fine-grained powders. And to take a grosser example, this is also what happens when we shuffle playing cards. At each stroke the cards undergo a permutation (analogous to that studied in the theory of substitutions). What will happen? The probability of a particular permutation (for example, that bringing to the $n$th place the card occupying the $\phi$ [$n$]th place before the permutation) depends upon the player's habits. But if this player shuffles the cards long enough, there will be a great number of successive permutations, and the resulting final order will no longer be governed by aught but chance; I mean to say that all possible orders will be equally probable. It is to the great number of successive permutations, that is to say to the complexity of the phenomenon, that this result is due.

A final word about the theory of errors. Here it is that the causes are complex and multiple. To how many snares is not the observer exposed, even with the best instrument! He should apply himself to finding out the largest and avoiding them. These are the ones giving birth to systematic errors. But when he has eliminated those, admitting that he succeeds, there remain many small ones which, their effects accumulating, may become dangerous. Thence come the accidental errors; and we attribute them to chance because their causes are too complicated and too numerous. Here again we have only little causes, but each of them would produce only a slight effect; it is by their union and their number that their effects become formidable.

We may take still a third point of view, less important than the first two and upon which I shall lay less stress. When we seek to foresee an event and examine its antecedents, we strive to search into the anterior situation. This could not be done for all parts of the universe and we are content to know what is passing in the neighborhood of the point where the event should occur, or what would appear to have some relation to it. An examination cannot be complete and we must know how to choose. But it may happen that we have passed by circumstances which at first sight seemed completely foreign to the foreseen happening, to which one would never have dreamed of attributing any influence and which nevertheless, contrary to all anticipation, come to play an important role.

A man passes in the street going to his business; some one knowing the business could have told why he started at such a time and went by such a street. On the roof works a tiler. The contractor employing him could in a certain measure foresee what he would do. But the passer-by scarcely thinks of the tiler, nor the tiler of him; they seem to belong to two worlds completely foreign to one another. And yet the tiler drops a tile which kills the man, and we do not hesitate to say this is chance.

Our weakness forbids our considering the entire universe and makes us cut it up into slices. We try to do this as little artificially as possible. And yet it happens from time to time that two of these slices react upon each other. The effects of this mutual action then seem to us to be due to chance.

Is this a third way of conceiving chance? Not always; in fact most often we are carried back to the first or the second. Whenever two worlds usually foreign to one another come thus to react upon each other, the laws of this reaction must be very complex. On the other hand, a very slight change in the initial conditions of these two worlds would have been sufficient for the reaction not to have happened. How little was needed for the man to pass a second later or the tiler to drop his tile a second sooner.

All we have said still does not explain why chance obeys laws. Does the fact that the causes are slight or complex suffice for our foreseeing, if not their effects *in each case,* at least what their effects will be, *on the average?* To answer this question we had better take up again some of the examples already cited.

I shall begin with that of the roulette. I have said that the point where the needle will stop depends upon the initial push given it. What is the probability of this push having this or that value? I know nothing about it, but it is difficult for me not to suppose that this probability is represented by a continuous analytic function. The probability that the push is comprised between $\alpha$ and $\alpha + \epsilon$ will then be sensibly equal to the probability of its being comprised between $\alpha + \epsilon$ and $\alpha + 2\epsilon$, *provided $\epsilon$ be very small.* This is a property common to all analytic functions. Minute variations of the function are proportional to minute variations of the variable.

But we have assumed that an exceedingly slight variation of the push suffices to change the color of the sector over which the needle finally stops. From $\alpha$ to $\alpha + \epsilon$ it is red, from $\alpha + \epsilon$ to $\alpha + 2\epsilon$ it is black; the probability of each red sector is therefore the same as of the following black, and consequently the total probability of red equals the total probability of black.

The datum of the question is the analytic function representing the probability of a particular initial push. But the theorem remains true whatever be this datum, since it depends upon a property common to all analytic functions. From this it follows finally that we no longer need the datum.

What we have just said for the case of the roulette applies also to the example of the minor planets. The zodiac may be regarded as an immense roulette on which have been tossed many little balls with different initial impulses varying according to some law. Their present distribution is uniform and independent of this law, for the same reason as in the preceding case. Thus we see why phenomena obey the laws of chance when slight differences in the causes suffice to bring on great differences in the effects. The probabilities of these slight differences may then be regarded as proportional to these differences themselves, just because these differences are minute, and the infinitesimal increments of a continuous function are proportional to those of the variable.

Take an entirely different example, where intervenes especially the complexity of the causes. Suppose a player shuffles a pack of cards. At each shuffle he changes the order of the cards, and he may change them in many ways. To simplify the exposition, consider only three cards. The cards which before the shuffle occupied respectively the places 123, may after the shuffle occupy the places

$$123, \ 231, \ 312, \ 321, \ 132, \ 213.$$

Each of these six hypotheses is possible and they have respectively for probabilities:

$$p_1, \ p_2, \ p_3, \ p_4, \ p_5, \ p_6.$$

The sum of these six numbers equals 1; but this is all we know of them; these six probabilities depend naturally upon the habits of the player which we do not know.

At the second shuffle and the following, this will recommence, and under the same conditions; I mean that $p_4$ for example represents always the probability that the three cards which occupied after the $n$th shuffle and before $n + 1$th the places 123, occupy the places 321 after the $n + 1$th shuffle. And this remains true whatever be the number $n$, since the habits of the player and his way of shuffling remain the same.

But if the number the shuffles is very great, the cards which before the first shuffle occupied the places 123 may, after the last shuffle, occupy the places

$$123, \ 231, \ 312, \ 321, \ 132, \ 213$$

and the probability of these six hypotheses will be sensibly the same and equal to 1/6; and this will be true whatever be the numbers $p_1 \ldots p_6$ which we do not know. The great number of shuffles, that is to say the complexity of the causes, has produced uniformity.

This would apply without change if there were more than three cards.

but even with three cards the demonstration would be complicated; let it suffice to give it for only two cards. Then we have only two possibilities 12, 21 with the probabilities $p_1$ and $p_2 = 1 - p_1$.

Suppose $n$ shuffles and suppose I win one franc if the cards are finally in the initial order and lose one if they are finally inverted. Then, my mathematical expectation will be $(p_1 - p_2)^n$.

The difference $p_1 - p_2$ is certainly less than 1; so that if $n$ is very great my expectation will be zero; we need not learn $p_1$ and $p_2$ to be aware that the game is equitable.

There would always be an exception if one of the numbers $p_1$ and $p_2$ was equal to 1 and the other naught. *Then it would not apply because our initial hypotheses would be too simple.*

What we have just seen applies not only to the mixing of cards, but to all mixings, to those of powders and of liquids, and even to those of the molecules of gases in the kinetic theory of gases.

To return to this theory, suppose for a moment a gas whose molecules cannot mutually clash, but may be deviated by hitting the insides of the vase wherein the gas is confined. If the form of the vase is sufficiently complex the distribution of the molecules and that of the velocities will not be long in becoming uniform. But this will not be so if the vase is spherical or if it has the shape of a cuboid. Why? Because in the first case the distance from the center to any trajectory will remain constant; in the second case this will be the absolute value of the angle of each trajectory with the faces of the cuboid.

So we see what should be understood by conditions *too simple;* they are those which conserve something, which leave an invariant remaining. Are the differential equations of the problem too simple for us to apply the laws of chance? This question would seem at first view to lack precise meaning; now we know what it means. They are too simple if they conserve something, if they admit a uniform integral. If something in the initial conditions remains unchanged, it is clear the final situation can no longer be independent of the initial situation.

We come finally to the theory of errors. We know not to what are due the accidental errors, and precisely because we do not know, we are aware they obey the law of Gauss. Such is the paradox. The explanation is nearly the same as in the preceding cases. We need know only one thing: that the errors are very numerous, that they are very slight, that each may be as well negative as positive. What is the curve of probability of each of them? We do not know; we only suppose it is symmetric. We prove then that the resultant error will follow Gauss's law, and this resulting law is independent of the particular laws which we do not know. Here again the simplicity of the result is born of the very complexity of the data.

But we are not through with paradoxes. I have just recalled the figment of Flammarion, that of the man going quicker than light, for whom time changes sign. I said that for him all phenomena would seem due to chance. That is true from a certain point of view, and yet all these phenomena at a given moment would not be distributed in conformity with the laws of chance, since the distribution would be the same as for us, who, seeing them unfold harmoniously and without coming out of a primal chaos, do not regard them as ruled by chance.

What does that mean? For Lumen, Flammarion's man, slight causes seem to produce great effects; why do not things go on as for us when we think we see grand effects due to little causes? Would not the same reasoning be applicable in his case?

Let us return to the argument. When slight differences in the causes produce vast differences in the effects, why are these effects distributed according to the laws of chance? Suppose a difference of a millimeter in the cause produces a difference of a kilometer in the effect. If I win in case the effect corresponds to a kilometer bearing an even number, my probability of winning will be $1/2$. Why? Because to make that, the cause must correspond to a millimeter with an even number. Now, according to all appearance, the probability of the cause varying between certain limits will be proportional to the distance apart of these limits, provided this distance be very small. If this hypothesis were not admitted there would no longer be any way of representing the probability by a continuous function.

What now will happen when great causes produce small effects? This is the case where we should not attribute the phenomenon to chance and where on the contrary Lumen would attribute it to chance. To a difference of a kilometer in the cause would correspond a difference of a millimeter in the effect. Would the probability of the cause being comprised between two limits $n$ kilometers apart still be proportional to $n$? We have no reason to suppose so, since this distance, $n$ kilometers, is great. But the probability that the effect lies between two limits $n$ millimeters apart will be precisely the same, so it will not be proportional to $n$, even though this distance, $n$ millimeters, be small. There is no way therefore of representing the law of probability of effects by a continuous curve. This curve, understand, may remain continuous in the *analytic* sense of the word; to *infinitesimal* variations of the abscissa will correspond infinitesimal variations of the ordinate. But *practically* it will not be continuous, since *very small* variations of the ordinate would not correspond to very small variations of the abscissa. It would become impossible to trace the curve with an ordinary pencil; that is what I mean.

So what must we conclude? Lumen has no right to say that the probability of the cause (*his* cause, our effect) should be represented necessarily by a continuous function. But then why have we this right? It is because this state of unstable equilibrium which we have been calling initial is itself only the final outcome of a long previous history. In the course of this history complex causes have worked a great while: they have contributed to produce the mixture of elements and they have tended to make everything uniform at least within a small region; they have rounded off the corners, smoothed down the hills and filled up the valleys. However capricious and irregular may have been the primitive curve given over to them, they have worked so much toward making it regular that finally they deliver over to us a continuous curve. And this is why we may in all confidence assume its continuity.

Lumen would not have the same reasons for such a conclusion. For him complex causes would not seem agents of equalization and regularity, but on the contrary would create only inequality and differentiation. He would see a world more and more varied come forth from a sort of primitive chaos. The changes he could observe would be for him unforeseen and impossible to foresee. They would seem to him due to some caprice or another; but this caprice would be quite different from our chance, since it would be opposed to all law, while our chance still has its laws. All these points call for lengthy explications, which perhaps would aid in the better comprehension of the irreversibility of the universe.

We have sought to define chance, and now it is proper to put a question. Has chance thus defined, in so far as this is possible, objectivity?

It may be questioned. I have spoken of very slight or very complex causes. But what is very little for one may be very big for another, and what seems very complex to one may seem simple to another. In part I have already answered by saying precisely in what cases differential equations become too simple for the laws of chance to remain applicable. But it is fitting to examine the matter a little more closely, because we may take still other points of view.

What means the phrase "very slight"? To understand it we need only go back to what has already been said. A difference is very slight, an interval is very small, when within the limits of this interval the probability remains sensibly constant. And why may this probability be regarded as constant within a small interval? It is because we assume that the law of probability is represented by a continuous curve, continuous not only in the analytic sense, but *practically* continuous, as already explained. This means that it not only presents no absolute hiatus, but that it has neither salients nor re-entrants too acute or too accentuated.

And what gives us the right to make this hypothesis? We have already said it is because, since the beginning of the ages, there have always been complex causes ceaselessly acting in the same way and making the world tend toward uniformity without ever being able to turn back. These are the causes which little by little have flattened the salients and filled up the re-entrants, and this is why our probability curves now show only gentle undulations. In milliards of milliards of ages another step will have been made toward uniformity, and these undulations will be ten times as gentle; the radius of mean curvature of our curve will have become ten times as great. And then such a length as seems to us today not very small, since on our curve an arc of this length cannot be regarded as rectilineal, should on the contrary at that epoch be called very little, since the curvature will have become ten times less and an arc of this length may be sensibly identified with a sect.

Thus the phrase "very slight" remains relative; but it is not relative to such or such a man, it is relative to the actual state of the world. It will change its meaning when the world shall have become more uniform, when all things shall have blended still more. But then doubtless men can no longer live and must give place to other beings—should I say far smaller or far larger? So that our criterion, remaining true for all men, retains an objective sense.

And on the other hand what means the phrase "very complex"? I have already given one solution, but there are others. Complex causes we have said produce a blend more and more intimate, but after how long a time will this blend satisfy us? When will it have accumulated sufficient complexity? When shall we have sufficiently shuffled the cards? If we mix two powders, one blue, the other white, there comes a moment when the tint of the mixture seems to us uniform because of the feebleness of our senses; it will be uniform for the presbyope, forced to gaze from afar, before it will be so for the myope. And when it has become uniform for all eyes, we still could push back the limit by the use of instruments. There is no chance for any man ever to discern the infinite variety which, if the kinetic theory is true, hides under the uniform appearance of a gas. And yet if we accept Gouy's ideas on the Brownian movement, does not the microscope seem on the point of showing us something analogous?

This new criterion is therefore relative like the first; and if it retains an objective character, it is because all men have approximately the same senses, the power of their instruments is limited, and besides they use them only exceptionally.

It is just the same in the moral sciences and particularly in history. The historian is obliged to make a choice among the events of the epoch he studies; he recounts only those which seem to him the most important. He therefore contents himself with relating the most momentous events of the sixteenth century, for example, as likewise the most remarkable facts of the seventeenth century. If the first suffice to explain the second, we say these conform to the laws of history. But if a great event of the seventeenth century should have for cause a small fact of the sixteenth century which no history reports, which all the world has neglected, then we say this event is due to chance. This word has therefore the same sense as in the physical sciences; it means that slight causes have produced great effects.

The greatest bit of chance is the birth of a great man. It is only by chance that meeting of two germinal cells, of different sex, containing precisely, each on its side, the mysterious elements whose mutual reaction must produce the genius. One will agree that these elements must be rare and that their meeting is still more rare. How slight a thing it would have required to deflect from its route the carrying spermatozoon. It would have sufficed to deflect it a tenth of a millimeter and Napoleon would not have been born and the destinies of a continent would have been changed. No example can better make us understand the veritable characteristics of chance.

One more word about the paradoxes brought out by the application of the calculus of probabilities to the moral sciences. It has been proven that no Chamber of Deputies will ever fail to contain a member of the opposition, or at least such an event would be so improbable that we might without fear wager the contrary, and bet a million against a sou.

Condorcet has striven to calculate how many jurors it would require to make a judicial error practically impossible. If we had used the results of this calculation, we should certainly have been exposed to the same disappointments as in betting, on the faith of the calculus, that the opposition would never be without a representative.

The laws of chance do not apply to these questions. If justice be not always meted out to accord with the best reasons, it uses less than we think the method of Bridoye. This is perhaps to be regretted, for then the system of Condorcet would shield us from judicial errors.

What is the meaning of this? We are tempted to attribute facts of this nature to chance because their causes are obscure; but this is not true chance. The causes are unknown to us, it is true, and they are even complex; but they are not sufficiently so, since they conserve something. We have seen that this it is which distinguishes causes "too simple." When men are brought together they no longer decide at random and independently one of another; they influence one another. Multiplex causes come into action. They worry men, dragging them to right or left, but one thing there is they cannot destroy, this is their Panurge flock-of-sheep habits. And this is an invariant.

Difficulties are indeed involved in the application of the calculus of probabilities to the exact sciences. Why are the decimals of a table of logarithms, why are those of the number $\pi$ distributed in accordance with the laws of chance? Elsewhere I have already studied the question in so far as it concerns logarithms, and there it is easy. It is clear that a slight difference of argument will give a slight difference of logarithm, but a great difference in the sixth decimal of the logarithm. Always we find again the same criterion.

But as for the number $\pi$, that presents more difficulties, and I have at the moment nothing worthwhile to say.

There would be many other questions to resolve, had I wished to attack them before solving that which I more specially set myself. When we reach a simple result, when we find for example a round number, we say that such a result cannot be due to chance, and we seek, for its explanation, a nonfortuitous cause. And in fact there is only a very slight probability that among 10,000 numbers chance will give a round number; for example, the number 10,000. This has only one chance in 10,000. But there is only one chance in 10,000 for the occurrence of any other one number; and yet this result will not astonish us, nor will it be hard for us to attribute it to chance; and that simply because it will be less striking.

Is this a simple illusion of ours, or are there cases where this way of thinking is legitimate? We must hope so, else were all science impossible.

When we wish to check a hypothesis, what do we do? We cannot verify all its consequences, since they would be infinite in number; we content ourselves with verifying certain ones and if we succeed we declare the hypothesis confirmed, because so much success could not be due to chance. And this is always at bottom the same reasoning.

I cannot completely justify it here, since it would take too much time; but I may at least say that we find ourselves confronted by two hypotheses, either a simple cause or that aggregate of complex causes we call chance. We find it natural to suppose that the first should produce a simple result, and then, if we find that simple result, the round number for example, it seems more likely to us to be attributable to the simple cause which must give it almost certainly, than to chance which could only give it once in 10,000 times. It will not be the same if we find a result which is not simple; chance, it is true, will not give this more than once in 10,000 times; but neither has the simple cause any more chance of producing it.

---

*The foregoing essays are Chapters III and IV of Poincaré's* SCIENCE AND METHOD.

# Pierre Simon de Laplace

## 1749–1827

The French encyclopedists of the eighteenth century imagined that they were not far from a final explanation of the universe by physical and mechanical principles. Laplace is representative of that confident age which joyfully overestimated the scope of the new physico-mechanical ideas.

Pierre Simon de Laplace was born at Beaumont-en-Auge in Normandy in 1749. His father owned a small estate. At the University of Caen, which he entered at the age of sixteen, he soon demonstrated his mathematical abilities. He was only eighteen when he was appointed professor of mathematics at the École Militaire of Paris.

He rose rapidly. In 1773 he took up one of the outstanding problems which until then had resisted all attempts at solution in terms of Newtonian gravitation: the problem of why Jupiter's orbit appeared to be continually shrinking while Saturn's was continually expanding. Newton had feared that the planetary system would need divine intervention from time to time if it was to be preserved in anything like its present order. Laplace was able to show that this phenomenon was of periodic nature and could be expected to right itself every 929 years.

Laplace's monumental work on astronomical gravitation, *Celestial Mechanics,* was published in five volumes between 1799 and 1825. It is a work of formidable abstraction, obscure in style, with great gaps in the arguments bridged by the phrase "it is easy to see." Nor is it entirely honest writing. He deliberately omitted references to the work of others, presenting the labors of three generations of mathematicians as the fruit of his brain. Nevertheless, it is a triumphant work.

Laplace's contribution in the field of probability is unequaled by any other single investigator. *The Analytical Theory of Probabilities* (1812) described a calculus for assigning a "degree of rational belief" to propositions about chance events. "Belief" seems a startlingly unscientific notion in this context. We order our daily affairs in the firm belief that the sun will rise tomorrow, but it does not seem to be an idea to which a definite quantity could be assigned. But, belief can be measured, said Laplace, and he set up the calculus for doing so.

Although the concept of probability has become one of the fundamental notions of modern science, the experts are still not able to agree on its meaning. The classic definition, formulated by Laplace, has, to a large extent, been replaced by the "relative frequency" interpretation developed by Charles S. Peirce, as expounded in his essay *The Red and the Black.*

*A Philosophical Essay on Probabilities* is a nontechnical introduction to the laws of chance. In establishing the ten principles which form the calculus, Laplace deals with "hope" as easily as he does with tossed coins; the principles of probability affect every phase of human life. Everything can be measured. Laplace saw no technical bar to an intelligence which would be able to predict the course of the universe in minutest detail with infallible accuracy. His was not an age of intellectual humility.

Modern science is more modest. In some ways the universe is more mysterious than it has ever been. Nature is no longer examined solely in terms of motion and matter. Laplace's celestial machine established the stability of the universe for a very long time indeed, but not for the "eternal duration" that he claimed.[1] The eighteenth

------

[1] For various theories about the ultimate fate of the universe, see selections from Arthur Eddington, pp. 565–580, and Sir James Jeans, pp. 585–596, in Vol. 8 in this set.

------

*Notes from the artist: ". . . an almost surrealist head study of Laplace, made up in part from the ancient symbols of the planets. The background is a facsimile of the constellations in the Northern Hemisphere as drawn by Albrecht Dürer in 1515."*

Pierre Simon
Laplace

century was unique in the history of ideas. Never before nor since has man been so sure of his ability to comprehend all of nature.

Laplace died in 1827. He surrounded himself with astronomers, physicists, naturalists, and mathematicians during his last years. Busy and happy, he received distinguished visitors from all parts of the world. His scientific genius earned for him the title of "the Newton of France."

Laplace has been criticized for his infinite adaptability to changing political environments; his contemporaries cynically referred to his "suppleness." During the turbulent times of the French Revolution he kept his head—literally—and prospered. As his books entered into successive editions, the introductions were changed to fit the times. Laplace dedicated the 1812 edition of *The Analytical Theory of Probabilities* to "Napoleon the Great"; in the 1814 edition he suppressed this dedication and wrote "that the fall of empires which aspired to universal domination could be predicted with a very high probability by one versed in the calculus of chance."

# Probability

## from *A Philosophical Essay on Probabilities*

### INTRODUCTION

This philosophical essay is the development of a lecture on probabilities which I delivered in 1795 to the normal schools whither I had been called, by a decree of the national convention, as professor of mathematics with Lagrange. I have recently published upon the same subject a work entitled *The Analytical Theory of Probabilities.* I present here without the aid of analysis the principles and general results of this theory, applying them to the most important questions of life, which are indeed for the most part only problems of probability. Strictly speaking it may even be said that nearly all our knowledge is problematical; and in the small number of things which we are able to know with certainty, even in the mathematical sciences themselves, the principal means for ascertaining truth—induction and analogy—are based on probabilities; so that the entire system of human knowledge is connected with the theory set forth in this essay. Doubtless it will be seen here with interest that in considering, even in the eternal principles of reason, justice, and humanity, only the favorable chances which are constantly attached to them, there is a great advantage in following these principles and serious inconvenience in departing from them: their chances, like those favorable to lotteries, always end by prevailing in the midst of the vacillations of hazard. I hope that the reflections given in this essay may merit the attention of philosophers and direct it to a subject so worthy of engaging their minds.

### CONCERNING PROBABILITY

All events, even those which on account of their insignificance do not seem to follow the great laws of nature, are a result of it just as necessarily as the revolutions of the sun. In ignorance of the ties which unite such events to the entire system of the universe, they have been made to depend upon final causes or upon hazard, according as they occur and are repeated with regularity, or appear without regard to order; but these imaginary causes have gradually receded with the widening bounds of knowledge and disappear entirely before sound philosophy, which sees in them only the expression of our ignorance of the true causes.

Present events are connected with preceding ones by a tie based upon the evident principle that a thing cannot occur without a cause which produces it. This axiom, known by the name of *the principle of sufficient reason,* extends even to actions which are considered indifferent; the freest will is unable without a determinative motive to give them birth; if we assume two positions with exactly similar circumstances and find that the will is active in the one and inactive in the other, we say that its choice is an effect without a cause. It is then, says Leibnitz, the blind chance of the Epicureans. The contrary opinion is an illusion of the mind, which, losing sight of the evasive reasons of the choice of the will in indifferent things, believes that choice is determined of itself and without motives.

We ought then to regard the present state of the universe as the effect of its anterior state and as the cause of the one which is to follow. Given for one instant an intelligence which could comprehend all the forces by which nature is animated and the respective situation of the beings who compose it—an intelligence sufficiently vast to submit these data to analysis—it would embrace in the same formula the movements of the greatest bodies of the universe and those of the lightest atom; for it, nothing would be uncertain and the future, as the past, would be present to its eyes. The human mind offers, in the perfection which it has been able to give to astronomy, a feeble idea of this intelligence. Its discoveries in mechanics and geometry, added to that of universal gravity, have enabled it to comprehend in the same analytical expressions the past and future states of the system of the world. Applying the same method to some other objects of its knowledge, it has succeeded in referring to general laws observed phenomena and in foreseeing those which given circumstances ought to produce. All these efforts in the search for truth tend to lead it back continually to the vast intelligence which we have just mentioned, but from which it will always remain infinitely removed. This tendency, peculiar to the human race, is that which renders it superior to animals; and their progress in this respect distinguishes nations and ages and constitutes their true glory.

Let us recall that formerly, and at no remote epoch, an unusual rain or an extreme drought, a comet having in train a very long tail, the eclipses, the aurora borealis, and in general all the unusual phenomena were regarded as so many signs of celestial wrath. Heaven was invoked in order to avert their baneful influence. No one prayed to have the planets and the sun arrested in their courses: observation had soon made apparent the futility of such prayers. But as these phenomena, occurring and disappearing at long intervals, seemed to oppose the order of nature, it was supposed that Heaven, irritated by the crimes of the earth, had created them to announce its vengeance. Thus the long tail of the comet of 1456 spread terror through Europe, already thrown into consternation by the rapid successes of the Turks, who had just overthrown the Lower Empire. This star after four revolutions has excited among us a very different interest. The knowledge of the laws of the system of the world acquired in the interval had dissipated the fears begotten by the ignorance of the true relationship of man to the universe; and Halley, having recognized the identity of this comet with those of the years 1531, 1607, and 1682, announced its next return for the end of the year 1758 or the beginning of the year 1759. The learned world awaited with impatience this return which was to confirm one of the greatest discoveries that have been made in the sciences, and fulfill the prediction of Seneca when he said, in speaking of the revolutions of those stars which fall from an enormous height: "The day will come when, by study pursued through several ages, the things now concealed will appear with evidence; and posterity will be astonished that truths so clear had escaped us." Clairaut then undertook to submit to analysis the perturbations which the comet had experienced by the action of the two great planets, Jupiter and Saturn; after immense calculations he fixed its next passage at the perihelion toward the beginning of April, 1759, which was actually verified by observation. The regularity which astronomy shows us in the movements of the comets doubtless exists also in all phenomena.

The curve described by a simple molecule of air or vapor is regulated in a manner just as certain as the planetary orbits; the only difference between them is that which comes from our ignorance.

Probability is relative, in part to this ignorance, in part to our knowledge. We know that of three or a greater number of events a single one ought to occur; but nothing induces us to believe that one of them will occur rather than the others. In this state of indecision it is impossible for us to announce their occurrence with certainty. It is, however, probable that one of these events, chosen at will, will not occur because we see several cases equally possible which exclude its occurrence, while only a single one favors it.

The theory of chance consists in reducing all the events of the same kind to a certain number of cases equally possible, that is to say, to such as we may be equally undecided about in regard to their existence, and in determining the number of cases favorable to the event whose probability is sought. The ratio of this number to that of all the cases possible is the measure of this probability, which is thus simply a fraction whose numerator is the number of favorable cases and whose denominator is the number of all the cases possible.

The preceding notion of probability supposes that, in increasing in the same ratio the number of favorable cases and that of all the cases possible, the probability remains the same. In order to convince ourselves let us take two urns, A and B, the first containing four white and two black balls, and the second containing only two white balls and one black one. We may imagine the two black balls of the first urn attached by a thread which breaks at the moment when one of them is seized in order to be drawn out, and the four white balls thus forming two similar systems. All the chances which will favor the seizure of one of the balls of the black system will lead to a black ball. If we conceive now that the threads which unite the balls do not break at all, it is clear that the number of possible chances will not change any more than that of the chances favorable to the extraction of the black balls; but two balls will be drawn from the urn at the same time; the probability of drawing a black ball from the urn A will then be the same as at first. But then we have obviously the case of urn B with the single difference that the three balls of this last urn would be replaced by three systems of two balls invariably connected.

When all the cases are favorable to an event the probability changes to certainty and its expression becomes equal to unity. Upon this condition, certainty and probability are comparable, although there may be an essential difference between the two states of the mind when a truth is rigorously demonstrated to it, or when it still perceives a small source of error.

In things which are only probable the difference of the data, which each man has in regard to them, is one of the principal causes of the diversity of opinions which prevail in regard to the same objects. Let us suppose, for example, that we have three urns, A, B, C, one of which contains only black balls while the two others contain only white balls; a ball is to be drawn from the urn C and the probability is demanded that this ball will be black. If we do not know which of the three urns contains black balls only, so that there is no reason to believe that it is C rather than B or A, these three hypotheses will appear equally possible, and since a black ball can be drawn only in the first hypothesis, the probability of drawing it is equal to one third. If it is known that the urn A contains white balls only, the indecision then extends only to the urns B and C, and the probability that the ball drawn from the urn C will be black is one half. Finally this probability changes to certainty if we are assured that the urns A and B contain white balls only.

It is thus that an incident related to a numerous assembly finds various degrees of credence, according to the extent of knowledge of the auditors. If the man who reports it is fully convinced of it and if, by his position and character, he inspires great confidence, his statement, however extraordinary it may be, will have for the auditors who lack information the same degree of probability as an ordinary statement made by the same man, and they will have entire faith in it. But if some one of them knows that the same incident is rejected by other equally trustworthy men, he will be in doubt and the incident will be discredited by the enlightened auditors, who will reject it whether it be in regard to facts well averred or the immutable laws of nature.

It is to the influence of the opinion of those whom the multitude judges best informed and to whom it has been accustomed to give its confidence in regard to the most important matters of life that the propagation of those errors is due which in times of ignorance have covered the face of the earth. Magic and astrology offer us two great examples. These errors inculcated in infancy, adopted without examination, and having for a basis only universal credence, have maintained themselves during a very long time; but at last the progress of science has destroyed them in the minds of enlightened men, whose opinion consequently has caused them to disappear even among the common people, through the power of imitation and habit which had so generally spread them abroad. This power, the richest resource of the moral world, establishes and conserves in a whole nation ideas entirely contrary to those which it upholds elsewhere with the same authority. What indulgence ought we not then to have for opinions different from ours, when this difference often depends only upon the various points of view where circumstances have placed us! Let us enlighten those whom we judge insufficiently instructed; but first let us examine critically our own opinions and weigh with impartiality their respective probabilities.

The difference of opinions depends, however, upon the manner in which the influence of known data is determined. The theory of probabilities holds to considerations so delicate that it is not surprising that with the same data two persons arrive at different results, especially in very complicated questions. Let us examine now the general principles of this theory.

## THE GENERAL PRINCIPLES
### OF THE CALCULUS OF PROBABILITIES

*First Principle.* The first of these principles is the definition itself of probability, which, as has been seen, is the ratio of the number of favorable cases to that of all the cases possible.

*Second Principle.* But that supposes the various cases equally possible. If they are not so, we will determine first their respective possibilities, whose exact appreciation is one of the most delicate points of the theory of chance. Then the probability will be the sum of the possibilities of each favorable case. Let us illustrate this principle by an example.

Let us suppose that we throw into the air a large and very thin coin whose two large opposite faces, which we will call heads and tails, are perfectly similar. Let us find the probability of throwing heads at least one time in two throws. It is clear that four equally possible cases may arise, namely, heads at the first and at the second throw; heads at the first throw and tails at the second; tails at the first throw and heads at the second; finally, tails at both throws. The first three cases are favorable to the event whose probability is sought; consequently this probability is equal to 3/4; so that it is a bet of three to one that heads will be thrown at least once in two throws.

We can count at this game only three different cases, namely, heads at the first throw, which dispenses with throwing a second time; tails at the first throw and heads at the second; finally, tails at the first and at the second throw. This would reduce the probability to 2/3 if we should consider with d'Alembert these three cases as equally possible. But it is apparent that the probability of throwing heads at the first throw is 1/2, while that of the two other cases is 1/4, the first case being a simple event which corresponds to two events combined: heads at the first and at the second throw, and heads at the first throw, tails at the second. If we then, conforming to the second principle, add the possibility 1/2 of heads at the first throw to the possibility 1/4 of tails at the first throw and heads at the second, we shall have 3/4 for the probability sought, which agrees with what is found in the supposition when we play the two throws. This supposition does not change at all the chance of that one who bets on this event; it simply serves to reduce the various cases to the cases equally possible.

*Third Principle.* One of the most important points of the theory of probabilities and that which lends the most to illusions is the manner in which these probabilities increase or diminish by their mutual combination. If the events are independent of one another, the probability of their combined existence is the product of their respective probabilities. Thus the probability of throwing one ace with a single die is 1/6; that of throwing two aces in throwing two dice at the same time is 1/36. Each face of the one being able to combine with the six faces of the other, there are in fact thirty-six equally possible cases, among which one single case gives two aces. Generally the probability that a simple event in the same circumstances will occur consecutively a given number of times is equal to the probability of this simple event raised to the power indicated by this number. Having thus the successive powers of a fraction less than unity diminishing without ceasing, an event which depends upon a series of very great probabilities may become extremely improbable. Suppose then an incident be transmitted to us by twenty witnesses in such manner that the first has transmitted it to the second, the second to the third, and so on. Suppose again that the probability of each testimony be equal to the fraction 9/10; that of the incident resulting from the testimonies will be less than 1/8. We cannot better compare this diminution of the probability than with the extinction of the light of objects by the interposition of several pieces of glass. A relatively small number of pieces suffices to take away the view of an object that a single piece allows us to perceive in a distinct manner. The historians do not appear to have paid sufficient attention to this degradation of the probability of events when seen across a great number of successive generations; many historical events reputed as certain would be at least doubtful if they were submitted to this test.

In the purely mathematical sciences the most distant consequences participate in the certainty of the principle from which they are derived. In the applications of analysis to physics the results have all the certainty of facts or experiences. But in the moral sciences, where each inference is deduced from that which precedes it only in a probable manner, however probable these deductions may be, the chance of error increases with their number and ultimately surpasses the chance of truth in the consequences very remote from the principle.

*Fourth Principle.* When two events depend upon each other, the probability of the compound event is the product of the probability of the first event and the probability that, this event having occurred, the second will occur. Thus in the preceding case of the three urns A, B, C, of which two contain only white balls and one contains only black balls, the probability of drawing a white ball from the urn C is 2/3, since of the three urns only two contain balls of that color. But when a white ball has been drawn from the urn C, the indecision relative to that one of the urns which contain only black balls extends only to the urns A and B; the probability of drawing a white ball from the urn B is 1/2; the product of 2/3 by 1/2, or 1/3, is then the probability of drawing two white balls at one time from the urns B and C.

We see by this example the influence of past events upon the probability of future events. For the probability of drawing a white ball from the urn B, which primarily is 2/3, becomes 1/2 when a white ball has been drawn from the urn C; it would change to certainty if a black ball had been drawn from the same urn. We will determine this influence by means of the following principle, which is a corollary of the preceding one.

*Fifth Principle*. If we calculate a priori the probability of the occurred event and the probability of an event composed of that one and a second one which is expected, the second probability divided by the first will be the probability of the event expected, drawn from the observed event.

Here is presented the question raised by some philosophers touching the influence of the past upon the probability of the future. Let us suppose at the play of heads and tails that heads has occurred oftener than tails. By this alone we shall be led to believe that in the constitution of the coin there is a secret cause which favors it. Thus in the conduct of life constant happiness is a proof of competency which should induce us to employ preferably happy persons. But if by the unreliability of circumstances we are constantly brought back to a state of absolute indecision, if, for example, we change the coin at each throw at the play of heads and tails, the past can shed no light upon the future and it would be absurd to take account of it.

*Sixth Principle*. Each of the causes to which an observed event may be attributed is indicated with just as much likelihood as there is probability that the event will take place, supposing the event to be constant. The probability of the existence of any one of these causes is then a fraction whose numerator is the probability of the event resulting from this cause and whose denominator is the sum of the similar probabilities relative to all the causes; if these various causes, considered a priori, are unequally probable, it is necessary, in place of the probability of the event resulting from each cause, to employ the product of this probability by the possibility of the cause itself. This is the fundamental principle of this branch of the analysis of chances which consists in passing from events to causes.

This principle gives the reason why we attribute regular events to a particular cause. Some philosophers have thought that these events are less possible than others and that at the play of heads and tails, for example, the combination in which heads occurs twenty successive times is less easy in its nature than those where heads and tails are mixed in an irregular manner. But this opinion supposes that past events have an influence on the possibility of future events, which is not at all admissible. The regular combinations occur more rarely only because they are less numerous. If we seek a cause wherever we perceive symmetry, it is not that we regard a symmetrical event as less possible than the others, but, since this event ought to be the effect of a regular cause or that of chance, the first of these suppositions is more probable than the second. On a table we see letters arranged in this order, *C o n s t a n t i n o p l e,* and we judge that this arrangement is not the result of chance, not because it is less possible than the others, for if this word were not employed in any language we should not suspect it came from any particular cause, but this word being in use among us, it is incomparably more probable that some person has thus arranged the aforesaid letters than that this arrangement is due to chance.

This is the place to define the word *extraordinary.* We arrange in our thought all possible events in various classes; and we regard as *extraordinary* those classes which include a very small number. Thus at the play of heads and tails the occurrence of heads a hundred successive times appears to us extraordinary because of the almost infinite number of combinations which may occur in a hundred throws; and if we divide the combinations into regular series containing an order easy to comprehend, and into irregular series, the latter are incomparably more numerous. The drawing of a white ball from an urn which among a million balls contains only one of this color, the others being black, would appear to us likewise extraordinary, because we form only two classes of events relative to the two colors. But the drawing of the number 475813, for example, from an urn that contains a million numbers seems to us an ordinary event; because, comparing individually the numbers with one another without dividing them into classes, we have no reason to believe that one of them will appear sooner than the others.

From what precedes, we ought generally to conclude that the more extraordinary the event, the greater the need of its being supported by strong proofs. For those who attest it, being able to deceive or to have been deceived, these two causes are as much more probable as the reality of the event is less. We shall see this particularly when we come to speak of the probability of testimony.

*Seventh Principle.* The probability of a future event is the sum of the products of the probability of each cause, drawn from the event observed, by the probability that, this cause existing, the future event will occur. The following example will illustrate this principle.

Let us imagine an urn which contains only two balls, each of which may be either white or black. One of these balls is drawn and is put back into the urn before proceeding to a new draw. Suppose that in the first two draws white balls have been drawn; the probability of again drawing a white ball at the third draw is required.

Only two hypotheses can be made here: either one of the balls is white and the other black, or both are white. In the first hypothesis the probability of the event observed is 1/4; it is unity or certainty in the second. Thus in regarding these hypotheses as so many causes, we shall have for the sixth principle 1/5 and 4/5 for their respective probabilities. But if the first hypothesis occurs, the probability of drawing a white ball at the third draw is 1/2; it is equal to certainty in the second hypothesis; multiplying then the last probabilities by those of the corresponding hypotheses, the sum of the products, or 9/10, will be the probability of drawing a white ball at the third draw.

When the probability of a single event is unknown we may suppose it equal to any value from zero to unity. The probability of each of these hypotheses, drawn from the event observed, is, by the sixth principle, a fraction whose numerator is the probability of the event in this hypothesis and whose denominator is the sum of the similar probabilities relative to all the hypotheses. Thus the probability that the possibility of the event is comprised within given limits is the sum of the fractions comprised within these limits. Now if we multiply each fraction by the probability of the future event, determined in the corresponding hypothesis, the sum of the products relative to all the hypotheses will be, by the seventh principle, the probability of the future event drawn from the event observed. Thus we find that an event having occurred successively any number of times, the probability that it will happen again the next time is equal to this number increased by unity divided by the same number, increased by two units. Placing the most ancient epoch of history at five thousand years ago, or at 1826213 days, and the sun having risen constantly in the interval at each revolution of twenty-four hours, it is a bet of 1826214 to one that it will rise again tomorrow. But this number is incomparably greater for him who, recognizing in the totality of phenomena the principal regulator of days and seasons, sees that nothing at the present moment can arrest the course of it.

Buffon in his *Political Arithmetic* calculates differently the preceding probability. He supposes that it differs from unity only by a fraction whose numerator is unity and whose denominator is the number 2 raised to a power equal to the number of days which have elapsed since the epoch. But the true manner of relating past events with the probability of causes and of future events was unknown to this illustrious writer.

## CONCERNING HOPE

The probability of events serves to determine the hope or the fear of persons interested in their existence. The word *hope* has various acceptations; it expresses generally the advantage of that one who expects a certain benefit in suppositions which are only probable. This advantage in the theory of chance is a product of the sum hoped for by the probability of obtaining it; it is the partial sum which ought to result when we do not wish to run the risks of the event in supposing that the division is made proportional to the probabilities. This division is the only equitable one when all strange circumstances are eliminated; because an equal degree of probability gives an equal right to the sum hoped for. We will call this advantage *mathematical hope*.

*Eighth Principle.* When the advantage depends on several events it is obtained by taking the sum of the products of the probability of each event by the benefit attached to its occurrence.

Let us apply this principle to some examples. Let us suppose that at the play of heads and tails Paul receives two francs if he throws heads at the first throw and five francs if he throws it only at the second. Multiplying two francs by the probability $1/2$ of the first case, and five francs by the probability $1/4$ of the second case, the sum of the products, or two and a quarter francs, will be Paul's advantage. It is the sum which he ought to give in advance to that one who has given him this advantage; for, in order to maintain the equality of the play, the throw ought to be equal to the advantage which it procures.

If Paul receives two francs by throwing heads at the first and five francs by throwing it at the second throw, whether he has thrown it or not at the first, the probability of throwing heads at the second throw being $1/2$, multiplying two francs and five francs by $1/2$ the sum of these products will give three and one half francs for Paul's advantage and consequently for his stake at the game.

*Ninth Principle.* In a series of probable events of which the ones produce a benefit and the others a loss, we shall have the advantage which results from it by making a sum of the products of the probability of each favorable event by the benefit which it procures, and subtracting from this sum that of the products of the probability of each unfavorable event by the loss which is attached to it. If the second sum is greater than the first, the benefit becomes a loss and hope is changed to fear.

Consequently we ought always in the conduct of life to make the product of the benefit hoped for, by its probability, at least equal to the similar product relative to the loss. But it is necessary, in order to attain this, to appreciate exactly the advantages, the losses, and their respective probabilities. For this a great accuracy of mind, a delicate judgment, and a great experience in affairs is necessary; it is necessary to know how to guard one's self against prejudices, illusions of fear or hope, and erroneous ideas, ideas of fortune and happiness, with which the majority of people feed their self-love.

The application of the preceding principles to the following question has greatly exercised the geometricians. Paul plays at heads and tails with the condition of receiving two francs if he throws heads at the first throw, four francs if he throws it only at the second throw, eight francs if he throws it only at the third, and so on. His stake at the play ought to be, according to the eighth principle, equal to the number of throws, so that if the game continues to infinity the stake ought to be infinite. However, no reasonable man would wish to risk at this game even a small sum, for example five francs. Whence comes this difference between the result of calculation and the indication of common sense? We soon recognize that it amounts to this: that the moral advantage which a benefit procures for us is not proportional to this benefit and that it depends upon a thousand circumstances, often very difficult to define, but of which the most general and most important is that of fortune.

Indeed it is apparent that one franc has much greater value for him who possesses only a hundred than for a millionaire. We ought then to distinguish in the hoped-for benefit its absolute from its relative value. But the latter is regulated by the motives which make it desirable, whereas the first is independent of them. The general principle for appreciating this relative value cannot be given, but here is one proposed by Daniel Bernoulli which will serve in many cases.

*Tenth Principle.* The relative value of an infinitely small sum is equal to its absolute value divided by the total benefit of the person interested. This supposes that every one has a certain benefit whose value can never be estimated as zero. Indeed even that one who possesses nothing always gives to the product of his labor and to his hopes a value at least equal to that which is absolutely necessary to sustain him.

If we apply analysis to the principle just propounded, we obtain the following rule: Let us designate by unity the part of the fortune of an individual, independent of his expectations. If we determine the different values that this fortune may have by virtue of these expectations and their probabilities, the product of these values raised respectively to the powers indicated by their probabilities will be the physical fortune which would procure for the individual the same moral advantage which he receives from the part of his fortune taken as unity and from his expectations; by subtracting unity from the product, the difference will be the increase of the physical fortune due to expectations: we will call this increase *moral hope*. It is easy to see that it coincides with mathematical hope when the fortune taken as unity becomes infinite in reference to the variations which it receives from the expectations. But when these variations are an appreciable part of this unity the two hopes may differ very materially among themselves.

This rule conduces to results conformable to the indications of common sense which can by this means be appreciated with some exactitude. Thus in the preceding question it is found that if the fortune of Paul is two hundred francs, he ought not reasonably to stake more than nine francs. The same rule leads us again to distribute the danger over several parts of a benefit expected rather than to expose the entire benefit to this danger. It results similarly that at the fairest game the loss is always greater than the gain. Let us suppose, for example, that a player having a fortune of one hundred francs risks fifty at the play of heads and tails; his fortune after his stake at the play will be reduced to eighty-seven francs, that is to say, this last sum would procure for the player the same moral advantage as the state of his fortune after the stake. The play is then disadvantageous even in the case where the stake is equal to the product of the sum hoped for, by its probability. We can judge by this of the immorality of games in which the sum hoped for is below this product. They subsist only by false reasonings and by the cupidity which they excite and which, leading the people to sacrifice their necessaries to chimerical hopes whose improbability they are not in condition to appreciate, are the source of an infinity of evils.

The disadvantage of games of chance, the advantage of not exposing to the same danger the whole benefit that is expected, and all the similar results indicated by common sense, subsist, whatever may be the function of the physical fortune which for each individual expresses his moral fortune. It is enough that the proportion of the increase of this function to the increase of the physical fortune diminishes in the measure that the latter increases.

---

*The foregoing consists of Chapters I-IV*
*of Laplace's* A PHILOSOPHICAL ESSAY ON PROBABILITIES,
*translated by Frederick W. Truscott and Frederick L. Emory.*

# Charles Sanders Peirce

## 1839–1914

Charles Sanders Peirce was born at Cambridge, Massachusetts, in 1839. He was the son of Benjamin Peirce, a Harvard professor and a leading mathematician. Peirce's early education, supervised by his father, was a strenuous experience. The elder Peirce was a forceful man and relentless in his determination to develop his son's mathematical talents. He sometimes kept the boy awake all night, training him in the "art of concentration" by playing rapid games of double rummy. When Charles began to read philosophers, his father would have him repeat their proofs and in a very few words would usually rip them apart and show them empty. This forced march to education gave young Peirce a wide background in experimental science, mathematics, logic, and philosophy, but it also may have contributed to his later unhappiness and chaotic personal life.

In Peirce's own words: "I insensibly put on a sort of swagger here, which is designed to say, 'You are a very good fellow in your way; who you are I don't know and I don't care, but I, you know, am Mr. Peirce, distinguished for my various scientific acquirements, but above all for the extreme modesty in which respect I challenge the world.'" This is a humorous self-portrait, but apt. Peirce really was a difficult man. He was unable to get along with others, careless about his appearance, impractical in money matters, forgetful, vain, and arrogant. He died in 1914 in poverty, unknown to the general public. Yet today he is recognized as one of the most influential thinkers this country has produced.

In 1861 Peirce joined the United States Coast Survey, in which post he remained for thirty years. He served as computer for the nautical almanac, made pendulum investigations, was in charge of gravity research and wrote a number of scientific papers. This government post left him enough time to teach and to engage in private research in science, philosophy, and logic. His contributions to the science of logic are undisputed. Though not extensive, his writings in pure mathematics were original and prophetic. He published only one book in his lifetime, *Photometric Researches* (1878), but most of his scattered writings have been published posthumously in six volumes, *Collected Papers* (1931–35).

Peirce was the founder of pragmatism, the philosophy that was elaborated by William James [1] and John Dewey.[2] Dewey and James diverged from the original doctrine, but all three represent an interest in relating the abstract to the concrete.

Peirce was deeply concerned with the theory of meaning. The main purpose of his investigations was to explain the pragmatic meaning of general terms as they are used by scientists. The following excerpts from an essay entitled *How To Make Our Ideas Clear* are representative of his doctrine:

> Our idea of anything is our idea of its sensible effects. . . . What a thing means is simply what habit it involves. . . . There is no distinction of meaning so fine as to consist in anything but a possible difference of practice. . . . The final upshot of thinking is the exercise of volition. . . .

It has been said that pragmatism is a characteristically American movement in philosophy. Its emphasis is on "doing."

Peirce was one of the first proponents of the frequency interpretation of probability. It is in keeping with his whole philosophy that this interpretation agrees with our everyday "common sense" concept. It is also the interpretation most widely used in applied statistics and measurement, and in many branches of the theoretical sciences.

*The Red and the Black*, the selection which follows, is one of the most charming essays on probability ever written. The mathematician-philosopher arrives, by logic, at the conclusion that he is indeed his brother's keeper. While this is an unusual argument for an ethical principle, it is not the first time that the laws of probability have been

---

[1] See Vol. 10, pp. 39–87, in this set.
[2] See Vol. 10, pp. 92–213, in this set.

invoked to support what is essentially an article of religious belief. Pascal, too, once urged mankind to consider the following odds. "Let us weigh the gain and loss in wagering that God is," he wrote. "Let us estimate these two chances. If you gain, you gain all; if you lose, you lose nothing. Wager, then, without hesitation, that He is."[3]

[3] Compare *Great Books of the Western World,* Vol. 33, pp. 214–216.

# The Red and the Black

The theory of probabilities is simply the science of logic quantitatively treated. There are two conceivable certainties with reference to any hypothesis, the certainty of its truth and the certainty of its falsity. The numbers *one* and *zero* are appropriated, in this calculus, to marking these extremes of knowledge; while fractions having values intermediate between them indicate, as we may vaguely say, the degrees in which the evidence leans toward one or the other. The general problem of probabilities is, from a given state of facts, to determine the numerical probability of a possible fact. This is the same as to inquire how much the given facts are worth, considered as evidence to prove the possible fact. Thus the problem of probabilities is simply the general problem of logic.

Probability is a continuous quantity, so that great advantages may be expected from this mode of studying logic. Some writers have gone so far as to maintain that, by means of the calculus of chances, every solid inference may be represented by legitimate arithmetical operations upon the numbers given in the premises. If this be, indeed, true, the great problem of logic, how it is that the observation of one fact can give us knowledge of another independent fact, is reduced to a mere question of arithmetic. It seems proper to examine this pretension before undertaking any more recondite solution of the paradox.

But, unfortunately, writers on probabilities are not agreed in regard to this result. This branch of mathematics is the only one, I believe, in which good writers frequently get results entirely erroneous. In elementary geometry the reasoning is frequently fallacious, but erroneous conclusions are avoided; but it may be doubted if there is a single extensive treatise on probabilities in existence which does not contain solutions absolutely indefensible. This is partly owing to the want of any regular method of procedure; for the subject involves too many subtleties to make it easy to put its problems into equations without such an aid. But, beyond this, the fundamental principles of its calculus are more or less in dispute. In regard to that class of questions to which it is chiefly applied for practical purposes, there is comparatively little doubt; but in regard to others to which it has been sought to extend it, opinion is somewhat unsettled.

This last class of difficulties can only be entirely overcome by making the idea of probability perfectly clear in our minds in the way set forth in our last paper.[1]

To get a clear idea of what we mean by probability, we have to consider what real and sensible difference there is between one degree of probability and another.

The character of probability belongs primarily, without doubt, to certain inferences. Locke explains it as follows: After remarking that the mathematician positively knows that the sum of the three angles of a triangle is equal to two right angles because he apprehends the geometrical proof, he thus continues: "But another man who never took the pains to observe the demonstration, hearing a mathematician, a man of credit, affirm the three angles of a triangle to be equal to two right ones, *assents* to it; *i.e.*, receives it for true. In which case the foundation of his assent is the probability of the thing, the proof being such as, for the most part, carries truth with it; the man on whose testimony he receives it not being wont to affirm anything contrary to, or besides his knowledge, especially in matters of this kind." The celebrated *Essay concerning Human Understanding* contains many passages which, like this one, make the first steps in profound analyses which are not further developed. It was shown in the first of these papers that the validity of an inference does not depend on any tendency of the mind to accept it, however strong such tendency may be; but consists in the real fact that, when premises like those of the argument in question are true, conclusions related to them like that of this argument are also true. It was remarked that in a logical mind an argument is always conceived as a member of a *genus* of arguments all constructed in the same way, and such that, when their premises are real facts, their conclusions are so also. If the argument is demonstrative, then this is always so; if it is only probable, then it is for the most part so. As Locke says, the probable argument is *"such as* for the most part carries truth with it."

---

1. [Peirce is here referring to his essay *How To Make Our Ideas Clear* (Ed.).]

According to this, that real and sensible difference between one degree of probability and another, in which the meaning of the distinction lies, is that in the frequent employment of two different modes of inference, one will carry truth with it oftener than the other. It is evident that this is the only difference there is in the existing fact. Having certain premises, a man draws a certain conclusion, and as far as this inference alone is concerned the only possible practical question is whether that conclusion is true or not, and between existence and nonexistence there is no middle term. "Being only is and nothing is altogether not," said Parmenides; and this is in strict accordance with the analysis of the conception of reality given in the last paper. For we found that the distinction of reality and fiction depends on the supposition that sufficient investigation would cause one opinion to be universally received and all others to be rejected. That presupposition, involved in the very conceptions of reality and figment, involves a complete sundering of the two. It is the heaven-and-hell idea in the domain of thought. But, in the long run, there is a real fact which corresponds to the idea of probability, and it is that a given mode of inference sometimes proves successful and sometimes not, and that in a ratio ultimately fixed. As we go on drawing inference after inference of the given kind, during the first ten or hundred cases the ratio of successes may be expected to show considerable fluctuations; but when we come into the thousands and millions, these fluctuations become less and less; and if we continue long enough, the ratio will approximate toward a fixed limit. We may, therefore, define the probability of a mode of argument as the proportion of cases in which it carries truth with it.

The inference from the premise, A, to the conclusion, B, depends, as we have seen, on the guiding principle that if a fact of the class A is true, a fact of the class B is true. The probability consists of the fraction whose numerator is the number of times in which both A and B are true, and whose denominator is the total number of times in which A is true, whether B is so or not. Instead of speaking of this as the probability of the inference, there is not the slightest objection to calling it the probability that if A happens, B happens. But to speak of the probability of the event B, without naming the condition, really has no meaning at all. It is true that when it is perfectly obvious what condition is meant, the ellipsis may be permitted. But we should avoid contracting the habit of using language in this way (universal as the habit is), because it gives rise to a vague way of thinking, as if the action of causation might either determine an event to happen or determine it not to happen, or leave it more or less free to happen or not, so as to give rise to an *inherent* chance

in regard to its occurrence. It is quite clear to me that some of the worst
and most persistent errors in the use of the doctrine of chances have arisen
from this vicious mode of expression.[2]

But there remains an important point to be cleared up. According to
what has been said, the idea of probability essentially belongs to a kind
of inference which is repeated indefinitely. An individual inference must
be either true or false, and can show no effect of probability; and, therefore, in reference to a single case considered in itself, probability can have
no meaning. Yet if a man had to choose between drawing a card from
a pack containing twenty-five red cards and a black one, or from a pack
containing twenty-five black cards and a red one, and if the drawing of a
red card were destined to transport him to eternal felicity, and that of a
black one to consign him to everlasting woe, it would be folly to deny that
he ought to prefer the pack containing the larger portion of red cards,
although, from the nature of the risk, it could not be repeated. It is not
easy to reconcile this with our analysis of the conception of chance. But
suppose he should choose the red pack, and should draw the wrong card,
what consolation would he have? He might say that he had acted in
accordance with reason, but that would only show that his reason was
absolutely worthless. And if he should choose the right card, how could
he regard it as anything but a happy accident? He could not say that if
he had drawn from the other pack, he might have drawn the wrong one,
because a hypothetical proposition such as, "if A, then B," means nothing
with reference to a single case. Truth consists in the existence of a real
fact corresponding to the true proposition. Corresponding to the proposition, "if A, then B," there may be the fact that *whenever* such an event as
A happens such an event as B happens. But in the case supposed, which
has no parallel as far as this man is concerned, there would be no real
fact whose existence could give any truth to the statement that, if he had
drawn from the other pack, he might have drawn a black card. Indeed,
since the validity of an inference consists in the truth of the hypothetical
proposition that *if* the premises be true the conclusion will also be true,
and since the only real fact which can correspond to such a proposition is
that whenever the antecedent is true the consequent is so also, it follows
that there can be no sense in reasoning in an isolated case at all.

These considerations appear, at first sight, to dispose of the difficulty

2. The conception of probability here set forth is substantially that first developed by
Mr. Venn, in his *Logic of Chance.* Of course, a vague apprehension of the idea
had always existed, but the problem was to make it perfectly clear, and to him belongs the credit of first doing this.

mentioned. Yet the case of the other side is not yet exhausted. Although probability will probably manifest its effect in, say, a thousand risks, by a certain proportion between the numbers of successes and failures, yet this, as we have seen, is only to say that it certainly will, at length, do so. Now the number of risks, the number of probable inferences, which a man draws in his whole life, is a finite one, and he cannot be absolutely *certain* that the mean result will accord with the probabilities at all. Taking all his risks collectively, then, it cannot be certain that they will not fail, and his case does not differ, except in degree, from the one last supposed. It is an indubitable result of the theory of probabilities that every gambler, if he continues long enough, must ultimately be ruined. Suppose he tries the martingale, which some believe infallible, and which is, as I am informed, disallowed in the gambling houses. In this method of playing, he first bets say $1; if he loses it he bets $2; if he loses that he bets $4; if he loses that he bets $8; if he then gains he has lost $1 + 2 + 4 = 7$, and he has gained $1 more; and no matter how many bets he loses, the first one he gains will make him $1 richer than he was in the beginning. In that way, he will probably gain at first; but, at last, the time will come when the run of luck is so against him that he will not have money enough to double, and must, therefore, let his bet go. This will *probably* happen before he has won as much as he had in the first place, so that this run against him will leave him poorer than he began; some time or other it will be sure to happen. It is true that there is always a possibility of his winning any sum the bank can pay, and we thus come upon a celebrated paradox that, though he is certain to be ruined, the value of his expectation calculated according to the usual rules (which omit this consideration) is large. But, whether a gambler plays in this way or any other, the same thing is true, namely, that if he plays long enough he will be sure some time to have such a run against him as to exhaust his entire fortune. The same thing is true of an insurance company. Let the directors take the utmost pains to be independent of great conflagrations and pestilences, their actuaries can tell them that, according to the doctrine of chances, the time must come, at last, when their losses will bring them to a stop. They may tide over such a crisis by extraordinary means, but then they will start again in a weakened state, and the same thing will happen again all the sooner. An actuary might be inclined to deny this, because he knows that the expectation of his company is large, or perhaps (neglecting the interest upon money) is infinite. But calculations of expectations leave out of account the circumstance now under consideration, which reverses the whole thing. However, I must not be understood as saying that insurance is on this account unsound, more than other kinds of business.

All human affairs rest upon probabilities, and the same thing is true everywhere. If man were immortal he could be perfectly sure of seeing the day when everything in which he had trusted should betray his trust, and, in short, of coming eventually to hopeless misery. He would break down, at last, as every good fortune, as every dynasty, as every civilization does. In place of this we have death.

But what, without death, would happen to every man, with death must happen to some man. At the same time, death makes the number of our risks, of our inferences, finite, and so makes their mean result uncertain. The very idea of probability and of reasoning rests on the assumption that this number is indefinitely great. We are thus landed in the same difficulty as before, and I can see but one solution of it. It seems to me that we are driven to this, that logicality inexorably requires that our interests shall *not* be limited. They must not stop at our own fate, but must embrace the whole community. This community, again, must not be limited, but must extend to all races of beings with whom we can come into immediate or mediate intellectual relation. It must reach, however, vaguely, beyond this geological epoch, beyond all bounds. He who would not sacrifice his own soul to save the whole world, is, as it seems to me, illogical in all his inferences, collectively. Logic is rooted in the social principle.

To be logical men should not be selfish; and, in point of fact, they are not so selfish as they are thought. The willful prosecution of one's desires is a different thing from selfishness. The miser is not selfish; his money does him no good, and he cares for what shall become of it after his death. We are constantly speaking of *our* possessions on the Pacific, and of *our* destiny as a republic, where no personal interests are involved, in a way which shows that we have wider ones. We discuss with anxiety the possible exhaustion of coal in some hundreds of years, or the cooling-off of the sun in some millions, and show in the most popular of all religious tenets that we can conceive the possibility of a man's descending into hell for the salvation of his fellows.

Now, it is not necessary for logicality that a man should himself be capable of the heroism of self-sacrifice. It is sufficient that he should recognize the possibility of it, should perceive that only that man's inferences who has it are really logical, and should consequently regard his own as being only so far valid as they would be accepted by the hero. So far as he thus refers his inferences to that standard, he becomes identified with such a mind.

This makes logicality attainable enough. Sometimes we can personally attain to heroism. The soldier who runs to scale a wall knows that he will probably be shot, but that is not all he cares for. He also knows that if all the regiment, with whom in feeling he identifies himself, rush forward at once, the fort will be taken. In other cases we can only imitate the virtue. The man whom we have supposed as having to draw from the two packs, who if he is not a logician will draw from the red pack from mere habit, will see, if he is logician enough, that he cannot be logical so long as he is concerned only with his own fate, but that that man who should care equally for what was to happen in all possible cases of the sort could act logically, and would draw from the pack with the most red cards, and thus, though incapable himself of such sublimity, our logician would imitate the effect of that man's courage in order to share his logicality.

But all this requires a conceived identification of one's interests with those of an unlimited community. Now there exist no reasons, and a later discussion will show that there can be no reasons, for thinking that the human race, or any intellectual race, will exist forever. On the other hand, there can be no reason against it; [3] and, fortunately, as the whole requirement is that we should have certain sentiments, there is nothing in the facts to forbid our having a *hope*, or calm and cheerful wish, that the community may last beyond any assignable date.

It may seem strange that I should put forward three sentiments, namely, interest in an indefinite community, recognition of the possibility of this interest being made supreme, and hope in the unlimited continuance of intellectual activity, as indispensable requirements of logic. Yet, when we consider that logic depends on a mere struggle to escape doubt, which, as it terminates in action, must begin in emotion, and that, furthermore, the only cause of our planting ourselves on reason is that other methods of escaping doubt fail on account of the social impulse, why should we wonder to find social sentiment presupposed in reasoning? As for the other two sentiments which I find necessary, they are so only as supports and accessories of that. It interests me to notice that these three sentiments seem to be pretty much the same as that famous trio of charity, faith, and hope, which, in the estimation of St. Paul, are the finest and greatest of spiritual gifts. Neither Old nor New Testament is a textbook of the logic of science, but the latter is certainly the highest existing authority in regard to the dispositions of heart which a man ought to have.

---

3. I do not here admit an absolutely unknowable. Evidence could show us what would probably be the case after any given lapse of time; and though a subsequent time might be assigned which that evidence might not cover, yet further evidence would cover it.

# GATEWAY TO THE GREAT BOOKS